MODERN MANAGEMENT SERIES

G. Jay Anyon MANAGING AN INTEGRATED PURCHASING PROCESS

John Fayerweather FACTS AND FALLACIES OF INTERNATIONAL BUSINESS

Myron S. Heidingsfield and Frank H. Eby, Jr. MARKETING AND BUSINESS RESEARCH

Thomas Moranian THE R & D ENGINEER AS MANAGER

Edward B. Shils AUTOMATION AND INDUSTRIAL RELATIONS

Automation
and
Industrial
Relations

▶▶▶▶▶▶▶▶▶▶▶▶▶▶▶▶▶▶▶▶▶▶

EDWARD B. SHILS

Associate Chairman, Industry Department
Secretary, Labor Relations Council

*Wharton School of Finance and Commerce
University of Pennsylvania*

18589

HOLT, RINEHART AND WINSTON

NEW YORK • CHICAGO • SAN FRANCISCO • TORONTO • LONDON

▶ ▶ ▶ ▶

Preface

The Government, unions, employers, and citizens are very much concerned with the possible effects of an accelerated development in fuller mechanization and automation. Will employment be increased or decreased? Will the large number of personnel displacements continue to plague the labor market? Will management's profits from automation be shared with the workers? Will markets increase as a result of lower unit costs, thus permitting fuller production and avoiding the unemployment problems that create fear and uncertainty in the minds of employees and union leaders? Will we be able to meet the competition from the European Common Market more effectively?

What occurs will be determined in part by the wisdom of our Government, our employers, and our unions. Will we run into vexing situations by being headstrong about adapting ourselves to the problems of automation? Or will we elect to improve our personnel administration techniques, to plan new machines in areas of labor shortage, and to defer hiring where we plan to introduce automation, thus permitting normal attrition to ease dislocation and unemployment?

What guarantees will labor unions demand in their contracts? Will more stringent work rules result? Will we have more or less featherbedding? Will the gradual change in the composition of the work force from blue-collar to white-collar workers affect the traditional influence of the presently powerful labor unions in the manufacturing industries?

iii

This book is partly an outgrowth of my interest in job evaluation and wage administration. For some years I have been teaching graduate classes in this area, and have noted that more and more of our discussions of the value of a job hinge on factors no longer controllable by the employee. The question, What is the basis of payment for workers? is now more unsettled than ever. Automation has removed the basis for the historic piece-rate system in which the operator controlled the speed of the machine. Unions tell us that there are many reasons for upgrading the newly automated job — for example, mental requirements and responsibility may be greater. This viewpoint, however, has been questioned by such an authority as Professor James Bright of Harvard. As the reader will perceive in the following pages, some jobs in the automated plant will result in upgrading and others will result in downgrading, because many of these new jobs have been de-skilled in the historic sense.

As secretary of the Wharton School Labor Relations Council, I have had the pleasure of discussing this and related problems with George W. Taylor, chairman of the Council. Dr. Taylor served as chairman of the War Labor Board in World War II, and more recently as a member of the President's Advisory Committee on Labor-Management Policy. He has been most helpful to me in discussions of work rules and the influence they may have on the freedom of management to proceed with fuller mechanization and automation.

One of Professor Taylor's recent responsibilities was the chairmanship of the Kaiser Steel Panel, a tripartite committee that attempted to solve many of the problems of automation and work rules during the normal contract period. In December 1962, this panel released a new "progress-sharing" agreement. These new developments may inspire management and labor to view the problems of automation as requiring joint consultation fifty-two weeks of the year, and not solely at the time of contract negotiation. Only by mutual activities in the field of productivity improvement will American labor and industry be able to survive in the face of the European Common Market and competitive inroads from the Far East.

I am likewise indebted to a number of directors of industrial relations, who regularly attended meetings of the Labor Relations Council at the University of Pennsylvania. These men represented member firms of the Council and were extremely helpful to me at a time when my studies in automation and industrial relations raised a number of perplexing questions that could be answered only by "practitioners" working in the nation's basic industries.

Without the help and personal interest of my wife, Shirley, this book would never have been written.

My thanks also to Mrs. Dalia Vilgosas and Miss Roberta Vellozzi for their help on the manuscript. Mr. Walter Duglin assisted me on some of the knotty problems of interviewing and research.

Penn Valley, Pennsylvania   E. B. S.
January 1963

▶ ▶ ▶ ▶

Contents

vii

▶ ▶ ▶ ▶ **1**

What Is
Automation?

Automation, according to Peter Drucker, is not "technical in character. Like every technology it is primarily a system of concepts, and its technical aspects are results rather than causes."[1]*

The technology of automation differs from the much earlier one of "individual production," since there, skill was an important principle. Neither does it focus on the "product," as did the Henry Ford concept of "mass" production. "Automation focuses on the *process*, which it sees as an integrated and harmonious whole."[2]

Definitions, History, and Application

Definitions In attempting to stabilize the "process," automation looks to maximum production at lowest costs and with minimum human effort. The new technology also emphasizes the principle of *control*, by requiring that which is significant to be the preset governor of the *process*. The mechanics of *control* are such that they must be built into the process — discarding what the process cannot handle or providing built-in, self-regulating adjustments to handle the variations of work.

Mechanization is not, however, Automation itself. It is only the result of automation and is not essential to it. We have plenty of examples of effective mass production without a single conveyor belt; for example, the sorting of checks in a clearing house. We will see examples of automation without a single "*automatic*" tool, let alone a single "pushbutton."

Techniques, tools and gadgets are thus in automation, as in every technology, specific to the task, and determined by it. They do not

*References are listed at the end of each chapter.

1

constitute automation; nor does automation consist in their application. Automation *is a concept of the organization of work*. It is therefore as applicable to the organization of distribution, or of clerical work, as to that of industrial production.[3]

The pace of technological change is increasing sharply, creating vast changes in the production and distribution of goods. For more than two decades, scientists and engineers have succeeded in bringing forth a variety of new developments and new concepts in electronics and production methods. Many of these techniques, first developed for military equipment and missiles, are now being applied to civilian use.

The new technology has been called by many names. For a time it was called "fuller mechanization." Today we use the term "automation," which started as a technical term, to describe certain types of methods used in production. Now it has a much broader meaning — and much more is ascribed to it.

Regardless of how we define the term, we know that it is rapidly making possible the automatic office and the automatic factory. In many industries the introduction of automated techniques is slow, but even in these there is much talk and planning.

Let us consider further some additional brief definitions of automation. The term, it is said, was first coined by D. S. Harder when he was a manufacturing executive with General Motors Corporation, who defined it as "the automatic handling of parts between progressive production processes." It was originally used to describe the linking of machine tools with automatic materials transfer and handling equipment.

Charles Killingsworth defines automation as "mechanization which emphasizes automatic control; also mechanization of computation, data processing and record keeping."[4] In the first part of this compound definition, Killingsworth appears to refer primarily to factory automation, whereas in the latter part he refers to office automation; yet the two are certainly related, for the latest developments in factory automation depend on automatic computation and data processing.

J. Diebold,[5] the "father" of automation, advises management in making its decision to automate, to be aware of the difference between "Detroit" automation, or advanced mechanization, and automation that is "feedback control."

The former, consisting of integration of machines one with the other, is limited to long runs of identical products. The latter, characterized by "self-regulation," can break through limits of mechanization and extend benefits of automatic production to job shops. "Feedback automation" also has the advantage of flexibility, not found in special-purpose machines of the Detroit variety.

During the 1950's a wave of mechanization took place in American industry. Fuller mechanization was widely applied to certain functions, and by 1960 it was possible to detect definite trends in application. These applications have become the backbone of "automation." According to James R. Bright of Harvard, the more prominent included:

1. Mechanization of more direct labor activities; in particular, the task of assembling parts.

2. Mechanization of material movement (material handling); including movement between machines, departments, buildings, common carriers, and in storage operations.

3. Mechanization of control activity; including the consolidation of controls for many machines in one control panel; program control, in which an intricate sequence of actions is directed by the control system; and feedback control, in which a high degree of self-regulation and correction is involved.

4. Mechanization of testing and inspection activities.

5. Mechanization of data processing through the computer.[6]

History   Automation is not entirely new, but since World War II it has acquired increasing importance, primarily as a result of the development of complex control devices used by the military during the war. Some industries, such as petroleum, chemicals, papermaking, ore refining, telephone, and cigarette manufacture, were highly automated even before the word was invented. Isolated examples of rather complete automation can be found far back in history.

The Romans used a water device for automatic control of temple doors. Jacquard used punched cards to control needle selection in his loom in the early part of the eighteenth century. In 1784, Evans designed and built a fully automatic grist mill. In more recent times the A. O. Smith Corporation had a highly automatic frame plant in operation in 1920; the Morris Automobile plant in England was using a transfer machine in 1924; and in this country, Graham-Paige was using transfer devices between machines in 1929.[7]

Thus, mechanical handling, processing, sensing, and automatic control equipment are the principal components of the automated plant, and each has been utilized in industry for a considerable time.

Mechanical handling of one sort or another dates back to antiquity. It is believed that processing of material commenced with the first weapons. Automatic control devices were used on clocks as far back as the fourteenth century. The automatic grist mill mentioned above was a complete integration of processing and handling of flour. In 1808 a pulley-block factory existed in Portsmouth, which had an output of 160,000 blocks a year.

The first industrial revolution replaced the muscle power of animals and human beings with steam- and electric-powered machines. Automation apparently is now ushering in a second industrial revolution. We find a new technology in which automatic control devices replace the human being in controlling and regulating the machine. The hand-tool worker went out with the first industrial revolution and was succeeded by the machine tender. In the new revolution the machine tender has become a supervisor of an automatically controlled operating system.

Application Automation refers to the design, manufacture, and use of automatic equipment for industrial or other processes. Most machines used in industry today have the power of self-motion, self-regulation, or self-action, but these characteristics in themselves do not provide the basis for the use of the term "automation." For more than a hundred years mechanization and electric power have been steadily increasing substitutes for direct human power and energy. All types of manufacturing make use of machines. The "unautomated" characteristics of the present-day machinery constitute feed, watch, and control of the equipment by the operator.

As the "muscle" functions of human beings were transferred to the machines many years ago, so were evident the properties of self-action involving repetitive activity, such as in the firing of cylinders in a gasoline engine, or the alternation of polarities in an electric motor. In these developments "muscles" were more important than the replacement of the "mental" functions of the operator. Today's equipment has supplied the built-in sensory functions not found in the nonautomated equipment of the period from 1900 to 1950.

In recent years, the linking up of special-purpose machines by conveyors and other work-handling devices to form assemblages termed "transfer machines" has permitted performance of long sequences of metalworking operations without operator intervention.[8]

Many persons are familiar with the Detroit production-line techniques. The use of "transfer machines" builds into the production-line layout *machine work-stations*, rather than men and machines in concert. Gradually industry perfects the substitution of machines for men until the stage of push-button automatic production is attained. Much of this development is now found in the automobile industry.

The type of "transfer-machine" line described here is excellent for a fixed sequence of fixed operations. The process is definitely not self-regulation. Dimensions for parts fabrication are preset. Controls assure that only one piece will arrive at a station at one time. Inspection is built in. Controls capable of disclosing worn-out parts are also built in, and signal the need for substituting new parts when permissible tolerances are exceeded.

Examples of this type of production machine set-ups are the rolling mills, knitting machines, paper-making machines, glass bottle molders, can sealers, bag fillers, carpet looms, rotary printing presses, screw machines, mechanical stokers, plastic molding presses, and die casting machines.

In automation not only are machines and production processes combined, but conveyors, chutes, and other related equipment successfully tie together different production processes into automatic and semiautomatic continuous-flow operations.

The new technology also involves mechanical and electronic devices that automatically control the operation of machines. It includes electronic computers — often called "giant brains" — that automatically perform such varied jobs as storing office records, controlling the operations of complicated machines, and preparing customers' bills and employee payrolls.

Related to this new technology are new products that aid in its development. Printed circuits and transistors are replacing electric wiring and electronic tubes in radios, television sets, and other electronic equipment. Radioactive isotopes, by-products of atomic reactors, are widely used in industry for testing the precise thickness of materials, detecting leaks in pipes, and testing metal structural parts for defects. New plastics are replacing metals for some purposes.

Automatic and semiautomatic methods are spreading into almost every type of work — in manufacturing industries, offices, communications, railroads, warehouses, large retail stores, and farming.

Radical changes in production methods, work flow, office procedures, and labor skills are taking place in numerous parts of the American economy.[9]

Concept of Self-Regulation

Electrical Energy Versus Human Energy   Why the recent emphasis on "automation"? The answer comes quickly to the electrical engineer, who knows that the cost of human energy is 480 times that of electrical energy. In recent years the advance in electrical techniques has been astounding. In many industries dielectric heating has effected great increases in production and savings. Induction heating has turned heat-treatment into an operation similar to that of machining. Ultrasonics, ultraviolet light, and electronic gauging have created fresh ideas of nondestructive testing. Mathematical computations, which otherwise might take a band of mathematicians days to complete, are completed in a matter of minutes by the electronic computer.

If automation served only to make the machine more and more automatic, this aspect alone would be a worthwhile contribution to technological progress. However, automation is more than mechanization — it is like a biological mutation in terms of new technology and innovation. As Rogers states:

> . . . full automation is the application of the theory of automatic control in technical innovations to make possible full automatic production with self-regulation as well as self-action. It contemplates the wholesale reproduction of the sensory and mental functions of human operators in production systems which go far beyond the fixed sequence-fixed operation variety of automatic production.[10]

Feedback and Automatic Control   An important aspect of this new technology is the concept of *feedback* control, or automatic self-correction. The thermostat, the most common example of this technique, automatically increases or reduces the furnace fuel supply when the temperature of the room goes above or below a preset level. When this concept is extended to industrial activity, it is clear what automation is attempting to achieve. The worker is not expected to operate the machinery; he only sets the controls and repairs the system in the event of breakdown.

The use of automatic control devices has attained its highest development in the petroleum refining industry. In this type of continuous-flow process, crude petroleum feeds in at one end of the plant, flows continuously through a series of automatically controlled chambers and pipes, and pours out a variety of finished products at the other end.

Eugene Ayres, a chemist at Gulf Research and Development Company, describes the oil refinery thus:

> It is a bewildering kind of factory, with metallic towers rising 20 stories high, hundreds of miles of pipe, and only an occasional modest building. A few lonely men wander about this special monster doing supervisory or maintenance work here or there. . . . Every day a quarter of a million barrels of oil flow unobtrusively into its maw and about as many flow out in the forms of dozens of finished petroleum products — all profoundly and specifically altered by processing. . . .
>
> The nerve center of this mechanical organism is the control room with its control panel. Here are ensconced the human operator-attendants upon the little mechanical operators of the plant. The human operators watch, they sometimes help or correct the instruments, but only occasionally do they take over the major part of operating responsibility. . . .
>
> On the control panel are many things — indicators of measurements, indicators of valve positions, indicators of the settings of controllers, knobs for changing these settings, facilities for shifting from automatic to manual control, knobs for effecting manual controls, alarms and safety devices, recording of measurements for operation analyses, and recordings of measurements for accounting. . . . Five hundred controllers, 400 motor operated valves, 15,000 indicators and 800 recorders are in slight but significant motion at all times — like the steering wheel of a speeding motor car on a straight road.[11]

Notion of Self-Regulation Whatever happens in a process may be used to affect the process to achieve a desired result. This principle is the same whether we describe *control* as "feedback," "closed-loop,"* or some other term.

It appears possible that almost any physical process controllable by man can be made to control itself. In addition, processes not controlled 100 percent by man may be made self-controlling.

The notion of *control* through *feedback* becomes clearer if we consider the housewife's problem in cooking soup. She looks at the

---

*In "closed-loop" control the man is replaced by a control unit that receives the information from the sensing head, compares it with information in its memory and corrects any deviation. A closed-loop system controlled by feedback of information is also called a "servo mechanism." (See Chapter 2.)

soup, smells it, tastes it, and analyzes the condition of the soup with
respect to the desired temperature. If it is too hot, back it goes into
the pot to cool; if it is not hot enough, she will turn up the gas. The
process continues, with the wife acting as the regulator in a loop
running from soup to housewife to stove, and back again to soup.
This is not an automatic control system, although the state of the
soup is "fed back," and results in action being taken to alter the
condition of the soup. In effect it is an "open-loop" control system
in which the operator's function must be inserted if the system is
to operate properly.

Closing the Loop   Again using the soup illustration, let us replace the housewife's attention with a temperature monitor and
regulating device. The control device will permit current to flow to
the heating unit so long as the soup temperature is below that set.
The current will be shut off when the set temperature is exceeded.
The soup will then be brought to the desired temperature and held
within a few degrees of it. This results in "closed-loop" automatic
control.

For satisfactory automatic control the process must be one that
can be controlled by a change in a regulating device (for example,
a valve, a brake, or variable resistance); that the variable to be
controlled be measurable; that the measurement and resulting regula-
tion take place fast enough to keep the controlled variable near the
desired value. Oscillation in a control system introduces several
problems requiring correction. For example, in our previous illustration, if the housewife wants the soup to be just right, she needs to
stand at the stove, raising and lowering the gas flame until it is time
for serving. Otherwise the soup, when desired, may be too hot or
too cold. This problem of oscillation must be worked out in control
systems as well, since there is a time lag between determination of
the need for correction and the start of the correction process. We
may also find *over-* or *undercorrection.* The solution is obtained by
sensitive monitoring devices to increase or decrease the frequency of
feedback. High-speed communicating devices are used to shorten
time lags, and secondary feedback loops are introduced to provide
corrections for corrections.

Mechanical Power Versus Automation   Any process performed
with mechanical equipment is said to be mechanized. Automatic
equipment is that which, although not needing an operator, is not
self-regulating. *Self-regulating* systems are those using feedback

control. Whenever the necessity for operator control of a mechanized process is eliminated, it may be inferred that automation has taken effect.

Information Handling and the Computer Automation may be regarded as the process of arranging to have one kind of machine run another kind. Automation depends more on the handling of information than any other single factor. Self-guided missiles use the closed-loop control system in order to stay on target and hit the correct position. Machines that commonly handle information are called *computers*. These electronic computers operate with closed-loop control and constitute systems in themselves. If clerical or computational routines are viewed as processes, then the automatic production of numerical results from data is similar to the automatic production of goods from materials.

It is possible to conceive of a single, large, fully automated computing and production unit which would eliminate the manifold tasks of recording and analysis of information which now accompany the planning and direction of business activities and tie together all management processes and production activities. Input information would consist of criteria to be satisfied by the plant's operation and data including prices, sales quantities and material qualities. Operation of the plant would be adjusted automatically towards an optimum with every change in external and internal conditions.[12]

A fully automated computing and production unit can be achieved through the use of a general-purpose digital computer.

Electronic Computers Computers can be divided into two main types, digital and analog. The digital computer can be put to work in the office on such problems as data processing; the analog computer can be put to work in the plant on such activities as the control of machine tools. Research involving the solution of scientific and engineering problems generally entails a combining of both the digital and the analog computer in problem solving. More details concerning the characteristics of computers and their uses will be found in Chapter 2.

Comparison of Automation in the Metalworking and the Flow-Process Industries

Application of Automation to Metalworking Industries The application of automation in the shaping and assembling of metal parts differs somewhat from that in the flow-process plant. In the former, individual units must be moved and fabricated. Automation moves them, holds them in position, and fabricates them. In addition to these direct operations, machine preparation, maintenance, inspection operations, and other nondirect activities can be automated.

It is more difficult to replace the operator in the metalworking plant than in the flow-process plant. However, mechanisms to position materials, to start and stop work, and to eject materials can all be used to reduce operator time and effort. Special setups, short runs, and the need for the operator to adapt the machine's function to a specific job order all limit the possibility of automating the general-purpose equipment usually found in smaller companies.

Where large volumes of material are to be handled, the problem of introducing automation in the metal industry is simplified. Instead of passing small pieces of metal back and forth in rolling mills, the use of continuous strip has been developed. In the machine tool industry, more rigid and powerful units for high-speed surface cutting have been designed. These firms employ tungsten carbide tools.

For small parts like screws, screw machines perform a sequence of operations on a piece. This sequence is built into the machines by the mechanical arrangement of several tools to engage the work piece progressively. Unit-type machines, consisting of a single machine tool element and a power source, such as a drill-head, may be flexibly assembled with other units into special-purpose combinations. Automatic handling, loading, and unloading devices with which standard machines can be linked together replace manual handling between operations in many applications.

The so-called push-button plants illustrate the ease with which some semblance of automation may be achieved without necessarily going in for closed-loop control. One production line automatically performing 555 drilling, milling, boring, reaming, countersinking, and tapping operations at fifty-three stations can turn out one hundred finished blocks an hour. Individual machine cycles are counted automatically, and when a predetermined number have been reached the unit shuts itself off so that a tool setup man can replace the dull tools. The only direct labor in the line is the initial positioning of the blocks in the loading station.[13]

In the auto industry, automation is found as well in forging and stamping plants. Automatic shell molding, automatic core-making machines, semiautomatic forging presses, plating equipment with which three men do the work of one hundred hand platers, electronically controlled spray painting equipment, and many other items are now common in auto fabricating plants.

Since, for the most part, the automobile industry is primarily interested in the mass production of components, only the first stages of automated operations are observed. When auto firms move into complete automation, the qualities of judgment and adaptability now found in the operators have to be reproduced in the machines.

Fully automatic control in the metal industry will be achieved by uniting the information-handling functions of computers to the fabricating machines by means of "numerical control." Under such control the observer will see a tool guided by instructions coded in numerical values on a punched paper tape, magnetic tape, or photographic film. The position of the punched holes, magnetized areas, or dark and light spots represents digits that will be read by the computer. Interpretation of the code by the computer results in its originating impulses, which actuate machine elements to move the tool or the work. A feedback system operates at the same time to detect and correct deviations from desired values.

Numerically controlled machine tools, which run almost untouched by human hands from instructions punched on tapes or cards, are beginning to revolutionize short-run metalworking production.

The coded tapes are usually prepared by methods devised at the Massachusetts Institute of Technology. This system requires an experienced machinist's direction for producing a part, which is then converted by a computer into coded tape instructions for hundreds or thousands of machine tool positions required to do the job. The tape can be re-used indefinitely.

The machine tools cut out the metal shapes automatically, by following "programmed" instructions through tape or punch card. These coded holes are "read" by the computer, which controls the motion of the machine tools.

The coded tape control of Kearney and Trecker Corporation's "Milwaukee-Matic" selects tools from a battery of thirty-one, stored in a drum. It can rotate the tool up to 4000 rotations a minute and can cut at speeds up to 99 inches a minute. The automatic machine can handle simple slopes and arcs; it can rough-cut, finish-cut, ream, tap, and bore. Tool changes take nine seconds.[14]

Business Week[15] reported a case study of automatic machine tools where machines automatically cut three-dimensional curves for parts in aircraft. The Sundstrand Machine Tool Company produces an automatic lathe that gauges each part as it is produced and automatically resets the cutting tools to compensate for tool wear. In addition, when the cutting tools have been worn down to a certain predetermined point, the machine automatically replaces the worn tools with sharp ones. The parts are automatically loaded onto the machine and are automatically unloaded as they are completed. Lathes can be operated at least five to eight hours without attention, except for an occasional check to make sure that the parts are being delivered to the loading mechanism.

Continuous Automatic Production   The machining department of the Ford engine plant in Cleveland is perhaps the best-known example of Detroit automation, or continuous automatic production. It also demonstrates the stepped-up pace of technological change. In 1952, Ford started operations in this plant to machine automobile engine blocks with a battery of seventy-one machines linked together into an automatic line about 1600 feet long. Automatic machine tools perform more than five hundred boring, broaching, drilling, honing, milling, and tapping operations with little human assistance. The timing of each operation is synchronized so that the line moves forward uniformly. In announcing the opening of this plant, the Ford News Bureau stated:

> Rough castings of engine blocks and heads that later emerge from the Cleveland plant in engines operating under their own power are seldom touched by workmen during their machining route to the final assembly line. . . . Electric nerve centers direct them, by mechanical arms and fingers, from one cutting machine to another in much the same manner that a policeman directs traffic.[16]

America's major industries never stopped the constant push for technical improvements. This was true at Ford's Cleveland plant. When the plant first commenced operations, it was estimated that 154 engine blocks an hour ran through the production line, requiring 41 workers, compared to 117 workers with the same production by use of older methods. In the years since 1952, the move at Ford toward automation made the 1952 plant appear obsolete. Bright reported that "in four research visits to the Ford Cleveland plant over an eighteen-month period, the cylinder block line never appeared the same twice. Always there were changes in machinery since the last visit."

Continuous automatic production methods are in operation throughout the automobile industry and are being utilized in the assembly of radio, television, and other electronic equipment components.

Continuous-Process Industries Automation may be applied in continuous-process industries operating on a continuous-flow principle with maximum effect. Principal among these are petroleum refineries and chemical plants. When the first workerless plant appears, it will in all probability be a "flow" plant.

In a continuous-flow plant ingredients flow through processes in an uninterrupted stream as they are converted from raw materials to products. Materials, generally liquids or gases, are confined in closed pipes or tanks during the production process. One does not see anything happening. A maze of valves and instruments must be observed in order to measure and interpret temperatures, pressures, liquid levels, and rates within and between processes. Extensive instrumentation is a necessity. Catastrophic results can be caused by loss of control of processes operating at high temperatures and pressures.

Process control in most modern flow plants is accomplished by a combination of operator control and automatic control. Automatic feedback instruments are constantly at work turning valves, starting and stopping pumps, and performing other operations, but recording instruments indicating the quality of the process are available at key points for observation by operators. The operator is usually in complete control only during start-up, shutdown, or emergencies. Most of the operator's time is spent in scanning dials and making minor corrections in the automatic control equipment settings aimed at maximum yield, or in changing product properties as indicated by laboratory analysis of samples.

The operation of a catalytic cracking unit in a petroleum refinery is a good illustration of the points involved. About 15 percent of current capital investment in petroleum refining facilities is for automation, and the direct labor costs in oil processing are less than 10 percent of total costs, yet this industry can travel still further to total automation. If a plant employing eight hundred people were automated (in the fullest possible way), it is said that the operating staff (not maintenance men) could be cut to about a dozen men!

In the flow-process industries — those producing petro-chemicals, synthetic fibers, plastics, paints, for example — the general trend is toward the development of greater instrumentation that will make it possible to determine automatically the internal state of the process and, therefore, to eliminate indirect measures. With new analyzers, sensing devices, and automatic logging mechanisms, centralized control under operator supervision can be achieved. In this manner, the programs of the computers will specify actions to be taken in response to every situation for the entire plant.

Automation and the Worker

Despite the problems of displacement and dislocation, the popular belief that the new technology will replace human labor by robots is not well founded or reliable. In the thirties it was believed that mass production would throw people out of work in appalling numbers. Time has proved the contrary. In fact, the skilled worker as a class grew strong, and the unskilled laborer, while eliminated for the most part, became the nucleus of the semiskilled class. The semiskilled worker today enjoys a better level of living and is much better educated than the former unskilled worker. Technological changes will move further in this direction, requiring large numbers of highly skilled and well-trained persons. A new type of manager and supervisor will be necessary to think the problems through, and technicians will be required to design the new equipment, to operate it, and to repair and maintain it.

Public Psychology about "Automation"   The term "automation" has broad significance among millions of working men, managers, clerks, and school children. To some it means the miracle of progress; to others job insecurity and displacement. In the early fifties the term was hardly known. Today, although it is a familiar word, it means different things to different people, and misunderstanding and controversy surround its use.

> For some, mention of automation conjures up an image of a world of robots in which humans do no work. For others automation suggests the intricate engineering problems of the self-regulating systems. To many, automation is practically synonymous with mechanization in industry. For most, however, the term is a vague one having something to do with electronics and automatic production. Just what it all means for the man in the street is not too clear.[17]

Concern by Congress for Human Factor   Within the past few years Congressional committees have been studying the impact of automation on the American worker. In the *Economic Report of the Congressional Joint Committee* (Subcommittee on Economic Stabilization), this statement was made:

> It is clearly wrong to discuss automation as nothing more than an extension of mechanization. We are clearly on the threshold of an industrial age, the significance of which we cannot predict and with potentialities which we cannot fully appreciate. . . .
>
> The fact that representatives of organized labor are watchful, lest the material gains of automation become the sole objective, without recognizing the individual hardships that may be caused by job losses and skill displacements, ought not be turned into a charge that labor, as such, is obstructive to new developments. . . .
>
> Whenever one has been in a position to have witnessed first hand the hardships experienced by the skilled and older worker in any line of endeavor — industrial or professional — suddenly wrenched from the job by the installation of a new machine, or new technology, one can scarcely be unmindful of the inequities which can come about where management and public policy have not given recognition to needs for retraining, relocation, severance pay and other programs which tend to soften the transition. . . .
>
> However much we may welcome the fruits of advancing technology — however optimistic one may be that the problems of adjustment will not be serious — no one dare overlook or deny the fact that many individuals will suffer personal, mental and physical hardships as the adjustments go forward. . . .
>
> The subcommittee recommends that industry, and management for its part, must be prepared to accept the human costs of displacement and retraining as charges against the savings from the introduction of automation.[18]

While we all want to share in the benefits of a prosperous America, we obviously want to avoid, whether we be employers or union representatives, the terrible toll of displacement, unemployment, and social disorganization. Let us hope that the various techniques suggested by Congress will hasten the advance of technology — and at the same time benefit workers. Although these two goals appear to be antithetical, they are, in fact, attainable, with proper planning at both the national level and the enterprise level.

As one union leader said recently:

> We in the union field are not afraid of automation — we believe that it could be a blessing to our nation — that men will work less and

produce more, thus permitting sufficient leisure time to progress culturally and develop as individuals. However, we are not certain that families will not starve, that breadwinners will not lose their jobs — that employers will not provide security through collective agreements. . . . Neither are we certain that, with innovation, new industries will spring up to employ those whose jobs pass away as a result of automation.[19]

Accept and Exploit   Thomas J. Watson, president of the International Business Machines Corporation, which has made a tremendous contribution to efficiency in industry, had this to say about the general problems:

> We can't argue that technological change and automation are not labor-saving devices. Of course they are. They do cause displacement of people. In fact to do so is one of their major purposes. They may also upgrade people or increase the prosperity of an industry so that more are employed.
>
> There are three main approaches that we might take toward handling technological change and the unemployment it creates: (1) Retard it, and spare ourselves the pain of adjusting to it. (2) Let it come on, and take the benefit of it in increased leisure, spreading employment around by adopting a shorter work week. (3) Accept it fully, push it *ahead* with vigor, and exploit its benefits while controlling its hazards.[20]

Further Automation in the Seventies?   In 1951 two Canadian physicists, E. W. Leaver and J. J. Brown, foresaw the results of automation in terms of the complete electronic management not only of industrial production, but also of business and government communication, financial movement, and commercial distribution. They outlined eight principles, which have not yet entirely materialized, but which, in 1951, they believed would bring about a new organization of work in society. Perhaps the late sixties and early seventies will justify their judgment. These principles are as follows:

1. Machines should replace men wherever possible.
2. Men should not be used for routine operations if machines can do the work.
3. Automaticity of machines should be encouraged.
4. Automaticity of men should be discouraged.
5. Men must be ancillary to machines.
6. Machines must be designed in terms of their function, not in terms of the final product.
7. Machines must be utilized in terms of common denomination of electronics.

8. Units must be adaptable so that they can be plugged into each other to make different combinations.[21]

These Canadian physicists concluded in the main that widespread automation might bring an era of peace and creative human development.

Effect of Work Conditions on Human Beings The real meaning of automation lies less in the machines involved than in how the machines will affect human beings and their conditions of work. Substantial changes can be expected in conditions of work, occupations, wages, job classifications, union membership, and even in the structure of the enterprise. Technical change will bring with it social change.

Conclusion

Automation has a long history. It goes back in part to the early Romans, and there have been many illustrations of it within the past two hundred years in Europe and the United States. Jacquard punch cards were used in the textile industry in the eighteenth century and in the twentieth century. Mass production, with its "full mechanization," began to take on many of the aspects of automation.

The major developments since "Detroit automation" with its transfer-machine linkage, have been the marvelous improvements in electronic technology that have permitted self-regulation of the machine with its "feedback" controls.

Automation is utilizing the computer in both the plant and the office at a rapid pace. It is having a revolutionary influence on business organization, plant management, and labor relations. The metalworking industry and the petroleum-flow process plants are already well advanced in these new technologies, and labor unions and Congress are beginning to show concern for the lack of reactivity of workers displaced by automation.

References

1. Peter Drucker, *The Practice of Management* (New York: Harper & Row, Publishers, 1954), p. 19.
2. *Ibid.*
3. *Ibid.*, p. 21.

4. Charles C. Killingsworth, "Automation in Manufacturing," (reprint). Industrial Relations Research Association, *Proceedings of Eleventh Annual Meeting* (Michigan State University Labor and Industrial Relations Center, 1958–1959), p. 2.

5. J. Diebold, "Integrating Automation into Our Economy," *Monthly Labor Review*, (May 1955), pp. 526–527.

6. James R. Bright, "Skill Requirements and Wage Aspects of Automation," presented at University of Pennsylvania Labor Relations Conference, November 18, 1960, p. 1 from *Industrial Relations in the 1960's: Problems and Prospects*, George W. Taylor and Edward B. Shils, eds., vol. 1 (February 15, 1961).

7. Killingsworth, *op. cit.*, p. 2.

8. Jack Rogers, *Automation — Technology's New Face* (Berkeley: Institute of Industrial Relations, University of California) 1958, p. 3.

9. "Labor Looks at Automation," AFL-CIO Publication no. 21 (July 1959).

10. Rogers, *op. cit.*, p. 8.

11. *Scientific American* (September 1952).

12. Rogers, *op. cit.*, p. 15.

13. *Ibid.*, p. 26.

14. AFL-CIO Publication no. 21, *op. cit.*

15. *Business Week*, April 4, 1959.

16. *Cleveland Plain Dealer* (September 1952), p. 13.

17. Rogers, *op. cit.*, p. 1.

18. *Automation and Technological Change*, Hearing, Joint Committee on the Economic Report, Congress of the United States, October 14–28, 1955 (Washington, D.C.: U. S. Government Printing Office, 1955), pp. 219–243.

19. William Gomberg, "American Workers' and Employers' Reaction to Automation," *Free Labour World* (Brussels), no. 60 (June 1955), pp. 11–14.

20. Thomas J. Watson, "Accept and Exploit," *Automation* (August 1961), p. 158.

21. E. W. Leaver and J. J. Brown, "Electronics and Human Beings," *Harper's Magazine* (August 1951), pp. 88–93.

▶▶▶▶ **2**

The Computer:
Its Use in the Plant
and the Office

When the first giant, all-electronic digital computer went into operation in 1946, fantastic predictions about its capabilities were heard. Such "giant brains," it was said, would speedily take over all the paper functions of business and the running of entirely automatic factories. Actually these impressive monsters have proved harder to tame and put to work than was first imagined. They are finally being domesticated, and computers are functioning on a day-to-day basis in a variety of tasks in the plant and the office.

Electronic Computers

Computers can be divided into two main types, digital and analog. The *digital* computer, as its name implies, operates with numbers represented in digital form, a digit being one of a definite set of symbols and used to represent numbers. Thus, this method depends primarily upon a relationship between number and quantity. The digital computer is used in electronic data processing. The *analog* computer, on the other hand, relies on an analogy of quantity; thus, it deals with physical quantities and not numbers. For example, a length of 12 inches in a digital computer might be represented by, say, a thousand units or pulses; in an analog computer, by a voltage of, say, 100 volts. Analog computers have scientific, engineering, and industrial uses.

The computer has a machine "language" consisting of patterns of electrical signals used as code symbols for numbers and letters of the alphabet, just as in telegraphy the Morse code is used to transmit messages from place to place. Because the computer communicates by means of electrical signals, it is able to translate information from

19

the patterns on punched cards or teleprinter tape, from impulses arising in modified typewriter keyboards, and from records made on magnetic tape. Also, by the use of teleprinter lines, it is able automatically to receive and transmit information over any desired distance.

The digital computer uses the basic arithmetic of addition and subtraction from which multiplication and division are derived. Because of the very high speed at which the computer works, these operations can be carried out at a tremendous pace.

Whereas the digital computer has recently stolen the limelight, the extended field of use of the analog machine must be mentioned, because it does fall within the fringe of automation. The uses of this kind of computer, besides that of machine-tool control, include the solution of scientific and engineering problems, in which a combination of digital and analog machines can be used when necessary.

Machine tools can be controlled by both the digital computer and the analog computer. A component must be specifically designed and dimensioned to suit the digital computer. Planning involves determination of coordinates at each point of change, type of curve, etc. The computer reads the tape input and produces continuous impulses on four channels so interrelated as to produce the required tool movement. Pulses are recorded on magnetic tape, and servomechanisms follow instructions from magnetic tape distances being measured by optical gratings. Thus any three-dimensional surface may be contained.[1]

Machine tools can also be controlled by an analog computer, which differs from the digital computer in that it deals with physical quantities and not numbers. For instance, a length defined in an engineering drawing may be represented by the number of pulses in a digital computer, but by voltage in an analog computer. A change in the input voltage will enable an analog computer to move the cutting tool from one point to another in the same line of motion, and three applied voltages will completely determine the position of the cutting tool.

The use of electronic computers is still at a fairly early stage in the control of machine tools and in the process industries; it is more advanced in business operations and in clerical work, and forms part of an important trend toward the automatic operation of the office. Computers are being used to unsnarl red tape between the office and the plant, to provide extra information for management decisions, and to reduce overhead in many ways.

Thinking Machines

Thinking Machine? Giant mechanical brain? You can't tell me there is any such thing. I can understand a watch that keeps accurate time or a derrick that lifts giant weights. But thinking is different. Machines can't think. Anyway I'm not sure I'd want one around if I could.[2]

Are these computers "brains"? More and more major companies are turning them out in large numbers. Where they are too expensive for one company to buy, they are shared or "rented" on a service basis. It is well known that digital computers solve weather problems, are used in reviewing income tax returns, and serve to run automated factories. Great credence is given to the statement that computers can solve in a few minutes problems which would take trained mathematicians and scientists fifteen years to work out.

Early Origins of the Computer

The computer was not an overnight phenomenon. It all started with simple counting in the days of Neolithic man, who by using his fingers could count from one to ten. Later, stones on the ground, pellets on a grooved board, beads on wires — all these evolved into the abacus, the ancient calculating instrument of the Far East.

The first adding machine, developed by Blaise Pascal in 1642, was an adaptation of the abacus. William Leibnitz, a German, followed in the late seventeenth century with a machine capable of adding, subtracting, dividing, and multiplying. In 1812 Charles Babbage, an Oxford mathematics professor, designed a "difference engine" and an "analytical engine," which were capable of doing advanced mathematics.

In 1872 Charles Seaton, a chief clerk at the U. S. Bureau of the Census, developed a mechanical tabulator that simultaneously registered horizontal and vertical sums and rapidly processed large amounts of data in sequence. Lord Kelvin, in 1875, gave the world the idea for a large-scale continuous variable machine (a differential analyzer), in a series of papers given before the Royal Society. The U. S. Census again made a major contribution through Dr. Herman Hollerith, who, in 1887, adapted a punched-paper control system to statistical work. His work, together with that of James Powers, was the forerunner of today's punched-card tabulating systems.

In 1919, in an article in *Radio Review*, W. H. Eccles and F. W. Jordon of the United States first described electronic "trigger circuits," which could be used for automatic counting.

In 1925 Dr. Vannevar Bush, while a professor of electrical engineering at M.I.T., designed and built the first successful differential analyzer — the first large-scale computing machine. In 1930, and again in 1942, he improved upon his earlier work by combining elements electrically and feeding in data by special tapes.

Units in a General-Purpose Digital Computer

A general-purpose digital computer is comprised of the following units:

1. *Input and output units* through which the machine communicates with the world of men, receiving information to be processed and returning it in intelligible form (read-out). Since the machine is electronic, information must be presented to it in electronic or electronic-convertible form.

2. *A control or programming unit* which sets up instructions for the machine including built-in or self-sequencing routines. Since the machine has no will of its own, it must be told electronically what to do, how to do it and when to do it. The instructions may involve routines and subroutines wired into the machine and on tap for use whenever needed.

3. *A memory unit* in which both instructions and data are stored. The data in the memory unit are essentially reference information which the machine requires in order to deal with the problems presented to it. A location of data within the machine is called an "address."

4. *An arithmetic unit* to add, subtract, multiply and divide. A machine which can add can do anything mathematical. Subtraction is only negative addition; it makes no difference to the machine whether it adds 70 and 60 impulses to make 130, or whether having recorded 130, it brings it back to 70 by wiping out 60. If the machine has no special circuits to multiplication and division, it can obtain the answers by multiple addition and subtraction. And, odd as it may seem, if one can compute fast enough it is feasible to solve complex mathematical functions by simple arithmetic, without resorting to the special techniques of higher mathematics.[3]

Training of Programmers Required

The value of these machines is their intensive memory, which is beyond the ability of human beings. These machines, however, depend on proper programming, which is the work of humans. What comes out will be wrong unless what goes in is proper and appropriate. Thus an entirely new employment area has become accessible. Young people will be interested in entering that branch of engineering leading to the construction of computers, either as inventors or designers.

For the "trouble shooters," thousands of jobs will be open to fixers, who will maintain and service computers. Each large computer contains thousands of tubes or transistors, all susceptible to maintenance and repair.

To those young persons interested in the feeding of problems to the computers, the field of coding might be attractive. Coders are greatly in demand today.

Those interested in mathematics will be valuable in computer work, as the mathematician is the key person in any computer laboratory. His role is deciding whether a problem is suitable for the workings of the "brain," and just how to break this problem down into a logical flow chart. These mathematicians must be able to speak the language of the economist, the scientist, the engineer, and anyone else who will need the service of the computer.

The computer will create a need for highly trained salesmen as well.

Harvard-Mark I

Mathematical researchers at MIT were used extensively by the Government during World War II for the preparation of ballistics data. It was soon obvious that there was need for a speed in calculation beyond the abilities of the analog computers then in existence. H. H. Aiken, working for Naval Ordnance and IBM at Harvard University in 1944, completed the first large-scale general-purpose digital computer, the Automatic Sequence Controlled Calculator, called "Harvard-Mark I." While the major contribution of this mechanical unit was greater accuracy than that of the differential analyzers, it was still not capable of outstanding speed. It had no vacuum tubes and lacked flexibility. Elaborate sequences could be completed much more quickly than desk calculators, as, for example, addition in three tenths of one second (ten to twenty times faster than an ordinary calculator). Nevertheless, the mechanical factor limited the action time. The Mark I project became the forerunner of a whole set of "alphabetical" cousins, each moving the world a bit closer to the design of today's computers.

Eniac, Seac, Ordvac, Edvac are abbreviations of somewhat lengthy computer names. The Oak Ridge atomic energy project uses a computer named "Oracle." This is not an oracle in the traditional sense. The last two letters of the name stand for "logical engine."

Eniac

J. Presper Eckert, Jr., and Dr. John W. Mauchly of the University of Pennsylvania were the inventors and developers of Eniac (Electronic Numerical Integrator and Computer), the first all-purpose, all-electric digital computer, completed and delivered to Army Ordnance in 1946. Eniac, with speeds one thousand times faster than those of the electromechanical predecessors, opened up an entirely new field of electronic computation. The first problem put to Eniac — a nuclear physics computation — would have taken one hundred engineers a full year to solve by conventional means. With the new techniques the answer was obtained in two weeks, only two hours of which were devoted to actual computation, the remainder being given to operational details and review of the results.[4]

In 1950 Binac was also invented by Eckert and Mauchly and produced by their own company. This electronic computer was the first machine to use the principle of self-checking. In 1951 Eckert and Mauchly sold their company to Remington Rand, and were responsible for delivery of Univac I to the Census Bureau. This event was responsible for the founding of today's $1,400 billion computer industry.

This new unit was the first computer to handle both numerical and alphabetical information equally well. It also utilized the principle of storage of information, and divorced the complex input and output problems from actual computation operation. With Univac, electronic data processing came of age. This was made evident as a result of a computer census made by John Diebold and Associates in mid-1961, which found that 5371 computers of all types were in operation at that time.

A new Univac was delivered in late 1961 to the University of Pennsylvania as a ten-year anniversary gift in appreciation of the earlier research work. The new computer, a solid-state 80 computing system, is the most up to date to be installed at any university, and utilizes such solid-state electronic devices as transistors, diodes, and printed circuitry. The computer performs 11,706 additions and subtractions a second and prints out the results of computation at the rate of six hundred lines a second.[5]

Univac Larc was recently built for the Navy and the Atomic Energy Commission. Larc is one hundred times faster than Eniac and works in billionths of a second, or nanoseconds. Today, laboratories such as the new Univac Engineering Center at Whitpain, Pennsylvania, are at work seeking speeds twenty times faster than the Larc in order to meet the time-control problems of the aircraft and missile industries. Similar refinements are continually being sought in other areas of performance — in memory storage, search, sort, and fact-updating facilities — so that computer applications and service can continue to diversify and improve. It is hoped that the selection and utilization of personnel to handle these units progress at the same pace as technical innovation.

Computer Users

It is estimated that 15 percent of the total computers, mostly of the analog type, are being used for scientific and engineering purposes. They are used extensively in the control of industrial processes as well as in fields of atomic physics, chemistry, and other physical science applications, such as pretesting flight performance, space flight communications and control, and satellite checking. These computers will speed up the application of scientific research and theory.

> The benefit of discoveries in thermodynamics of the American mathematician and physicist, J. Willard Gibbs, was denied the world for many years because of the absence of adequate computing devices. It took several years of careful and laborious computing to produce the tables and other data required in designing and building heating, refrigeration, air-conditioning, and other modern heat-exchange equipment.[6]

Forty percent of all computers are involved in military applications. Rockets, radar, and supersonic speeds are to a large extent dependent upon electronic computers, used for fire control, ballistics, rocket tracking, computing logistics problems, tracing submarines, and early warning systems against surprise attack — for example, Sage, Norad, and similar systems. The Armed Forces are also using many computers on the management level.

The number of Federal employees running electronic computers has grown from 4000 in 1958 to 9000 in 1961. If present projections are correct, the number will grow to 30,000 by 1965.[7] In 1960 the Federal Government had 524 electronic computers on nonclassified work and about another 100 on classified work; state and local governments used 131 in all.

Business data processing systems account for the remaining 45 percent of the computers in use. Large-scale computers are used by over five hundred United States firms. The first application of the computer was to routine paper work — payroll, accounting, bill handling, record-keeping. Now, marketing and production have begun to feel the influence of computer application. The outlook for business applications in the future is breath-taking. There are currently on order double the number of computers now in use. Thousands of smaller computers are being used in department stores, factories, and other businesses.

Programming

A set of instructions is called a *program*. The reading in of the data proceeds as the steps in the program are executed. Punched cards, tape, or some other medium can be used. As the medium is moved through the reader, it translates the data and instructions into circuit states. Instructions and data are held in the computer pending their use, and results must be held until they are read out. The data storage unit or "memory" performs this function. Information is held in a computer memory as a state of the device. For example, as the rotating drum passes a reading head, a magnetic drum memory stores information as magnetized spots on its surface, which can be detected as pulses. Each location on the drum has an "address," to which the control unit may route a signal and from which it may recall as needed. Thus the instruction program of a computer contains step-by-step directions for the storage of data or specified addresses, recall of the data for manipulation, and storage of the results.

Reading-out devices operate in an opposite way from read-in devices. The output data are translated as they emerge from the main body of the computer in binary coded form or as pulses into some physical form. The output may be punched into cards or paper tapes, recorded on magnetic tapes, or printed out as numbers and letters.

Computers and Automatic Devices

Engineers and scientists dreamed of the day when machines would run machines. This has now occurred in the petroleum industry with the advent of the computer. On March 12, 1959, the Texas Company added an electronic computer to provide central automatic controls for its Port Arthur Texas Refinery, which had been set up with automatic devices in 1942. The automatic devices, which control the oil refining processes, are now regulated and controlled automatically by an electronic computer.

Monsanto Chemical Company and B. F. Goodrich Chemical Company have each begun computer installations in an effort to achieve fully automatic industrial processing. A recent article on this new development at Port Arthur discussed it as follows:

> Automatic remote controls in the plant long ago cut the crew requirements to three men per shift. A human operator simply can't look about at 50 recorder-controls that indicate pressure, temperature and flow; then relate the readings that indicate the level of activity of the reaction or condition of the catalyst; then calculate the complex interrelationships of the process, all in time to reset the controls to keep the plant operating at maximum efficiency. . . . Texaco's RW-300 computer, on the other hand, has no difficulty doing that job every five minutes, twenty-four hours per day.[8]

Computers and Numerical Control

As was indicated, an oil refinery in Texas is completely controlled by a giant computer. It does a better job than the former human operators. The Air Force has a computer which is the key component of a machine that translates Russian into English. It now translates 40 words a minute; shortly it may do 2400 words a minute. Bell Telephone is working on a device by which a statement made in English at one end of the line will come out in French at the other end.

The metalworking industry is combining computers with mechanical or electrical control devices, a technique called numerical control, which is like the old-fashioned player piano. Technicians take engineering drawings and, using a special computer language, feed information into the computer. The computer makes the necessary calculations and works out the detailed instructions, which are recorded on tape or punch cards. The tape or punch cards are then plugged into a control unit on a machine tool, after which step the operation becomes automatic. The control unit can even inspect the work of the machine tool and make instantaneous corrections while the work is in progress.

The significance of numerical control lies in its ability to reduce machine time and increase quality. The cost of one large aircraft part was reduced from $18,500 a unit by conventional methods to $1950 by numerical control, a reduction of 90 percent. The machining time on one part used in electrical manufacture was reduced from sixty hours to forty-five minutes, and the rejection rate dropped from 50 percent to 2 percent with numerical control.[9] In 1960 the U. S. Steel Corporation opened a new rolling mill in Chicago, utilizing numerical control techniques. It is estimated that this technique is feasible on 90 percent of present-day metalworking operations.

Value and Saving in Office Work

The computer becomes a powerful tool in the paper-work area because of its memory and speed of recall. Where man-days are now required, jobs can be done in seconds. In making up payrolls under present methods, a firm may involve itself with many repetitive steps. Pay rates are applied to hours worked by each employee, various deductions are calculated, and checks and earnings statements are written out. When this job is handled by the automatic data processing systems, manual operations are not required after transcription of the data in machine language. A deck of punched cards with information on hours worked plus "exceptions" to the usual deductions is fed into the system. The pay and deductions of each employee are computed automatically by applying the proper rates previously fed into the "memory" of the system, are recorded, and the check and earnings statement are printed automatically.

Value of Data Processing

The same paper-saving techniques can be applied in summarizing voluminous information on sales invoices into tabular form by items, product lines, outlets, territories, or time periods. In inventory control, withdrawals from and additions to stock are registered in the computer memory so that a particular stock balance can be extracted in seconds from the memory.

In the future most functions of analysis and control in business will be performed by electronic equipment. Not only will routine data processing be handled, but in addition process control computer elements will be lined together, as well as with those programmed for analysis — then the computer will get into the realm of business decision making.

Decision making is certainly possible in production scheduling where a firm keeps track of use versus capacity in each department. New orders are tested against production time available and entered on a master schedule. Alternative schedules may be examined in terms of their costs and optimal loadings determined. Some day, with completely automated plants, the computer will transmit signals directly to equipment controls, and progress information will be fed back to the scheduling computer without human intervention.

The amazing feature of computers is that, besides having memory, they have fantastic speed. In the tracking of man-made satellites, orbits can be predicted by computers by making 42,000 mathematical calculations a second. Hundreds of clerks would be helpless in the face of this assignment.

From a report made by Armstrong-Cork Company on the use of a medium-sized computer it was learned that in about eight hours the computer can make all the calculations required to determine the gross payroll, deductions, and net pay for the 3000 employees where formerly about 225 man-hours of calculations were required.

A special-purpose computer in a Chicago mail order house is reported to handle 90,000 tallies a day, keeping track of inventory on the 8000 items in the firm's catalogue. One government check-writing machine can turn out 80,000 checks a day. The Bell system's long-distance dialing, direct from the subscriber's phone, is made possible by automatic message accounting. This system uses a combination of electronic units to record both local and long-distance calls, to assign these calls to the proper subscriber's account, and to prepare and print the telephone bills automatically.

The New York Life Insurance Company uses a computer to calculate premiums and dividends for over $20 billion of life insurance policies. The machine also types out premium notices for mailing. The U. S. Social Security accounts for 80,000,000 persons are reviewed four times a year by two electronic data processing machines.

American Airlines has a "Magnetronic Reservisor." Any one of separate sales offices in the New York area can quiz the central drum of a computer to find out the availability of seats for a specific flight. A light flashes on the keyboard of the interrogating unit located in the sales office, indicating whether the seat is available. The clerk informs the customer of a reservation by using a key system.

The National Cash Register Company has on the market a "Sales-Tronic" complete register for retail stores. This machine rings up a sale and punches on tape the following information: clerk's number, customer's account number, classification of sale (cash, charge, c.o.d.), color of item, size, stock number, various taxes, and other related information. A clerk can write this up in one operation. Add a computer to this method and the store could have rapid reports on inventory, departmental comparisons, fast and slow items, commissions due clerks, and other data.

Widening Application

In numerous bakeries, biscuits and bread are prepared, baked, and packaged by automatic and semiautomatic equipment. In meat packing, semiautomatic hide-pulling machines strip the hides off slaughtered cattle. Huge chemical plants operate with a few production and maintenance workers. Steel mills, pulp and paper plants, large saw mills, printing plants, public utility plants and textile plants are going into fuller mechanized or automated operations.

Retail supermarkets are more and more using automatic or semiautomatic equipment, turntables at check-out counters, automatic bagging, automatic wrapping machines for the prepackaging of goods, semiautomatic scale and labeling machines, and conveyor belts and chutes.

In warehousing, electronic selection mechanisms, automatic conveyors, and automatic loading and unloading machines have combined to make warehouse operations almost fully automatic.

Robot track-laying equipment, automatic signaling and communications systems equipment, devices for the automatic handling and dispatching of freight cars are among the new developments in transportation.

The morning papers are being printed, folded, and assembled with automatic equipment. Food and drink are cleaned, processed, inspected, wrapped, boxed, canned, and bottled by automation. It is getting more difficult to find a mass-produced item that has not had automatic handling somewhere along the line.

Conclusion

The computer technology is advancing so rapidly it is making many skills obsolete. With work made easier by use of computers and automated equipment, a better way of life is certainly possible. There is, however, a transitional period wherein the computer and the fully automated plant will cause severe unemployment and labor displacement. The succeeding chapters will discuss the roles of management, labor, and Government in alleviating the growing pains of an advancing technology in the face of what appears to be a slowing down in the rate of American economic expansion.

References

1. *Automation*, Department of Scientific and Industrial Research (London: Her Majesty's Stationery Office, 1956), p. 19.
2. Saul Gorn and Wallace Manheimer, *The Electronic Brain and What It Can Do* (Chicago: Science Research Associates, Inc., 1956), p. 2.
3. Carl Dreher, *Automation: What It Is, How It Works, Who Can Use It* (New York: W. W. Norton & Company, 1957), pp. 76–77.
4. *Pennsylvania Gazette*, November, 1961, vol. 60, no. 2, p. 21.
5. *Ibid.*, p. 16.
6. *Ibid.*
7. *Ibid.*, p. 22.
8. *Business Week*, April 4, 1959.
9. Charles C. Killingsworth, "Effects of Automation on Employment and Manpower Planning," reprint, No. 37 (Michigan State University Labor and Industrial Relations Center, 1960–61), p. 5.

▶ ▶ ▶ ▶ # 3

Impact of
Automation on National
Economic Security

Personnel experts have admitted in recent years their inability to cope with the increasing complexity of employment problems stemming in part from displacement of workers as a result of automation. A major part of the problem is the lack of specific data on causes of unemployment. The phrases "structural unemployment" and "displacement because of automation" are bandied about without sufficient examination or evidence. The need for a better understanding of the causes of unemployment is taxing the tempers of citizens, employers, labor leaders, Government officials, and, of course, the unemployed themselves.

The economist is wrestling with the matter of full employment; the personnel director, with increasing productivity without injuring union-management relations; national and state legislators, with problems of retraining and unemployment; the sociologist, with aged workers whose retirement should be accelerated; and all good citizens, whether businessmen or employees, are greatly concerned with their own futures in this great age of progress — the age of fuller mechanization and automation.

No longer can it be assumed that the science of personnel administration is a staff function alone. To solve the problems of human obsolescence, management must come up with a "new personnel administration." This must be a knowledge that will guide management in making the correct human, as well as the correct economic, decisions.

We need now to provide both the teacher and the active personnel worker with the necessary points of view about the automation age. Our training in scientific management and in technological know-how has surpassed our training in what to do about the people who are our responsibility, the kind of culture lag that is typically American. We are beating the speed of sound and blasting our way into space, but the by-products of the new technical knowledge have not always brought us industrial peace, or even prosperity.

When line management puts its engineering innovations into operation, it must exercise responsibility over the maladjustments affecting the work force. In many companies a lack of planning, for the most part, characterizes managerial decisions with respect to automation. This shortcoming adds to the total unemployed, creates distressed areas, and stimulates national legislators to introduce retraining legislation. If each company, through its line managers and staff personnel directors, were to study in advance the results of applying technological changes, the nation as a whole would benefit by this prudence.

Causes of Joblessness

Employers, labor unions, and the Government have mutual responsibilities to the unemployed. Secretary of Labor Arthur J. Goldberg, in March 1961, stated that the equivalent of 7,000,000 additional jobs would have to be created "in the next twelve months to bring idleness down to the true level," in line with President Kennedy's yardstick. The President had fixed a 4 percent jobless rate as his target for full employment attainable without inflation. In March 1961, the Bureau of Labor Statistics reported 5,500,000 unemployed, a rate of 6.9 percent.

The problem of keeping the unemployed from being put into a frozen pool of unwantedness is made more difficult by the fact that the labor market is flooded by millions of new workers, the vanguard of a generation born since World War II. These young persons are trooping into the labor market at a rate 40 percent faster than in the fifties.

This outpouring of youth into the employment market is coming at a time when the new technology is revolutionizing work methods in distribution, in farms, in offices and factories, and in mines and transport. Fuller mechanization, automation, and other industrial innovations promise vast possibilities of producing greater quantities of goods with fewer and fewer workers.

The United States population has risen sharply — it was about 125,000,000 in 1930 and is estimated at 208,000,000 in 1970. The heavy annual crop of babies is continuing and people are living longer. In the next decade the number of workers and those looking for jobs will grow faster than the population, according to the U. S. Labor Department. In 1930 the labor force amounted to about 52,000,000; by 1970 it is expected to reach 87,000,000.

It is important to note also that the number of young persons reaching working age is increasing rapidly. In 1960 about 2,600,000 boys and girls passed their eighteenth birthday. By 1970 the total will be 3,800,000 a year. Some will go to college, but most will hunt jobs.

Economic Upturns and Unemployment

Our Government is concerned that the number of unemployed persons may increase in future years, despite expected economic upturns. In January 1962 the nation had almost two million workers on the short workweek, men and women who normally work full time. When business improves, however, these persons will in all likelihood be put on full time before those who have been dropped from the payrolls will be recalled.

In the manufacturing industries as of April 1961, the average workweek ran a full hour below the level of the previous year. Thus an equivalent of about 350,000 jobs will apparently be filled by lengthening the present workweek of those already employed, rather than by bringing back those furloughed from work.

Output per Man-Hour Versus Manpower Requirements

When demand for goods and merchandise increases as a result of better business and improved business psychology, business and industry will be found increasing the productivity of the present work force. Poor business and austerity in the downturn have driven hard to eliminate waste, to increase output, and to introduce fuller mechanization, which creates more output per hour for each worker. Use of more efficient equipment, plus a desire of workers on incentive to take home more pay, after a period of lean earnings, increases productivity by double and triple the normal rate. Meanwhile the idle remain idle.

The Farm Precedent

What has happened in agriculture the past ten years is a dramatic example of what is happening in manufacturing. In the last decade farms produced 28 percent more food and fiber with 28 percent fewer men, women, and children at work, the climax of fifty years of the gradual supplanting of workers with machinery. Machine planting and machine harvesting have reduced farm employment from one third of the national work force to one tenth, and still there is a farm surplus. Moreover, new machinery may soon eliminate the migrant farm workers, who number about one-half million persons with annual incomes of less than $1,000 a year. How will these uneducated and unskilled workers, unused to city ways, find jobs in urban industries when the better educated and more highly skilled are in fear of technological unemployment?

The Railroads — An Example of Our National Dilemma

In the last forty years railroad employment in the United States has dropped from 2,000,000 to 800,000. To some extent this has been caused by improvement in equipment and method; to some extent, also, by competition from airlines and trucks. What worries us still, and makes the railroads a national problem, is a claim by railroad management that $600,000,000 a year is being wasted by "feather-bedding." Rail unions, on the other hand, are asking the Federal Government to stop further rail mergers, since those now contemplated would add 200,000 job displacements to the 400,000 claimed to have been abolished in the past years.

Concern of Office Workers

The awareness of severe job dislocations in manufacturing industries has caused fears among office workers that the marvelous developments in computers and other technological innovations will create the same situation in the office that has taken place in the factory. What of the high school and college graduates? Will the doors be locked to them in order to protect present workers in clerical, professional, and administrative positions?

Need for 13,500,000 Additional Jobs

The Department of Labor estimates that 13,500,000 new jobs will be necessary in the sixties, to keep up with the expected growth in the national labor force. An average rate of 25,000 new jobs a week is needed to accomplish three important things: (1) take care of entrants into the labor force; (2) place the unemployed in jobs; and (3) replace jobs made unnecessary by automation and fuller mechanization.

In 1960, 2,500,000 more workers entered the labor market than left it as a result of old age, death, retirement, or other reasons. This was more than double the average annual growth of 850,000 jobs a year for the past decade. By 1970, 3,000,000 young persons a year will be looking for jobs, compared to about 2,000,000 a year at present. The nation can look ahead to unemployment troubles of a kind not observed since the thirties, unless post high school and college opportunities are made available for a larger percentage of these young persons. As the face of industry changes, more and more the high school graduate finds himself relatively unskilled and unqualified. An awareness of this problem by the educators has led to the community college, offering a two-year program in which young men and women may acquire mathematical and technical skills desired by the more automated society.

Unemployment by Age Groups

Eighteen percent of workers aged 19 or under in the active labor market were unemployed as of January 1962. In the age group 20 to 24, the rate dropped to 14 percent. As might have been expected, this was three times as great as the 6 percent total for males between the ages of 35 to 44. It is unfortunate that the very young must drop out of school before completing high school. The drop-out rate in many large industrialized cities, where the socioeconomic level is low and the number of in-migrant Negroes from the South is substantial, is as high as 50 percent in the eleventh and twelfth grades. The Department of Labor estimates the national drop-out rate at about 30 percent.

Unemployment by Skill Groups

In the group of workers who are 21 and over, unemployment has been most severe in the unskilled and semiskilled groups in manufacturing, mining, and transportation. One out of five laborers is jobless. One out of every eight semiskilled factory hands or mechanics is jobless. Many of the jobless are unskilled workers in the Negro and other minority groups.

By contrast, one out of fifty professional or technical workers was unemployed in January 1962; one out of every forty executives or managers, and one out of twenty office employees and sales clerks, was out of work. The argument labor economists present is that the recessions always hit the hard-goods industries, such as auto and steel, more severely than they do other industries. Other experts of labor-force trends believe that the nation is seeing at last the beginning of a long-term shift in the economy from production to service industries. In 1960 blue-collar jobs for men dropped by 1,300,000, but white-collar jobs rose by 600,000. For women, white-collar jobs increased by 700,000, whereas the number of production jobs remained about static.

Women in the Labor Force

One of the growing social problems is the fact that many male heads of families are unemployed while their wives are working either full time or part time. More and more women are being employed in lighter manufacturing, particularly in the electronics and garment industries. More and more men in heavy industry are being replaced by machines.

It has been estimated that about two fifths (2,400,000) of the jobless are male heads of families and that 40 percent of these either have working wives or are being partly supported by working children. The Department of Labor expects that, in 1970, 6,000,000 more women will be in the labor force than in 1960. This will increase the number of females to 30,000,000, out of a total work force of some 87,000,000, if the estimates of the Government are correct. The growing dependence on automated labor-saving devices will give the female high school graduates much greater opportunities in industry than ever before. It has also been estimated that by 1970 there will be a 25 percent increase in women workers, with only a 15 percent increase in male workers.

Negro Workers

The movement of many Negroes from the South to the North has exposed Negro children for the first time to laws applying to public school attendance. Cities such as New York, Philadelphia, and Chicago have laws requiring children to attend school until age 17 or until they attain a high school diploma. In some cases work certificates may be granted before age 17 — thus an increase in the level of education in Negroes of the current generation. Integration in the South will likewise increase the opportunities for a superior education. However, because of cultural and financial limitations, the number of Negro students in colleges and professional schools is still negligible. Moreover, in spite of greater educational opportunities, the Negro, whether educated or uneducated, may for some time be faced with an employment problem, because of limitations on available job opportunities.

Despite state and local antidiscrimination laws, which are supposed to protect the Negro from job bias, integration has been slow in many industries, trades, and professions. The current unemployment rate among Negroes is double that of the white worker. Negroes have tended to find the most stable employment opportunities in mine, factory, and dock operations — and these activities lend themselves most readily to automation. Today laborers represent the principal category of unemployment. Unless the Negroes in the United States can be trained or retrained for job opportunities in this technological age, they will continue to be found among the ranks of the "reliefers" and the chronically unemployed.

Mobility and Length of Unemployment

The unemployment period of the worker is gradually increasing. During the years 1951–1953 those unemployed fifteen weeks or more averaged about one-quarter million. In the period 1959–1960 this number increased to about one million; since 1960 it has increased to two million.

Much of this increase has resulted from two factors. First, the advent of the Supplemental Unemployment Benefit (SUB), as characterized by the Steel, Ford, and Pittsburgh Plate Glass plans, has given the unemployed worker the opportunity of earning almost 80 percent of his take-home pay without obtaining a new job in some other industry. Changes in state unemployment compensation laws permit a worker to draw unemployment compensation while drawing a supplemental benefit from his company. This factor limits the worker's mobility and tends to increase the number of unemployed for long periods.

Second, the interstate battle for industry has caused a large-scale transfer of work from established production centers in the East and Midwest. The efficiency gains permitted by automation (as well as escape from the union) have impelled many companies to avail themselves of offers to move into community-built plants and thus to enjoy tax privileges not available in their old locations. Moreover, the possibility of entering the European Common Market or of procuring cheaper labor (thereby lowering the unit cost of a product) has motivated many American companies to establish plants in Europe and other parts of the world.

American plants in England, West Germany, France, and Ireland are not uncommon. Profit reports are very satisfactory. American unions are becoming more worried by this trend, which may affect the patterns of their future demands. Over $3 billion a year is going into new plants abroad. Such investments may be considered an export of American jobs, particularly when much of the foreign production is shipped back to this country for sale.

The resistance to President Kennedy's plan for aiding distressed areas stemmed from the fear of the more industrialized states that the granting of subsidies to the needy regions would prompt still more employers to move to areas where they could get ultramodern plants free, lower labor costs, and perhaps reprieves from union controls. National studies reveal that the growth of industry in California, Florida, and seven Southwestern states has resulted in an increase in the employment rate more than double the national average, while all the eighteen Eastern and Midwestern states have lagged behind the average.

Other Factors in Automation and Efficiency

Millions of jobs have been jeopardized by lower priced foreign imports, particularly from Japan and other low-wage nations. Competition in steel from Europe has also been impressive. Manufacturers are now cost- and price-conscious. The raising of a price to meet a union demand may lose a customer to a foreign product. Even the garment industry is looking to automation.

In addition, jobs are being eliminated through the pooling of facilities and through business consolidations and mergers. The

Government can visualize an increase in gross national product to $540 billion, with little or no reduction in the size of the unemployment problem.

Several years ago it was not apparent — certainly back in 1955 — that automation would have a significant influence on employment.

Hearing Before Joint Committee

It is easy to prognosticate when times are good and everyone looks through rose-tinted glasses at a changing world. In 1955 the 84th Congress held two weeks of hearings concerned with the economic and social effects of advanced technology. The experts did not see automation as much of a threat to the American working man. Today, of course, these same experts may have cause for concern.

Among the statements made at that time were the following: the shift to automation was taking place against a background of relatively high employment levels and a prosperous situation; all elements in the American economy would accept and welcome progress, change, and increasing productivity; new industries had arisen and would be expected to increase further because of automation, and more goods and services would thus become available.

The experts foresaw new employment opportunities in the service industries and only a small portion of the labor force affected by automation. They also mentioned that marginal workers would have some difficulty in adjusting, but that there would be a greater shortage of scientists, technicians, and skilled labor.[1] Hence, what appeared in 1955 to be an authoritative report has proved to be a poor guess.

The Economics of Automation

Y. Brozen has stated that "automation is the least to be feared among the many episodes of change human society has endured."[2] Effects differ, of course, depending upon the forces leading to its application. He has pointed out that there would surely be changes in the marginal productivity of labor, wages, and employment. He has concluded that the forces leading to automation in a given industry include a rising stock of capital, technological changes in other industries causing a rise in marginal productivity of labor, capital-saving inventions applied in other industries causing them to release capital and capital- and labor-saving inventions.

W. S. Buckingham, Jr., in an address before the National Conference on Automation of the CIO Committee on Economic Policy, April 14, 1955, stated:

"[Automation will bring on] decentralization, concentration of markets, less secondary investment — and a necessity for more vigorous anti-trust enforcement."

Brozen[3] believed that the change-over in the nature of the automated job would turn machine operators into either machine tenders or machine maintenance men. He also felt that automation would have an alarming effect on wage rates. For, although automation would raise the average productivity of the work force, wage rates, which depend on marginal productivity, might be decreased. If an industry introducing newly invented automatic techniques drains large amounts of capital from other industries and releases workers, the capital ratio in the other industries will fall and marginal productivity and wage rates will decline, despite the rise in average productivity and national income.

Government View of Automation Economics

E. Weinberg describes the following factors as being the most important in determining the limits of automation: ". . . cost, reliability of equipment and availability of trained personnel."[4] He believes that despite price reductions, some plants will fail to expand output sufficiently to absorb displaced workers, because of an inelastic demand for the product. The Government therefore sees the greatest shift of the displaced worker from production to the service industries.

J. C. O'Mahoney has stated that "public policy must accept automation and encourage its progress to the extent that it improves living conditions for an expanding number of people."[5]

He warns that the human costs of material progress must be kept at a minimum. The greatest obstacle to the advancement of automation and to the realization of its benefits lies in the possibility that the economy may not find useful work for those displaced. If human resources are wasted, the whole objective of increased production would be wasted. Public policy must be concerned with possible and probable displacement of personnel, possible shifts and distortions in the distribution of the mass purchasing power, and sound and equitable distribution of expected gains in productivity. O'Mahoney states that the Government must make provision for the unemployed workers and must provide necessary training and retraining of old and new workers.

Economic Growth Necessary?

If the economy should increase at the rate of 3.5 percent a year and if expansion in the labor force and productivity make possible a yearly increase of 5 percent, the gradual increase will be achieved at the cost of labor displacement and rising unemployment. Only when sales rise rapidly enough to provide jobs for our growing labor force can we enjoy continuing levels of high employment.

What is economic growth? It is generally understood to mean the rate of increase in the volume of total national production of goods and services. The rate of economic growth between 1959 and 1960 was 2.6 percent, when the real volume of total national production rose from \$490.6 billion to \$503.2 billion (in 1960 dollars after accounting for price changes). Between 1909 and 1960 the average yearly increase in real national output was about 3 percent.[6]

If we want to maintain present living conditions and public service, the national output must rise as fast as the population. From 1959 to 1960 the United States population increased from 177,080,000 to 179,922,000, or 1.6 percent, while the total national production rose 2.6 percent. The rise in production was enough to account for the population increase and to provide a small margin for goods and services.

This margin was very small and the thin margin for improvements amounted to only \$27 for each man, woman, and child.

The Rockefeller Brothers Fund Report, "The Challenge to America," pointed out that unless the nation achieves a 5 percent growth rate, it will have to hold back otherwise desirable expenditures in the governmental field and keep the growth of private expenditures below a level commensurate with its aspirations.

Many business economists and academicians do not believe in the possibility of a 5 percent rate of economic growth. They say the normal potential is 3 to 3.5 percent. President Kennedy's Council of Economic Advisors makes a 3.5 percent estimate for 1962 and for several years following. The difference between a 5 percent rate and a 3.5 percent rate is substantial. Each year it amounts to \$7.5 billion of goods and services and is responsible for three-quarter million jobs.

The difference is greater in terms of basic economic policy. President Kennedy's Council of Economic Advisors, for example, states that a 3.5 percent pace is not good enough. To increase the potential rate, the Council suggests the need for cutting the share of total national production that goes into consumer activities and increasing the share of national output that goes into business investment.

Forced-draft advocates place great emphasis on a reduced tax burden for business as an incentive to additional investment in plant and machines. Such measures may increase the power of the economy to produce, but if consumer and Government buying lags, a capital goods boom could still collapse in a recession. A lack of balance between the nation's capacity to produce and lagging sales is the basis for frequent recessions and a slow economic growth. The productivity of capital investment is also increasing, as is labor productivity. New plants, machines, and production methods are more efficient than older ones. Output of new equipment is generally greater than that from old equipment, even when the latter was new. The rising productivity of plants and equipment places an increasing burden on the economy's need for rapidly expanding sales of the goods and services that can be produced. Only in this way will increased productivity lead to an improvement in the standard of living for all Americans.

Labor-Management Advisory Council's First Report

President Kennedy's nineteen-man labor-management advisory council presented a series of recommendations designed to relieve unemployment. It called for a higher rate of economic growth, possible tax reductions in periods of heavy unemployment, more public works spending, Federal standards for state unemployment compensation programs, and many other recommendations. The report was entitled "Benefits and Problems Incident to Automation and Other Technological Advances."

While the Council agreed that "unemployment had resulted from displacement due to automation and technological change, it was impossible to isolate that portion of present unemployment resulting from these causes."[7]

This vague reference to an important problem points out the dangers of big discussions with little research. Many of these commendations and recommendations appeared to be aimed at easing unemployment generally, rather than at the subject of automation specifically.

Shorter Hours Rejected as Solution to Automation

The Council in its report supported the President's position on a maintenance of a standard forty-hour week by having a panel majority agree to this statement:

> [We consider] the development of programs aiming at the achievement of full employment as being more significant at the present time than the consideration of a general reduction in the hours of work. . . . However, there well may develop in the future the necessity and desirability of shortening the work period either through collective bargaining, or by law, or by both methods.[8]

The labor men consisting of George Meany, AFL-CIO president; Walter Reuther, United Auto Workers Union president; and David McDonald, Steelworkers Union president suggested a statement such as the following: "If unemployment is not substantially reduced in the near future, we will have to resort to a general shortening of the work period through collective bargaining and by law."[9] They were not successful, however, in getting the majority of the panel to adopt the statement.

Conclusion

The U. S. Labor Department and the President's Council of Economic Advisors are struggling with the problem of full employment in the United States. How much of the current unemployment is due to automation and how much is due to the business cycle remains to be seen. An improvement in the statistical procedures for providing data to the Government would be helpful. The problem of automation affects not only the jobless head of the household, but also the youth group, which is pouring out of high school and college in greater number each year because of the high birth rates of post-World War II. Present joblessness of minority groups, who lack industrial skills, as well as the great total of secondary wage earners (women), add to the complexity of the problem of unemployment. Lack of worker mobility and an inability of public employment offices to match skills and job opportunities are apparent. Perhaps Government retraining programs will be a partial solution.

References

1. *Automation and Technological Change*, Report on the Hearings Before the Joint Committee on the Economic Report, October 14–28, 1955,

84th Congress (Washington, D.C.: U. S. Government Printing Office, 1956), 644 pages.

2. Y. Brozen, "The Economics of Automation," *American Economic Review* (May 1957), pp. 339–350.

3. Brozen, "Automation: Creator or Destroyer of Jobs," *Iowa Business Digest* (February 1956), pp. 3–8.

4. E. Weinberg, "A Government View — The Economic Aspects of Automation," *Advanced Management*, vol. 21, no. 5 (May 1956).

5. J. C. O'Mahoney, "Public Policy Implications," *The Challenge of Automation* (Washington, D.C.: Public Affairs Press), 1955, pp. 1–11.

6. "Labor's Economic Review," Department of Research, AFL-CIO, *AFL-CIO American Federationist*, July 1961.

7. *Wall Street Journal*, January 12, 1962, p. 3.

8. *Ibid.*

9. *Ibid.*

▶ ▶ ▶ ▶ **4**

Automation
Challenges
the Government

Automation is not a respecter of state lines. Over-all economic growth is a national problem. Thus the essential environment for rapid growth and the specific problems involved point to responsibility at the Federal level. Neither local and state efforts nor private attempts can achieve a scope sufficient for the size of the problem.[1]

As the Holland Subcommittee on Unemployment and the Impact of Automation of the House Labor and Education Committee recently found, "It is the responsibility of the government to create conditions conducive to economic expansion."[2] The Holland studies presented testimony of some leaders of industry. Ralph Cordiner, of the General Electric Company, said, "Both industry and government have a recognized responsibility to help families in periods of transitional unemployment."[3] Don G. Mitchell, of General Telephone and Electronics, also testified as follows: "It is the responsibility of government to anticipate and to identify those trends which will create chronic unemployment in the future . . . and to participate in the solutions."[4]

The Economic Role — Employment Act of 1946

The big thrust of automation will not only push into the basic economic sectors, but will also reach those fields formerly considered capable of absorbing workers displaced by machines in factories — the white collar occupations and the service trades. What is not automated may be further mechanized and jobless workers will still be unemployed, regardless of whether or not the college professors term the situation "displacement" or "unemployment," or whether its cause is mechanization or automation. Automation will not wait for the answers. A plan is necessary to ameliorate any of the short-run negative aspects of technical progress.

At the executive level of our Federal Government, the Council of Economic Advisors, set up by the Employment Act of 1946, has a mandate to look for necessary targets in the over-all economy that will provide healthy economic growth. This responsibility is clearly specified under the Act, which aims at "maximum employment, production and purchasing power." These terms are usually interpreted, respectively, as the lowest possible levels of unemployment, the lowest number of idle plants, and a reasonable stability of prices.

The public is entitled to have the Council of Economic Advisors provide a working plan of what technical change is doing to the balance between employment and consumption. Private decision making would be much better if businessmen and citizens at large could know what changes in output, in employment, in personal consumption, in business investment, and in Government spending could sustain full employment.

The Role of Congress

Given the proper perspective of the influences of the changing technology on the national economic machine and the world market influences on American production, Congress could enact programs consistent with the spurring of maximum employment, production, and purchasing power. Federal spending, tax policies, and monetary policies could be designed with a view to full employment without inflation. Congress should appropriate monies for studies by the executive departments of the Government, so that full information will be available at all times.

Need for Department of Labor Surveys

Despite what appears to be the sharp impact of automation today, plans startling to the ordinary citizen are on the drawing boards. Corporations are planning to be more competitive with the European Common Market — which means that all are concerned with a drive toward efficiency and lower unit costs.

With changes in machinery and equipment, it is necessary to know more about the kinds of skills required, the kinds of training desired, and the possible labor-management efforts needed to smooth out change without undue harm to workers and the economy. The

Secretary of Labor should prepare studies showing what new processes and machines are planned in certain industries. Confidential information provided to a Government department would help in national planning. Information on wages is collected by the Government on a company-by-company basis, but is not released to the public in any form other than an aggregate figure. Similarly, information on automation plans could be held in confidence by the Government, thus protecting the individual firm releasing such information. The Labor Department could make detailed studies that would be invaluable in training, retraining, and placement. Only by knowing what kinds of skills will be needed can there be intelligent planning for the problems of displacement and re-employment in the sixties. Secretary of Labor Arthur Goldberg took an important first step in solving the problems of technological unemployment by establishing an Office of Automation and Manpower within the Labor Department. One of the first studies made by the President's Labor-Management Advisory Committee of 21 also involved the subject of automation. This action, too, is a step in the right direction by the Government.

Report of President's Labor-Management Advisory Committee

On January 11, 1962, the President's Advisory Committee on Labor-Management Policy released its report on "The Benefits and Problems Incident to Automation and Other Technological Advances." There was common agreement on major matters involving these three central propositions:

1. Automation and technological progress are essential to the general welfare, the economic strength and the defense of the nation.
2. This progress can and must be achieved without the sacrifice of human values.
3. Achievement of technological progress without sacrifice of human values requires a combination of private and governmental action, consonant with the principles of a free society.[5]

In attempting to attain a more effective use of the work force, the Committee in its report indicated the magnitude of the problem. Among the factors it pointed out were the following:

1. The recent rate of economic growth in the United States has been insufficient to reduce unemployment to a tolerable level.

2. The exact extent of unemployment attributable to automation and technological change is unknown, since it is greatly complicated by other factors, such as:

a. The economic recession of 1960–61.

b. The unusually high entrance rate into the labor market, caused by the great postwar population increase. In the next 10 years it is expected that there will be a net gain in the labor force of 13½ million workers.

c. Chronic unemployment in distressed areas.

d. The effects of the rapid advances which have been made by foreign competitors.

e. Changing consumption patterns.

f. The changing nature of jobs which often leaves a gap between job requirements and qualifications of applicants. During the 1950's there was a 58 percent increase in the number of skilled technical and professional workers. Unskilled workers, with only a limited education, found it more difficult to get, or hold, a job. In this connection, the Department of Labor projections indicate that unless steps are taken to reduce the dropout rate among high school students, some 7½ million of those new workers joining the labor force in the 1960's, or more than 30 percent, will not have completed high school, and over 2½ million of them will not even have completed grade school.

g. Discrimination against workers on the basis of age, sex, race, and creed.

h. Multiple jobholding by individuals.

i. The continuing movement of workers away from the farms.[6]

3. Public employment service facilities have been inadequate as well as seriously uneven in their effectiveness with respect to helping workers find new jobs, counseling them as to the kind of jobs which are liable to be available in the future, and advising them as to job prospects in other geographical areas.

4. The mobility of workers is reduced by factors running contrary to the demands of a dynamic society, and an economy in transition.

a. The nontransferability of pension, seniority, and other accumulated rights may result in an employee's being dependent upon his attachment to a particular job as the sole means of protecting his equities.

b. Desirable and essential mobility is affected by reluctance to leave home — because of personal ties or because other members of the family may be working; by the cost of moving and possible losses on local property; and by the insecurity of jobs in a new locality.

5. Educational and informational facilities have been inadequate in that:

a. The requirements for general education prior to vocational and professional training have not kept pace with the shift in job opportunities.

b. The required types of vocational and technical training and retraining are often not available, e.g., for workers leaving the farm.

c. There has been an inadequate liaison among school systems, industry and government with respect to future job requirements, and in fact, there is insufficient information about the nature of such jobs.

d. There has been inadequate financial support for needy students.

e. Counselling facilities have been generally inadequate.

6. Proper retraining facilities and a system of financial support for workers while retraining have been lacking.[7]

This excellent report pointed out that a combination of responsible private and public action will be necessary to permit the advancement of automation and technological improvement without the sacrifice of human values, and that such combined efforts will be able to cope satisfactorily with the unemployment problem, including that which would inevitably arise from the introduction of mechanized and automated devices. The recommendations of this study committee will be examined in the final chapter, "Conclusions and Recommendations."

Federal and State Employment Services

With the need for increased mobility in a technological world, and with a growing demand for skilled workers in technical and administrative areas, the state employment services working in close conjunction with the Federal employment service can be utilized by the Department of Labor to do a more effective job of placement. The present state offices cannot do the best possible job because they are poorly coordinated with the Federal Government and lack funds and personnel needed to do a satisfactory job. Nationwide coordination is required to improve the counseling services and to work toward a goal of motivational training, particularly in the urban areas.

Manpower Development and Training Act of 1962

On March 15, 1962, President Kennedy signed and approved Senate Bill 1991, which had been introduced in the Senate by Senator

Joseph Sill Clark of Pennsylvania. Thus, the widely discussed measure, to be officially known as the "Manpower Development and Training Act of 1962," was made into law, (Public Law 87-415). The new statute contains appropriations of $97,000,000 for training costs in 1963, $161,000,000 in 1964, and a like amount in 1965. Title I, Section 102, of the Act requires the Secretary of Labor to:

(1) evaluate the impact of, and benefits and problems created by automation, technological progress, and other changes in the structure of production and demand on the use of the Nation's human resources; establish techniques and methods for detecting in advance the potential impact of such developments; develop solutions to these problems . . . .

(2) establish a program of factual studies of practices of employers and unions which tend to impede the mobility of workers or which facilitate mobility . . . .

(3) appraise the adequacy of the Nation's manpower development efforts to meet foreseeable manpower needs and recommend needed adjustments, including methods for promoting the most effective occupational utilization of and providing useful work experience and training opportunities for untrained and inexperienced youth;

(4) promote, encourage, or directly engage in programs of information and communication concerning manpower requirements, development and utilization, including prevention and amelioration of undesirable manpower effects from automation . . . .

Section 103 specified that, with respect to skill and training requirements, the Secretary of Labor shall:

. . . develop, compile and make available . . . information regarding skill requirements, occupational outlook, job opportunities, labor supply in various skills, and employment trends on a National, State, area, or other appropriate basis which shall be used in the educational, training, counseling, and placement activities performed under this Act.

Section 104 provided that the Secretary of Labor should furnish annually to the President a Manpower Report and that:

. . . the President shall transmit to Congress within sixty days after the beginning of each regular session (commencing with the year 1963) a report pertaining to manpower requirements, resources, utilization and training.

It is now apparent that the needs of the state employment offices will be recognized by the new manpower statute and this will make for more effective job placement in the field. The experiences gathered in the administration of the Area Redevelopment programs, discussed in Chapter 3, should also prove valuable in implementing the new Act.

Retraining

Labor unions believe, as do many industrialists, that while retraining is under way unemployment compensation or some sort of subsistence should be made available. Such payment has been provided for by the Manpower Development and Training Act of 1962.

Retraining calls for more exploration into the psychological needs of the displaced worker to find ways to convince him that retraining will be not only possible for him, but profitable for all concerned. Successful retraining, like the basic reshaping of education programs, depends on exploring the biggest question in the field of automation — retraining for what? Kinds of skills necessary, degree of training, upgrading or downgrading of already acquired skills — all these and many other factors are unknown, although such information may be found in individual company files. Coordination at every level is necessary to find out what is needed.[8]

Subsistence During Federal Retraining Programs

Title II, Section 203, of the Act provides for training and retraining programs in schools and "on the job" for periods not to exceed fifty-two weeks. Grants are to be made to the states as:

> . . . agents of the United States, to make payment of weekly training allowances to unemployed persons selected for training . . . . ;
> training allowances [shall be paid] only to unemployed persons who have not had less than three years experience in gainful employment and are either heads of families, or heads of households as defined in the Internal Revenue Code of 1954 . . . Provided, That the Secretary in defraying such subsistence expenses shall not afford any individual an allowance exceeding $35 per week . . . except that he may pay training allowances . . . not exceeding $20 a week to youths over nineteen but under twenty-two years of age where such allowances are necessary to provide them with occupational training, but not more than 5 per centum of the estimated total training allowances paid annually . . . may be paid to such youths.

There is nothing in the Act applying specifically to "older workers," although data on the unemployed generally tend to show a severer impact of unemployment caused by automation in the 55–60 age range than in the 35–40 age range. The chances of re-employing a younger head of the household are much greater than they are an older worker. Younger men can take retraining with the assurance of a better chance for new employment. This makes the curriculum very important in the retraining of workers of advanced age. Older workers are generally less mobile than younger workers. Title II, Section 202, states:

> Before selecting a person for training, the Secretary shall determine that there is a reasonable expectation of employment in the occupation for which the person is to be trained. If such employment is not available in the area in which the person resides, the Secretary shall obtain prompt assurance of such person's willingness to accept employment outside his area of residence.

Aside from the coverage on "heads of households," it is interesting to note that the problems of youth are recognized, but with a reduced subsistence, if they are eligible. The vast majority of the funds for subsistence, however, will be spent on the more mature displaced worker.

Trade Expansion Act of 1962

The Trade Expansion Act of 1962 became Public Law 87-794 on October 11, 1962. This Act was designed "to promote the general welfare, foreign policy, and security of the United States through international trade agreements and through *adjustment assistance* to domestic industry, agriculture, and labor, and for other purposes."

Although the objectives of the Act are principally to stimulate economic growth of the United States, it appears that in the short run many American manufacturing companies will be adversely affected by that portion of the Act which will make for tariff adjustments on competitive goods coming from abroad.

Sections 321, 322, and 323 of Chapter 3 of the Act provide for trade readjustment allowances for those workers whose employers have been forced to lay them off because of the adverse competitive results of tariff adjustments. The new law provides that displaced workers who take training in approved programs under the Manpower Development and Training Act of 1962 or the Area Redevelopment Act may receive a combination weekly grant (trade readjustment allowance) greater than that normally provided to workers displaced by automation or to unemployed workers in distressed areas. This provision may create some complications.

In any event, the law does limit the total trade readjustment allowance to 75 percent of the worker's average weekly wage when employed. The new Act will also permit recipients of trade redevelopment allowances to receive a combined income including unemployment insurance.

Older Workers

The increasing problem of adjustment for older workers in the new technology is a genuine one. First, the older worker's psychological problems and occupational needs are different from those of the younger worker. Studies in motivation are necessary to discover what is needed to convince the older worker he should take retraining. Studies in placement of older workers are also very important. The feasibility of early retirement should be considered as part of the over-all problem.

One suggestion made by the AFL-CIO is that:

> Some form of partial retirement system for older workers during a recession [should be made available]. For example, a provision could be made for older unemployed workers, age 60–65, to receive retirement benefits after unemployment insurance benefits have been exhausted, whenever the unemployment rate exceeds a specified percentage. Such a program would help maintain income for the older jobless workers.[9]

There is much room for research on the problem of the older worker. L. Landon Goodman, a British expert on automation, adds these thoughts to a possible solution of the problem:

> A man may have spent 30 or 40 years or more in a particular calling, possibly tied to a machine which has now become outdated. He may not be able to learn a new trade and achieve anything like the skill he acquired when he was young. What is to happen to him? The situation raises a great humanitarian question to which a solution must be found. It is not a problem which can be left to settle itself within 20 years time. In the words of a pensioner, the government never realizes just how precious time is to the elderly.[10]

It appears that the older man, in order to gain employment, would have to be downgraded. However, this problem may not be as intractable as it appears. Young trainable people will be attracted to the new opportunities in automated plants. With an improvement in the counseling and placement services, it may be possible to place the older workers in the conventional plants that still exist. Goodman believes that if an orderly deployment of older workers is not possible, Government should step in. He states: "There is a good case for asserting that retirement benefits [in England] should be payable, regardless of age, to any individual who cannot find employment as a result of technological change."[11]

Labor Mobility

In 1961 the Chamber of Commerce of the United States pointed out that there would be adequate labor mobility in this nation if the displaced and the unemployed had sufficient labor market information about where to seek employment. This is a very valid criticism of the Government's present inability to shed light in this important area of need, and may be corrected by the Manpower Development and Training Act of 1962. The Chamber's comments are as follows:

> By and large labor mobility between industries, occupations, and areas is high in our economy. In manufacturing in years of high employment, monthly voluntary quits total 2% of the labor force. This rate of turnover, if guided by adequate information on job opportunities, generally is high enough to take care of large scale structural displacement by the normal process of attrition. In the economy as a whole, according to one study there are some $11\frac{1}{2}$ million job shifts every year, involving $8\frac{1}{2}$ million different persons. Almost half of these shifts are to a different industry and a different occupation; another 20% to a different industry, but to the same type of job; an additional 8% to a different type of job in the same industry. Even these figures do not reveal the full extent of occupational mobility; many workers change their type of work without changing employers. Residential mobility is also high. Every year 11 million people move to a different county, half of them crossing state lines.[12]

Labor immobility is usually a result of special situations rather than a general problem. Where labor in a community is heavily dependent on a single dominant industry, with limited alternative employment opportunities, workers and their families are often slow to move as the industry declines and finally disappears. One major problem is that information on local job opportunities comes to the attention of the job hunter much more quickly than opportunities available in other areas. The unemployed cannot afford to seek jobs in distant communities with the same economy that he can look for a job at home. Many of the unemployed cannot afford the high cost of moving, even if jobs are available elsewhere. Older workers are relatively immobile. They often are homeowners; and if they have to sell their homes, the price may not be right or a buyer may not be available. Often, all their savings are invested in the home. In a new community they might have to pay rent, as compared to their present situation. Homeownership is a definite bar to worker mobility.

Seniority, pension rights, and vacation and sick benefits are also a bar to mobility of the older workers. They are reluctant to forgo these benefits. Perhaps all these labor-immobilizing factors ought to be reviewed by a joint labor-management committee in view of the problems of automation and the displacements of the sixties. Eventually, a standardization of benefits and a vesting of all benefits into an over-all program similar to social security would increase the mobility of the older worker and cut down on the unemployment costs of the states and the National Government.

> Older workers are less mobile also because they receive higher pay, possess greater skills, and consequently are likely to suffer larger cuts in pay when they are forced to move out of a depressed industry or occupation. They also face greater difficulties in re-employment on account of age and thus are more reluctant to cut the ties to their former industry and employer. Several states have passed legislation forbidding hiring discrimination on the basis of age. Since the number of workers over 45, and even their percentage of the total labor force, is on the rise, it is important to consider special problems of improving mobility, retraining, and re-employment prospects for older workers.[13]

Influence of Automation on Employment and Living Standard

Jack Rogers made a forceful statement on the influence of automation, employment, and the standard of living in his classic work at the Institute of Industrial Relations, University of California:

> In simple terms, if national output is not expanded and new job opportunities are not created as fast as the labor force grows, unemployment can result. If productivity increases from automation are devoted mainly to decreasing costs so that output does not increase in proportion to population growth, the standard of living will fall. That automation will displace people from jobs is indisputable. The questions are (1) whether there will be other jobs and (2) whether workers displaced

can fill them. The *rate* of introduction of automation is crucial to the answer to the second question.

To introduce automation in firms in such a way that employment is not decreased is by itself not enough, for if new employment is not created at somewhere near the rate of new entrants to the labor market, there will be general unemployment due to the absence of jobs. Even if new employment is created, however, there can be transitional unemployment as workers whose jobs disappear are unable to find jobs suitable to their experience and training. The *more rapid* the introduction of automation the more serious the problem of frictional unemployment will be.[14]

If automation is to be of real benefit to American society, the rate of economic growth must increase. Production is but one side of the growth picture — the other side is that the demands for goods and service must increase in proportion to production. Unions have expressed fear in this respect. This fear is shared by Norbert Weiner, recognized as one of the pioneers in automation:

> Let us remember that the automatic machine, whatever we may think of any feelings it may have or may not have, is the precise economic equivalent of slave labor. Any labor which competes with slave labor must accept the economic conditions of slave labor. It is perfectly clear that this will produce an unemployment situation, in comparison with which the present recession and even the depression of the thirties will seem a pleasant joke.[15]

All of which means that machines are good producers and poor consumers!

How Much Automation and How Soon?

A 1955 survey of more than one thousand companies, conducted by the Research Institute of America, provided insight into the degree in which automation had already influenced management thinking. On the question "How soon do you expect automation to be extensive in your industry?" the following thoughts were expressed: 16 percent of the companies replied that it was already extensive in the industry; 23 percent believed that it would be used extensively by 1964; 8 percent thought it would be used extensively by 1965 or later; the balance of 53 percent thought it would never be used, or stated they were uncertain about the possibility of its use.

In response to the question "When will you use automation in your company?" 18 percent indicated they were using it already;

17 percent expected to use it by 1964; 5 percent were to use it after 1965; 60 percent either planned never to use it or were uncertain about its use.[16]

Automation Generally Used by Larger Firms

The size of the company and the capital investment in equipment generally dictate the possibility of following automation principles. In the study just mentioned, it is quite clear that automation is more prevalent in the larger companies. According to this study, 12 percent of the companies employing 100 employees or less used automation; 16 percent of the companies with 101–500 employees used automation; and in the largest group — companies with over 500 employees — 29 percent used automation techniques.[17]

Growth of Industries Making Control Devices

Between 1947 and 1954 the electrical measuring industry, which includes integrating instruments, indicators, recorders, and testing equipment doubled its sales. In 1954 total shipments of scientific instruments were nearly six times those of 1947. The mechanical measuring instruments industry also doubled its sales during the same period.[18]

In 1962 it was judged that unit sales of control products will have increased by 50 to 75 percent over the 1954 sales. In the past two decades the control products industry has risen from a volume of $100 million to about $2.5 billion. By 1965 it is estimated that the industry will reach annual sales of $6 billion.

Investment in Automation

A McGraw-Hill survey of the sums being invested by metalworking firms in automated equipment in 1958 showed that about 30 percent of all expenditures for tools and equipment was being earmarked for the "new technology." The survey showed that in those firms already somewhat automated, the outlay devoted to automation was being raised to 40 percent, whereas in the automobile industry the automated outlay was to be about 60 percent.[19]

European Investment in Automation

There appears to be a world-wide movement toward automation. Many new plants, at least as advanced as American plants, are being built in Europe. The Soviet Union has a ball-bearing factory where the product is processed from raw stock to sealed and labeled cartons without being touched by human hands.[20] Russia is beginning to place great importance on automation. A Ministry of Instruments and Automation was established in Russia as early as 1956.[21] The development of the Sputnik indicates the degree of excellence of advanced automatic-control techniques.

Some experts do not believe that a "tidal wave" of automation is in prospect, and yet before long attainments in automatic production may stun the forecasters of a few years ago.

Fear of the Computer

The brains of automation are furnished by the computers. They can perform a thousand tasks from rolling steel to deciding how many bottles of milk should be left on doorsteps in the 4700 block of North 10th Street in Philadelphia on a cold Wednesday in December.

Computers can design in a few hours new chemical plants that would take platoons of engineers a year, monitor space vehicles on their way to the moon, coach baseball players, govern switches and signals on 35,000 miles of railroad track from a single remote-control center, collect eggs in electronic henhouses, refine oil, issue insurance policies, operate acres of industrial machinery, and provide the guideposts for billions of dollars of corporate decisions.[22]

These are some of the things that computers can do. But how can these constructive actions be weighed against uncertainties developing in this nation as a result of the computer? More and more we move toward push-button factories, automated transport systems, "robot" marketing, and automatic communication devices.

The problem of man versus machine is occupying the minds of important government personnel who try to find answers to the growing displacement problem. Will the best data processing decisions come in the future from machines or men? Will the "old-fashioned" conveyor continue to become obsolete, while factory workers are replaced with automated assembly lines? Can we estimate how soon or how rapidly, and in what measure, future displacement of manpower will take place? Even a computer could not give us the answers.

Automation Identified With Job Displacement

Competition with the United States from Europe, with its newer factories, is becoming more intense. Automation in western Europe and Russia is being encouraged through research and the development of pilot plants. Testimony given to Congress by Walter W. Heller, chairman of President Kennedy's Council of Economic Advisors, indicated that, in 1962, from the competitive point of view, two thirds of our plant and equipment were obsolete.

There is a tendency to associate automation with job displacement rather than with economic efficiency. According to John Diebold, in recent testimony before a Congressional Committee investigating the impact of technological change on manpower, industry and the Government are holding back orders for automated equipment and machine tools because of the immediate high level of joblessness in the heavy-goods field. He indicated that new orders for automated machine tools would pep up business and cut military costs. He reported that the Pentagon had turned down a recommendation from Wright Field, Ohio, that $40,000,000 be appropriated for purchase of electronically controlled machines for making missiles and war planes. He stated that the ostensible reason for the refusal to purchase these new items was that the Defense Department did not wish further automation when so many millions were already jobless.

The Efficiency Dilemma

Economic expansion in the hard-goods industries depends on an upswing in efficiency and the maintenance of improved cost controls. The more rapidly industry moves in an upsurge of new efficiency, the harder it becomes to find jobs for the skilled and semiskilled manual workers who are displaced. Union leaders press the Government for action to stop further automation in their industries. They report that the number of blue-collar workers in manufacturing had fallen by 1,500,000 jobs even before the 1960–1961 recession.

In February 1961 the U. S. Labor Department reported that steel employment failed to keep pace with the rise in output. In a special release, the Department stated: "Steel mill employment has failed to keep pace with the rising steel output, and automation and other technological changes are expected to limit the rate at which displaced workers are recalled for the balance of 1961."[23] More steel was poured in the twelve months ending February 1961 by 460,000 workers than was poured in 1951 by 540,000 workers.

Labor points out that in New York City alone, 40,000 elevator operators were displaced by automatic lifts. In the switch from planes to missiles, it was reported that 200,000 aircraft workers lost their jobs.

Labor talks of voice-controlled automatic typewriters, which will cancel the jobs of 1,500,000 typists, and of factories that will make automobiles, washing machines, and television sets while supervisors stare at the self-regulating automatic controls.

Inability of Government to Get Information on Automation

How can the human impact of automation be softened and thus moderate the climate of apprehension? This fear that has acted as a brake on the installation of the new technological developments in many industries is now a matter of top-level attention in the Government.

It appears that no one in Government is fully informed about the dimensions of the problem, or about the timetable as to when the most serious impact will occur. The issue is so explosive in labor relations that many companies are treating as top military secret information about the manpower effects of future automated installations or office automated equipment.

The Labor Department is moving to overcome the gap in information by organizing a special unit to collect and monitor reports on how smoothly the transition goes in companies introducing great technological change. The 1962 Manpower Development and Training Act should be of help in this respect.

Increased Efficiency Limits Re-employment Opportunities

An analyst writing in the *Wall Street Journal* reports that the nation's factory workers found more jobs in 1962, but probably not enough to put back to work everyone who was furloughed in the recent recession.[24]

Advancing production efficiency is allowing many manufacturers to turn out more goods with the same number of employees. The West Virginia Pulp and Paper Company reported that "employment in some of our converting operations has increased because of improved business, but improving manufacturing techniques have enabled us to maintain primary paper production levels with fewer people."[25]

"We are doing normal hiring for the season, but not any unusual hiring," says the American Machine and Foundry Company. "While sales are increasing," an official declared, "we are getting out a higher sales volume per worker, so sales have gone up a lot faster than our employment."[26]

Although there appeared to be a need in 1962 for hiring in the steel and automobile industries, the development of increased efficiency and automated techniques reduced the gross need in these basic industries. Kaman Aircraft Corporation, a Bloomfield, Connecticut, helicopter maker, was able to raise sales 10 percent in 1961 to a new volume of nearly $60,000,000 with only a 5 percent gain in employment for the year. This was done by centralizing the warehouse and machine shop work.[27]

Personnel directors interviewed in the *Wall Street Journal* analysis reported that there was no problem in recruiting skilled or semiskilled workers for the production lines; but for skilled workers in automated maintenance the story was quite different.

Problems With Unions

As jobs disappear with increased efficiency of industry, the pressure for a shorter work week is sure to grow, particularly if the only answer to technological displacement appears to be severance pay and retraining for nonexistent jobs. Earlier retirements and longer vacations may also be on labor's lists of demands.

More flexible seniority rules, pension and benefit programs, overhaul of the wage system to put more stress on income guarantees, allowances by the employer or the Government for moving workers from one city to another — all of these are in the wind.

Some unions have already started to press for shorter workweeks. Among these are the National Maritime Union, with a demand for a thirty-hour week, and the United Steel Workers of America, who are pressing Congress with a demand to reduce the provisions of the Fair Labor Standards Act from forty hours of straight-time pay to thirty-two hours a week.

Private Plans

The Government committees investigating the impact of automation on unemployment have been very much interested in private measures to soften the blows of automation. Among these are the West Coast Dock Plan, the Armour Plan, and the Kaiser Plan, which are covered in detail in Chapter 10. These plans stem from union-management contract negotiations.

Place of Automation in Next Twenty Years

Automation may attain its maximum growth rate by 1970, and by 1980 it will be relatively mature. It is not expected to influence the majority of the work force; but it will have tremendous impact on the economy through its influences on productivity.

If we are to have automation and full employment, too, our economy must adjust or adapt perfectly to automation. If our progress in this new technology permits its adaptation by the labor force, and if the potentially deflationary effects of automation are headed off by expansion of output, automation should result in a more productive economy and an improvement in the living standard of the American worker. There will be severe transition problems, but undoubtedly great technological progress will provide the same dividends as in past years in our history.

Conclusion

The nation is faced with structural unemployment, depressed areas, and increasing problems of automation. These problems are not brand-new, but in combination appear to be getting worse. Subsidies to depressed areas will not, in themselves, solve the problem for those areas. What is needed is to facilitate labor mobility and to step up plans for retraining through both private and public sources.

Improved Flow of Information   An improved flow of information is needed. Under this category are the following points:

a) Collection of improved information on current job openings, by skill, number, and locality.

b) Utilization of this information by the United States Employment Service and other agencies concerned with placing unemployed workers.

c) Advance notice by employers of plans for mechanization or automation that will displace substantial numbers of workers, combined with announcement of the alternatives available to the displaced workers and the steps management is undertaking to minimize the problems.

Improved Training and Retraining There must be an improvement in vocational counseling, guidance, personnel selection, and training and retraining programs, both public and private:

a) Better local vocational counseling and guidance, on the basis of prospective supply-demand situations for various skills and occupations.

b) Restructuring vocational curriculums in high schools and elsewhere to train workers for the skills of the future, rather than the skills of the past, thus entailing the training and retraining of vocational teachers as well as changing of curriculums.

c) Expanded efforts by employers and unions to retrain workers on a continuing basis as a means of averting skill obsolescence and to minimize structural unemployment by retraining displaced workers for needed skills where feasible.

d) The assistance of the Federal Government in joint Federal-state retraining programs, such as that now going on under the Area Redevelopment Act and under the Manpower Development and Training Act of 1962, introduced by Senator Joseph S. Clark of Pennsylvania, and signed by President Kennedy on March 15, 1962.

Increased Labor Mobility There must be increased labor mobility through better information on job opportunities and through training to prepare for the skills that are in demand.

Removal of Obstacles to Labor Mobility Obstacles to labor mobility should be eliminated, if at all possible. These obstacles include (a) the sacrifice of seniority rights and other fringe benefits as a result of switching employers; (b) severe financial losses as a result of moving to new communities; and (c) barriers barring the way to the employment of older workers.

Moderation of Union Demands If unions were to cooperate further in analyzing their own positions with respect to automation, there might be some moderation of demands that lead only to a substitute for labor through fuller mechanization and automation. Rigid wage policies should be re-examined, particularly in the depressed areas.

Additional Investments Continued pressure should be exerted for an adequate rate of investment in new jobs to facilitate reemployment of the workers displaced by progress. Government should encourage new investment and venture capital. Government should continue to apply fiscal policies to moderate and reduce the frequency of recessions. Finally, Government should stimulate research and development on the part of industry.

References

1. "The Impact of Automation — A Challenge to America," *AFL-CIO American Federationist* (August, 1961), vol. 68, no. 8, p. 13.
2. Hearings before the Subcommittee on Unemployment and Impact of Automation of the Labor and Education Committee, U. S. House of Representatives, March 1961.
3. *AFL-CIO Federationist op. cit.*, p. 13.
4. *Ibid.*, p. 13.
5. "The Benefits and Problems Incident to Automation and Other Technological Advances," The President's Advisory Committee on Labor-Management Policy, January 11, 1962, released by U. S. Department of Commerce, Washington, D.C., p. 1.
6. *Ibid.*, pp. 1, 2.
7. *Ibid.*, p. 3.
8. "The Impact of Automation," *op. cit.*, p. 15.
9. *Ibid.*, p. 16.
10. L. Landon Goodman, *Man and Automation* (Harmondsworth, Middlesex: Penguin Books, Ltd., 1957), p. 154.
11. *Ibid.*, p. 154.
12. "Automation and Unemployment," Chamber of Commerce of the United States, Washington, D.C., (1961), p. 26.
13. *Ibid.*, p. 27.
14. Jack Rogers, *Automation — Technology's New Face* (University of California, 1958), pp. 41–43.
15. Norbert Weiner, *The Human Use of Human Beings* (Boston: Houghton-Mifflin Co., 1950), p. 131.
16. Rogers, *op. cit.*, p. 41.
17. *Ibid.*, p. 42.
18. U. S. Bureau of the Census, 1954.
19. *American Machinist*, (October 21, 1957), p. 179.
20. Peter Trippe, "Russia's Automatic Factory," *American Machinist*, (January 15, 1957), pp. 147–154.
21. "Automation: A Brief Survey of Recent Developments," *International Labor Review*, (October 1956), pp. 384–403.
22. A. H. Raskin, *New York Times*, April 7, 1961.
23. *Ibid.*
24. *Wall Street Journal*, December 19, 1961, p. 1.
25. *Ibid.*
26. *Ibid.*
27. *Ibid.*, p. 14.

5

Factors
Determining a Firm's
Ability to Automate

Consideration of Elements Involved in Automation

While most industries could benefit from some aspects of automation, the degree will depend on the previous history and condition of the firm. Rarely would it be possible to jump directly from manual operation to automated operation in one step. Nor would it be wise. Automation is generally introduced in stages, and ultimately the stages and the departments are linked together in one process. The necessary steps in introducing automation to a manufacturing plant should be considered in the following order:

1. Check to make certain that at least part of the required technological knowledge cannot be found in the organization.
2. Launch a study of all production operations in order to mechanize them.
3. Study production design and methods. Processing must be changed in order to achieve mechanized materials handling, integration of materials handling and materials processing, instrumentation and control, and finally full automation. (At this stage automation is only an objective.)
4. Improve materials handling with view to eliminating it altogether or mechanizing it.
5. Integrate materials processing and materials handling equipment for individual operations, combined with instrumentation and control; later extend the integration to several operations.
6. Throughout the *whole* production sequence, integrate materials handling and materials processing equipment and combine with over-all instrumentation and control.

Risk for Employers Contemplating Automation   Employers, both as managers and businessmen, are faced with new problems as a

66

result of planning for partially or fully automated production. A great many of these problems are financial and technical; many involve labor. Banks, customers, contractors, middle supervisors, and labor unions tend to ask more guarantees of management and to urge employers to accept more risk and more responsibility. Life becomes very difficult, indeed, for the employer who contemplates automation.

Employers have achieved many innovations in production that have raised living standards and increased the number of well-paying jobs. Employers are responsible for the success or failure of an enterprise and the livelihoods of the workers and their families. Automation and other technological improvements currently require greater risks by management. Planning for current automation is as important as any previous planning for technological change during the Industrial Revolution and the mass-production era. It will be evident later on in this text that, on the whole, employers are very conscious of the social implications of automation, are willing to bear their fair share of the cost of technical progress, and are anxious to assure their employees that work disruption or job displacement will be kept to a minimum.

As decision making becomes more and more mechanized and as automation increases in the office as well as in the factory, many basic management concepts will have to be scrapped. Changes in the relations between managers and workers will require new attitudes and a new kind of management skill. Problems of human relations will become more important.

Certain high-level decisions involving such matters as choice of production line, diversification of plant location, and long-range planning are "natural" for centralized decision making. On the other hand, because of high costs involved in breakdowns of automated machinery at a decentralized location, certain decision-making responsibilities must be vested in middle management. The extent of the potential loss at the decentralized location, however, makes mandatory an immediate review of the matter at the decentralized location.

Mutual Learning Emphasis today falls on learning on the part of both management and workers. As a result of the technological advance, there may be management displacement as well as labor displacement.

In suggesting the implications of automation for management, one observer described the need as follows:

> The manager who will control the "automatic managers" will have to become increasingly aware of how decisions are made and how they should be made. He will have to deal with increasingly complex organized systems of men and machines. He will, therefore, need as much knowledge as possible about organizational behavior and how to fill by scientific method the gaps in his knowledge.
>
> He can learn on the job and in a relatively short time about the machines and processes he controls. But knowledge of scientific method, and the ability to apply social science, cannot be efficiently learned on the job. It is in these two areas that the education of managers should be concentrated.[1]

The British Institute of Management has been studying management requirements in the light of rapid technological progress. In one of the papers presented to a national management conference in November 1955, emphasis was placed on the need for more and better "human management," a need that would grow not in simple proportion to technological progress but more nearly as a cube function. As in the United States, stress was to be laid on developing greater qualities of human understanding in the next generation of managers, on whose shoulders so much of the burden of transition will rest.[2]

It is more than likely that the technical changes now in process are ushering in a new era of social and moral responsibility for management, both in the factory and in the community.

Employment Stability within the Firm   With automation there should be a reduction in the use of direct labor and a resultant reduction in direct-labor costs. At the same time capital costs should increase greatly. If the old technique was to reduce costs by reducing the number of employees, this should not apply equally under automation, since over-all capital costs will remain the same, whatever the production level.

The objective of management should be to keep production and output as high as possible. Once management has automated, there will be little advantage in further discarding labor, and the economists believe that changes in demand will be met by price adjustments. Thus, once automation hits an individual firm, those still employed in it will have more stable employment.

Will Competition Require Automation?   Buckingham, Dreher, and Boyce all have slightly different ideas about how widely and how quickly automation will take over. Buckingham, in his new book *Automation: Its Impact on Business and People* (published in 1962 by Harper & Row), states: "Since automation creates new jobs as it destroys old ones, the rate of automation is a critical factor." Buckingham also indicates that he believes automation appears to be limited to "process manufacturing and clerical work." It is difficult to accept this limitation when one observes the tremendous strides made in the communications, transportation, and service industries. Dreher, who is quoted below, also errs in believing that automation will not accelerate until a depression arrives. The author believes that the emphasis on international competition today will push automation "to the hilt." Boyce, whose ideas also follow, is apt to be the most correct of the writers mentioned here.

Will automation develop gradually or will it arrive with a rush? Dreher gives his opinion:

> As long as prosperity shines, automation may be expected to proceed more or less at the present rate, varying in different fields and at different times but on the whole not developing too fast for more or less orderly adjustment. But should the shadow of the Depression, or merely sharply lowered corporation profits, advance over the land, automation will advance as rapidly. It will be a race to beat falling prices with falling costs. Not everybody will be in a position to automate. Those will automate who have the resources and the hardihood, and from those who have not, will have taken away even that which they have. It will be an automation shakeout, and it will hit the smallest, hardest.[3]

Some businessmen, fearing they will be left behind in the race for American and foreign business because of high costs, say "automate or die." Boyce forecast the automated future:

> Some companies — and perhaps whole industries — will become economically sick as short-sighted management or far-sighted competitors (and generally a combination of both) put the skids under individual segments of our industrial society. . . . [As for individuals, executives, as well as mechanics who will bear the brunt of automation], new technology is exposing management to ideas that were not dealt with in textbooks and the classroom of ten or fifteen years ago, much less thirty or forty. The executive who does not keep his ideas modern by constant aggressive learning from every available source will increasingly often be called on to make decisions on problems he cannot grasp. . . . because something was good or bad in the past doesn't mean it will necessarily be either good or bad in the future.[4]

Organization and Management   Automation should bring sharp modification in operations, which will require an organization that can provide the closest teamwork possible. Quick decisions will be necessary, particularly on problems encountered by the preventive maintenance team. The manager must know how to train and maintain a work force to deal with this type of problem.

The advantages to management will not come through manpower slashes but through tighter production controls and greater potential yields. Better management planning and control will be possible through feedback controls and information retrieval. Productivity will go up through the better conversion of raw materials.[5]

Problem Solving   Carr[6] points out that management will be in a much better position to calculate in advance the penalties for making the wrong decisions because of unproved information resulting from the use of the electronic digital computer. Various approximation techniques can be used to solve most problems relating to repetitive arithmetic in the plant. Such problems could always be solved with the knowledge and use of mathematics, but problem solving was so elongated that it was less costly to make mistakes. Now the digital computer, with its high-speed addition, subtraction, multiplication, and division, can do the job that was too costly to do before. In addition, alert management is using the technique of simulation of real life situations, as well as the solution of systems of linear equations, to provide, a priori, that which formerly only adverse experience could have pointed out in the conventional plant.

Automation is a means of analyzing, organizing, and controlling production resources — mechanical, material, as well as human. The automated line must be regarded as a system, not a number of individual components. The form of management organization and reporting channels suited for automation will depend on the individual firm, its traditions, its economic environment, its operations, and its personality.

Drucker points out that whole processes will have to be considered and managed in a new way, or else the danger of overdiversity will become one of the major management problems resulting from automation.[7]

Great challenges and great opportunities face management. Management will have to develop people who can take responsibility for working with unions, employees, and supervisors during this period of change.[8]   Drucker believes that, to do the right job of management planning for automation, it takes at least five to eight years of preparation. If planning is not systematized, automation will fail because of public resistance and lack of skilled manpower.[9]

In his study of the automated plant at Cleveland belonging to the Ford Motor Company, Harder[10] gives management good insights to what problems may be expected from automation. The advantages of automation were clearly borne out through lower production costs, increased machine speed, improved quality of product, and fewer accidents.

Maintenance became something of a problem; and the manager is therefore cautioned to consider rising maintenance costs, the need for a program of preventative maintenance, and the importance of teamwork between the maintenance and production personnel. At the Cleveland plant, there was a decrease in the need for direct labor, and an increase in the need for indirect labor, required to service the machines. Manpower was utilized to watch various operating mechanisms, so that defects could be sighted before they became major breakdowns. It became necessary to standardize tools, methods, and specifications. Industrial standards were necessary on equipment, process, and materials. Such standardization assisted the purchasing and the stocking of supplies. Coordination problems became immense and early planning was proved to be vitally important.

More rigorous business planning is necessary in the move toward automated production, which may prove inflexible as products and markets undergo change. Because of the inherent dangers of inflexibility, management must supplement its experience and intuition with such important aids as operations research and statistical decision making.

Management thinking must become more philosophical and conceptual. It must approach management problems in the same way that a design engineer would approach the problems of automation. In terms of concepts, management will have to abandon the "batch" concept of manufacturing in favor of the "continuous flow" concept.[11]

Hurni advised his readers of three real problems created by automation. The first is the need for good communications and a "feedback," with emphasis on quantitative information. The second is the need for management to rely more on its specialists than was true traditionally. The last is the important requirement of "broad thinking" by management.

Product Variation and Its Relation to Cost-Inflexibility   Top management must take a position on product variation in the automated plant. Seaman points out that unless this variation can be controlled, costs will rise sharply.[12] Management will have to balance all factors, and take into consideration all aspects, of manufacture in order to produce a progression of maximum total sales. Minimum costs will have to be reviewed against the cost of financing further maximum sales and against the possibility of further reductions in costs.

Management Considerations   P. W. Cook, Jr., in a talk before the Industrial Relations Association in Chicago in 1955, pointed out that automation would result in management's becoming more professional and probably more decentralized, with top management exercising more review functions and less intervention functions.

The experts (among them J. B. Cunningham) agree generally that before leaping into automation in either processing or machine tools, management should give serious consideration to the production line of the new part or machine; the number of shifts to be worked per day; the current manpower requirements; present production per hour; and the evaluated costs in dollars per year of each worker replaced. Also to be considered should be installation costs and tryout time. The successful performance of the machine depends mostly on the thoroughness and practicality of the design. An often-observed factor in the design and operation of automated equipment is the accessibility to, and the cost of, maintenance required to keep it running.

D. G. Osborn[13] makes the point that, under automation, space and labor force become much less important, and instrumentation becomes much more important, as factors in the selection of plant sites. Automation diminishes both the amount of space required and the labor force necessary to turn out a given unit of product. Whereas the problem of adequate plant location is somewhat freed of control of site and labor force, human occupancy is nevertheless brought closer to the ideal of possible decentralization.

Automation will improve the speed and service in transportation and should alter the role of accessibility to resources and markets. The absence of facilities for servicing instruments may, however, deter the industrial location and adoption of automation in some areas.

With the high capital investment needed for automation, multi-shift working becomes of great importance. This idea is stated as follows by L. Landon Goodman, an English writer, in *Automation, Today and Tomorrow.*

> It is surely national madness to scrape to the bone in order to save money nationally through budget surpluses and privately through individual savings — for investment in buildings, plants, machinery, power stations, etc., and then only use them for 8 hours per day or forty hours per week. Double-day shift working must come, for it will not be possible to find money to invest in industry for a plant utilization of 25 percent, nor will it be possible to compete with nations on a 50 percent basis.[14]

Factors Involved in Ability to Automate

Competition and Rising Costs   The business enterprise wishes to conserve its resources and to operate competitively. Automation offers opportunities for increased productive and managerial efficiencies. At what point, however, are the time and atmosphere correct for installing this new technology, without the aggravations of union harrassment, reduction of employee morale, and other attendant problems?

Concerns faced with rising per-unit labor costs, shortages of skilled help, unsatisfactory relationships with customers on account of delayed deliveries resulting from a shortage of production facilities, poor quality — all are ripe for self-improvement derived from the successful application of automation.

Where concerns are already mass-producing, where the sales are steady throughout the year, and where the company is in a good enough financial position to make substantial equipment investment — these firms would find it difficult to resist the ideas of automation.

If a firm is faced with seasonality — where production consists of short runs of varying items or where operators lead the machines and apply a great deal of skill and judgment (as in the garment industries) — then the idea of automation is far off. Add to this factor the inability of smaller firms to raise money easily and the lack of specialized staff assistance — then automation recedes still further as a goal.

Regardless of whether automation is desirable from the point of view of the size of the company, access to funds, and other factors, a firm must often follow the lead of its competitors if it wishes to remain in business. Therefore, intelligent management must and should investigate the possibilities of greater manufacturing efficiencies, whether by means of automation or other work improvement methodology.

Increased Control By Elimination of Personnel   Reduction of the labor force is only part of the automation story. Most managements do not want to lay off workers. They know that machines cannot buy merchandise.

Aside from a reduction in labor costs by linking men and machines, management has other goals in introducing automated equipment. This equipment can work faster, longer, and more steadily than can operator-controlled equipment. Automatic equipment can do hazardous work where human life might be in danger. Fortunately or unfortunately for society, the greatest attraction is that machines can be controlled better than men. Management is attempting to regain some of its traditional prerogatives lost through successive years of union contract negotiations.

Managerial flexibility has, for the most part, gone out the window, thus contributing to restrictive work rules, pay premiums, and higher unit labor costs. When the United States had a virtual world market and prices rose faster than labor costs, vast inefficiencies were swallowed without profit margins shrinking. Today, however, with competition from the European Common Market and a generally admitted cost-price squeeze, management would like to regain some control over the costs of the production process. The tendency of wage expenses to become fixed costs through the ever-growing benefit or fringe programs contributes to persistent management review of automation.

Ability to Handle Objections of the Union   When it becomes easier for a worker to produce goods through fuller mechanization or automation, the unions for the most part still take the position that established piece-rate methods of pay or job classes should be maintained. How can a firm finance its new equipment, which makes possible added productivity, if historic unit costs are maintained? This is the dilemma faced by employers today, but it appears to be an unfair basis for discussions. When work becomes easier, a worker is able to turn out more units. Although management would be wise to pass back a part of its savings to the workers, yet their contributions alone have not caused the increased production, which, clearly, has resulted principally from the owners' investment in new machinery and equipment.

Unions will adhere to the old formula of assigning so many machines to an operator, even when the control rationale changes because the type of machine changes. Many unions take a dim view of job reclassification necessitated by obvious changes in operative duties and responsibilities. Featherbedding, work restriction, and many other obstructive techniques by the work force and union's representatives greet management attempts to modernize operations. Workers will often hold back in company retraining programs, and long and costly grievances ensue, generally resulting in compromises by arbitrators who seldom hold their hearings in the plant environment but usually far away in some unrealistic office building atmosphere.

Ability to Plan and Prevent Dislocation   One fear preventing management from moving ahead in modernization and automation is that workers will lose jobs; that it will be impossible to transfer the affected employees to new jobs in other departments; or that the affected workers do not have the abilities to be upgraded or retrained.

The degree of obstruction management can expect from the workers or the union will depend to a large extent on the honesty of the atmosphere in the company. Where these matters are discussed with unions well in advance of changes, and where workers know that without modernization their employers will not survive, workers are more readily willing to share and participate in the problem of survival, and to adjust to new responsibilities under automation. Nor is it fair always to blame the union for management's inertia. Often the company is too busy with the solution of daily problems to know what is going on in the world outside, and ignores process improvements possible through automation.

Financial Side of Automation   Will automation pay off? This is a natural question asked both by management and stockholders. If the firm lays out money for plant and equipment, will the expenditure of funds be justified within a reasonable time by reduced material and labor costs, by decreased indirect costs, by increased output, or by various combinations of these advantages?

Costs are difficult to estimate, since it is not often financially practicable to replace all present production facilities and switch to full automation. As most firms cannot easily raise vast sums for total automation, they turn to partial or piecemeal replacement of existing facilities; hence, they cannot easily estimate savings. Should a firm move now into superior equipment, or should it wait a while and get even better equipment in a few years? After all, the rate of obsolescence in this type of equipment is very rapid.

Automation based on a hopeful market expansion is tantamount to a direct road to bankruptcy. Management must be sensitive to demand; increased production could result in falling prices, which could be disastrous.

Production and Design Flexibility   It is also very difficult to estimate the effect of automation on all aspects of a company's operations. Products may have to be changed slightly, work methods altered more than originally estimated, material specifications amended, capacities of supporting operations increased, and other adjustments may have to be made. Indirect costs may increase, because products may have to be redesigned; many trial runs may have to be adjusted to the new controls; operators retrained; and equipment re-engineered if it does not operate as successfully as was contemplated. During the change-over period, the loss in production may be severe, power requirements may soar, and much more extensive maintenance may be required than formerly. Rogers lists a set of principles as a minimum guide in planning a conversion:

1. A complete analysis of all aspects of production is necessary to determine the need for and the applicability of automation.
2. Automation should not be justified solely on the basis of the amount of labor saved versus expenditure for equipment; there are other significant benefits and potential disadvantages.
3. Technical feasibility should not be taken for granted.
4. Planning should be based on the worst that can happen, both with respect to revenues and costs.[15]

Ability to Procure Information About Automation   With some firms automation is simply an extension of the rapid development occasioned by fuller mechanization. In other firms automation represents a brand-new set of ideas. Often a mistake is initially made by focusing on the equipment of automation rather than on the picture of the production system as a whole. If one looks for the answer in the designing of automatic equipment to replace that run manually, he may be making a mistake because of a "set" in thinking. This method may only accumulate the present productive inefficiencies. But an equally bad mistake can be made if the responsibility of conversion is turned over to the company engineers, who may not know of the side effect of automation.

It is not prudent to entrust either the human side or the business side of the problem to the engineers alone. A number of concerns have set up project committees, which include people who know the business well — its functions and activities. These committees can often foresee the effect of certain changes on organization and operations — changes that have eluded those technicians introspectively involved with equipment design and development. Committees are helpful in the early stages of information procurement, but later the company needs an action group or staff unit to serve as an adjunct to management in the installation period.

A surprising amount of information about automation may be procured from equipment manufacturers through visits to other automated concerns and participation in conferences and lectures. The automation planners must familiarize themselves with the field before making costly moves. As the managerial study group begins to understand the new technology, other persons in operations and administration can be advised about it and their support enlisted in the new program. The backing of top management is always a most important ingredient. Employment of consultants who are specialists on automated installations often works out beneficially.

Automation and Optimum Company Size   There is danger that overdiversification makes a business unmanageable. Such an effect is possible particularly in those businesses which originated in a common technology, such as electrical engineering, or in firms involved in chemistry. Drucker points out that the giant oil companies have always been highly complex, but nevertheless closely integrated. However, when the petro-chemical industry came along, the oil companies had to put these new businesses into separate companies, retaining financial ownership but giving the management job to new firms. Drucker believes that the danger of overdiversity in the new technology of automation is the most serious problem of manageability. He states:

> ... Automation does not require larger businesses — it may well make smaller ones possible in many industries. But it requires that each process be conceived of and managed as a separate integrated whole. Management policies and decisions taken for one *process* may not fit another; and management policies and decisions taken for one function or one area rather than for the entire process may not fit all. This not

only makes federal organization essential; it also may well set narrow limits to the diversity of product businesses, any one top-management can administer. It is, I think, no accident that the oil companies have chosen not to integrate their chemical businesses but to separate them out; after all, the oil companies had Automation long before the word was invented. And larger companies in the industries that are about to move into the new technology might well consider the oil industry's example.[16]

Ability to Plan Employment Stability   Automation, by raising productivity and living standards, may cause more jobs to be created than are eliminated. However, various situations may develop in a firm or an industry where this principle may not be in evidence. The worst possible situation would be that in a firm or industry where fewer new jobs will be created than are eliminated; or where new ones will be possible only after a lapse of time, and therefore the affected individuals will not be able to transfer to new work. The *ideal* situation would be one where more new jobs are created than are destroyed by automation and all affected individuals immediately have new jobs. The *actual* situation will fall somewhere between these two situations. When automation is adopted in an intensive fashion, some employees will never be unemployed; some will be only temporarily unemployed; others will be unemployed for a long time; some will eventually get better positions; others poorer ones.

When a firm is a major employer in an area, reduction in the normal size of the working establishment may result in such a community dislocation that new opportunities with smaller firms will not be enough to offset the major impact of automation on the town or city. If at all possible, it would be better for some firms to build new automated plants in new locations rather than expand or modify old plants.

While this point of view may seem to be altruistic, it would probably be acceptable to the union involved in the multiplant operations. As attrition takes place over a period in the older plant, it may then be possible to modify the production processes on an automated basis. If this is not done, then employees in these automated plants who cannot transfer to other regions will be stranded, thus causing a local situation.

As a solution to job dislocation and displacement, an employer could examine the possibility of moving workers. But labor mobility does not provide an easy solution. Unemployment cuts income, and moving costs are high. Moreover, the quick sale of a house or other property usually results in a loss. The worker faces a loss of his seniority and often a disruption of pension rights and other job-connected benefits, such as vacation. Finally, the other members of the worker's family may not want to move because they are attending school or have jobs.

The unions tend to make work-force changes less attractive to employers. They want to broaden seniority classifications, thus creating "bumping" of shorter term employees in other departments. This creates chaos for management and slows them down in their approach to automation. Early discussions with unions about plans to automate, say in two years, might very well eliminate this type of obstruction.

Theory of Automatic Reabsorption of Displaced Labor Some employers believe that there is a law of nature which states that when a man loses his job on a machine, he will always find another job elsewhere. The "theory of automatic reabsorption of displaced labor" has some degree of validity. Its supporters would have to concede, however, that it is a long-run, not a short-run, theory. Most people have to live in the short run. A classic comment was that made by the famous economist J. M. Keynes that "in the long run we are all dead."[17]

In a strong growth industry like the auto industry, from 1900 to 1950 a rising demand for products more than offset the laborsaving effects of mechanization. But the fact is that the nation is undergoing a shortage of major growth industries at present. Blue-collar employment in manufacturing has actually been falling off in the last few years, even though output has been rising, owing in very large measure to automation and fuller mechanization. It is significant that much more than a proportionate share of hard-core unemployment in the distressed areas is composed of workers whose last jobs were in manufacturing.

Another difficulty of the automatic reabsorption theory is that the mobility of the unemployed workers is severely limited. Long-run adjustments may well take a lifetime.

The May 1961 report of the Conference of Economic Progress describes the relationship of employment to technological progress for the years 1947–1960. With the average of 1947–1949 as a base and with an index number of 100, production workers declined steadily to only 90, as a percent of total manufacturing employment. Total employment in manufacturing as a percent of gross national product declined from 100 in 1947–1949 to 73 in 1960.

The worst picture of all is that production workers in manufacturing, as a percent of gross national product, declined from 100 in 1947–1949 to 65 in 1960. Gains in gross national product are coming about, despite static or even declining employment among production workers. Although some of the gains in gross national product come about as a result of inflation, most are attributed to gains in productivity resulting from higher capital investment per worker in machinery and automated equipment.

Motives for Automation Other Than Cutting Labor Costs

The justifying of automation through labor savings alone is a short-sighted position for a firm to take. Bright studied motives for automation in thirteen firms and found an astonishing range of motives. He discovered that firms rarely quantified anything but labor savings, and he concluded this was "a bad mistake," besides being extremely inflammatory to the labor unions.

Among the advantages Bright lists are the following:

1. The cutting of lead time. A parts firm cut it from 19 to 3 days; an oil refinery from 4 days to 5 hours; a feedmill from 2 manhours to 5 manminutes. It is obvious what the constructive influences might be on customer service, production planning and reduction of inventory by the technique of automation.

2. One firm justified automation on a basis of reduction in scrap. Another improved working conditions to such an extent that it was possible to hire and hold women workers in a tight labor market.

3. Certain engine plants were able to gain one-third in productive capacity without extra investment or plant expansion. This was accomplished by increasing equipment utilization from about 60 to 80 percent.

4. One fertilizer plant adopted automation because it enabled immediate push-button mixing of any of 500 formulations. Up to that time such product flexibility had never been contemplated in a conventional plant.

5. One oil refinery was actually able to reduce capital investment by automation. This possibility is entirely foreign to planners in other heavy industries. One firm visualized lower maintenance costs! Personnel savings alone do not constitute the greatest argument for automation.[18]

The oil refinery illustration shows clearly that automation may possibly cost less than a conventional system. The automation oil plant was to be an integrated system, eliminating much in-process tank storage and associated piping and pumping mechanisms. It required only one control center as compared to four previously. The automated cost came to $700 a barrel of daily output compared to $1000 a barrel for the conventional equipment. The reduction in cost was due to the fact that less equipment was necessary under automation, not that each ton of equipment was cheaper.

When the shrinkage of equipment volume is great enough, building and facilities requirements shrink as well. As a result, great reductions in cost will occur.

Economy Studies Important in Decisions on Automation   In contemplating automation, a manufacturer must contrast the difference between the present conventional operation and the proposed operations in all its aspects. When this is done, it will be noted that the complex calculations include those factors which are cost-raising and those which are cost-lowering. The net impact on investment requirements is by no means certain to be greater. It depends on the relative weight of the factors.

It is easy to generalize about equipment costs and the high investment necessary in automated plants. However, industries vary a good deal in their requirements. Conclusions for one industry do not hold for all. The automotive industry normally faces heavy development costs because each piece of automation is "a unique piece of machine design."[19] Many process industries, however, have assemblages of fairly standard components. The use of standard components reduces the investment and costs of the automated plant.

Many of the costs included in the price of automation are the price of ignorance, poor planning, carelessness, and human error. The cost of automation is not "so much proportional to the automaticity, but to the amount of novelty and uniqueness [attempted] . . . ."[20]

Maintenance Cost Reduction Possible   Many unions hope that where workers are laid off because displacement occurs in direct production, they will be upgraded and retrained as maintenance men in the same company or industry. Yet the facts indicate that fewer maintenance personnel may be required than before.

Bright[21] reports that conventional oil refineries usually assign about 60 percent of the work force to maintenance. He mentions one automated refinery where maintenance workers represent only 20 percent of the work force. This reduction is ascribed to the fact that there is less machinery to contend with. Many pipes, valves, controls, and pumps have been eliminated. Maintenance is proportional not to the amount of automaticity but to the total amount of machinery. Apparently automation itself is not a reason for increased maintenance costs, since automatic machinery can be very reliable and can have few breakdowns. That which does require costly service is not straight maintenance, but is a result of trial and error and the troubles that develop in the installation of new equipment.

Bright makes the point that the "thing called maintenance is usually a blend of . . . installation . . . debugging . . . routine servicing . . . downtime for tool replacement . . . housekeeping . . . maintenance of tooling fixtures (not production equipment) . . . and . . . breakdowns."[22]

Bright and other authorities believe that maintenance costs may be grossly exaggerated as a liability of automation. In fact, the cost differential is bound to decrease through reduction in the volume of machinery required compared to conventional setups. More functions will be compounded on fewer machine bases; higher production will be obtained from smaller but faster machines; and higher machine utilization and efficiency will be brought about by mechanical work-feeding and interlocking control. Required floor and building space will be reduced by less machinery, less in-process storage space, less space for operators, and fewer traffic aisles, since the material is mechanically moved into the production machine.

Severity of Maintenance Problems   The retraining of operators will not be too difficult, but the problem of increased maintenance will have a genuine influence upon personnel activities. The managers and the personnel directors of companies looking to automation ought to consider those aspects of the operation which will increase the maintenance requirements.

According to Bright, these are:

> . . . increased mechanization across the span of the production system . . . higher proportion of moving parts . . . greater complexity in the machinery . . . and of the controls . . . more novelty and uniqueness present in the mechanism. . . . The increased extent to which the machinery and control mechanisms employ new technologies, particularly electronics . . . higher proportions of electro-hydraulic-pneumatic actuation of controls and machinery as opposed to mechanical linkage. . . . The increased extent to which the machinery operates near design

limits of speed, temperature, precision and capacity . . . the inexperience of the maintenance force with the new machinery and controls.[23]

At the same time factors that decrease the severity of the maintenance problem must be considered. Already mentioned is the reduction in the total amount of machinery because of the smaller size of the plant and the compounding of production equipment. Controls and control mechanisms, it must be admitted, have been greatly standardized and in some ways simplified. Each year managers, supervisors, and engineers have accumulated more experience in design engineering and have had operational and maintenance experience with the new automated equipment.

Much progress has been made in avoiding trouble by mechanization of trouble prevention (safety switches and other devices) and the use of trouble-signaling systems, which forestall serious failure and damage. Mechanization is now extended to portions of the maintenance job — for example, automatic lubrication and adjustment for wear. The development of new techniques for instruction, such as the color coding of circuits, testing circuits, detector panels, is another case in point. It has also become easier to remove and replace parts and assemblies rapidly and to observe those which should be removed. The net impact on any plant is a combination of positive and negative factors, always keeping in mind, however, the maintenance problems that existed in the former conventional plant.[24]

Supply and Demand in Skills   In the study of the thirteen automated plants made by Bright (previously referred to), the researcher found that automation did not place management in a position of having to take drastic measures because of increases in operator skill requirements. He admitted a scarcity of maintenance electricians trained in electronics work, but found that only between 10 and 25 percent of all electricians involved in automated plants required this training.

The researcher also found that competent hydraulic and pneumatic repairmen were not in any liberal supply, but that only a few firms under study ran into great difficulty on account of this shortage. Those firms, however, that designed and built their own machinery saw a distinct shortage of machine designers, engineers, and mechanics with machine-building skills.

Bright[25] concluded that if the firm considering automation were to ask the question "can we go into automation with our present work force and succeed in running the new plant?" the answer would be "yes."

As to necessary retraining, suppose a company were to ask: "Will we face a difficult retraining problem?" Bright would answer "no," with due allowance for minor exceptions and for a few maintenance jobs. In fact, it appears that skill requirements might possibly be lowered and that the training period might be reduced for many operating positions.

Misrepresentation of Displacement Facts by the Press The community, the unions, and the workingman sometimes get so upset about the effect of automation on the employment picture that the "grapevine" gets to work, doing real harm to fair management proposals for expanding the business and making healthier opportunities for workingmen.

The press will occasionally pick up these rumors and run a harmful series of stories. Therefore, when management is considering automation or fuller mechanization, it must be public-relations conscious and must see that the facts reach the public in advance of feature stories on massive job displacement.

The labor impact of automation is often distorted by the way the percentage labor savings is expressed relative to a minute part of the operation:

> In a foam rubber mattress plant . . . displacement was quoted in the trade press as being 50 percent of the working force. However, on checking the figures closely, I found that displacement amounted to 45 percent of the people in the *pouring operation only*. They represented just 16 percent of the total employed on the foam rubber mattress line. Further, this production line was only a piece of the entire plant's activities, and the number of displaced people amounted to about $1\frac{1}{2}$ percent of the total working force! (Absorbed, incidentally, in other operations.)[26]

Time after time, Bright found similar drastic percentage displacement or labor savings figures widely quoted, which, in fact, applied only to very small segments of the total production activity.

Conventional Management Improvement Coincident with Automation Planning Unions will often take exception to the introduction of automatic machinery but not to other management improvements. The truth is that the great strides in production in this nation stem not so much from automaticity as from other improvements in manufacturing techniques.

The spatial rearrangement of machinery to provide a more efficient sequence of activity (as, for example, Ford's contributions to the idea of moving lines for chassis assembly); assembly lines pushed by rope (1913), by hands, or by chain-drive, or mounted on rails (1941) — all accounted for fantastic increases in productivity without much emphasis on mechanization.

Often, a change in material will advance the automatic aspect of production technique. Bakeries are not always continuous-flow systems, because the dough-mix must sit for several hours until the yeast rises. A new type of yeast material for rapid fermentation is under development. If it is successful, a flow process, and hence greater automaticity, will be possible.

Most of the dramatic improvements come from change in processes that facilitate mechanization; for example, stampings and castings versus machine parts.

Changes in product designs facilitate greater automaticity. The automatic TV chassis assembly process is the result of a new concept in design that permits the use of etched wiring on a flat board to connect the leads of the mounted components. The "printed circuit" design opened the way for automatic production.

Bright completes this thought with the following statement:

> Thus to look to automatic machinery as the sole hero or villain of automatic production, productivity increases and/or labor displacement is industrial naivete of the first order. We must not forget that the product designer who eliminates a part does something for productivity that surpasses any mechanization we might dream of. And when he so much as eliminates two of four fasteners, he decreases labor content 50 percent without spending one cent on equipment.[27]

Management ought to tell the worker that automation will provide him with a number of opportunities not available to him under the conventional methods of operation. This is particularly true for workers in operating levels. Why not tell it to him when you plan to automate? All he hears is the contrary side.

Work will become easier, both physically and mentally. Job variety will possibly develop through changes that make the tasks more interesting. Workers may find their jobs more satisfying through a sense of responsibility for a larger part of the end result. The working environment may become more pleasant, and higher pay may be earned through increased productivity.

Several experts make the point that there will be an increase in prestige and job satisfaction as a result of working in an outstanding plant in the community or the nation. Since automation follows the needs of competition for better tools, either workers in these changing plants may have better job security or the competitive position of the firm improves. This security will be gained at the expense of workers in other competing firms.

Workers in automated plants may have more continued employment, a safer job, and an opportunity to learn more about the total production process and machinery. To the pride of running a fine machine will be added the experience of working with modern equipment — experience that will prove more valuable to the worker as time goes on.

These cited advantages, of course, do not relate to the net effect on employment opportunities, which are still uncertain.

Conclusion

It is true that it took more than one hundred years for the steam engine to be widely adopted by industry. Today new techniques are more quickly adopted. In the early days of the computer, utilization appeared to require years of planning. Today computers are less costly and are being "miniaturized." Computer quality has been improved while costs have been lowered.

The incentive to go "automated" is strong. One aircraft manufacturer predicted that through the use of "numerical control" techniques, he could pay for a $500,000 machine in ninety days. If a manufacturer can make such quick saving, he can borrow the money easily without worrying about large investments.

The speed of automation will depend on the industry involved. However, when one reviews the entire pattern, it appears safe to assume that automation is coming faster than might have been expected at one time, partly because of the billions being poured into military research and development. Most of the numerically controlled machines in use are actually owned by the Air Force.

The automobile industry has always had rapid obsolescence. For example, a five-year-old engine line is obsolete from the competitive standpoint. Even the smallest and weakest auto manufacturers are going in heavily for automation. Mechanization is going swiftly in the bookkeeping and clerical fields — much more than might have been expected — and will continue to move rapidly.

References

1. R. L. Ackoff, "Automatic Management: A Forecast and Its Educational Implications," *Management Service*, vol. 2, no. 1 (October 1955), pp. 55–60.
2. R. Craig Wood, "Training the Manager of the Future," *The Manager*, vol. XXIV, no. 12 (December 1955).
3. Carl Dreher, *Automation: What it is, How it Works, Who Can Use it* (New York: W. W. Norton and Co., Inc., 1957), p. 13.
4. Carroll W. Boyce, "What Automation Means to America," *Factory Management and Maintenance* (September 1955).
5. A. F. Aperry, "The Nature of Automation," *Keeping Pace With Automation, Practical Guides for the Company Executive*, Special Report no. 7, American Management Association, 1955.
6. W. J. Carr, "Solving Scientific Problems," *Control Engineering*, vol. 3 (January 1956), pp. 63–70.
7. Peter F. Drucker, *The Practice of Management* (New York: Harper & Row, 1954).
8. Drucker, "The Management Horizon," *The Journal of Business* (July 1955), pp. 155–164.
9. Drucker, "Integration of People and Planning," *Harvard Business Review*, vol. 9, no. 6 (November–December 1955), pp. 35–40.
10. D. S. Harder, *The Automatic Factory* (Michigan: Ford Motor Co., Manufacturing Engineering Office, March 26, 1953).
11. M. L. Hurni, "Must Management Change to Prepare for Automation?" *Advanced Management*, vol. 19, no. 5 (May 1954), pp. 25–28.
12. M. Seaman, "Automation — Some Problems for the Boardroom," *The Automatic Factory, What Does it Mean?* (The Institution of Production Engineers, London, Conference Report on Margate Discussions, June 16–19, 1955), pp. 91–95.
13. D. G. Osborn, *Automation of Industry — A Geographical Consideration* (Chicago: University of Chicago Press, September 1953).
14. L. Landon Goodman, *Automation Today and Tomorrow* (London: Ioata Services, Ltd., 1958), p. 9.
15. Jack Rogers, *Automation — Technology's New Face* (Berkeley: University of California, Institute of Industrial Relations, 1958), p. 65.
16. Drucker, *The Practice of Management, op. cit.*, p. 235.
17. Charles C. Killingsworth, "Effects of Automation on Employment and Manpower Planning," LIRC, Reprint Series no. 37, Michigan State University, 1960–1961, p. 5.
18. James R. Bright, "Myths and Fallacies of Automation," a paper presented before the Society of Automotive Engineers, Inc., New York, January 14, 1957, p. 3.
19. *Ibid.*, p. 7.

20. *Ibid.*
21. *Ibid.*
22. *Ibid.*, p. 8.
23. *Ibid.*, Table 3, Appendix.
24. *Ibid.*, p. 8.
25. *Ibid.*, p. 11.
26. *Ibid.*, p. 14.
27. *Ibid.*

▶▶▶▶ **6**

Challenge to
Management of Machines and
Men in the Automated Plant

With the advent of automation, management begins to assume new responsibilities over both machines and men. Personnel functions that, for a long time, were the special province of the staff specialists must now be assumed in part by the line managers. The opportunities of automation will present great changes and new problems for management.

Operating Inflexibilities

In the early stages of automation, management will be confronted by a reduction in flexibility. For a long time the typical setup will consist of special toolings and single-purpose machines designed around one product. Equipment costs will be very expensive, so that revision for product change would be too costly. "The fixed costs of specialized production facilities will be high in comparison to variable costs of operations, so even if the operating rate can be slowed, costs cannot be appreciably reduced by cutting output."[1] In some future, more highly automated stage it may be possible to build more highly flexible production units to turn out a variety of products, but at present stages of development this is unlikely.

Where plants are designed to operate continuously near maximum capacity, it may not be possible technically or economically to operate above or below the designated rate.

Another problem is that the labor force will consist of salaried technicians and maintenance men, whose salaries go on for the entire week, month, or year, so they must be on the job regardless of the rate of productivity. Labor costs will be unresponsive to changes in rate of operations or output. The overhead organization in engineer-

89

ing and administration will be relatively large and its minimum size will tend to be fixed.[2]

Planning Most Important

These management inflexibilities will require advance planning to prevent gearing the automated department to what might be over-production. Where variations in output are required, planning will be necessary to achieve them with minimum dislocation. All business functions — sales, finance, and procurement — should be integrated to the maximum with production.

As automation demands integration of line activities and management, so it magnifies the consequences of error. Decisions and judgments must be made on a basis of detailed analysis rather than on hunches. Shortages of materials, excessive equipment down time, and poor production planning occurring in a manual plant might have only a negligible cumulative effect. However, in an automated plant these conditions might stop production for hours over the entire plant.

How are large quantities of standardized items to be marketed? Where are the skilled technicians of automation to be recruited? How are new industrial relations problems created by shorter hours, changed skill requirements, and new working conditions to be handled? From what source comes the money required for continued plant changes? These problems will belabor management after the beginning steps of automation are taken. Managing a business with automation may be a tougher job than managing one without it!

Aids to Management

Automation in the office will continue to parallel the progress of automation in the plant. Automatic data processing will be valuable to the managers in their struggle with the new production problems. The employment of computers for managerial purposes will speed up information flow, so that prompt decisions may be forthcoming. Inventory control by computers can provide management the answer in seconds, compared to the older methods of looking into last week's or last month's reports.

Data will be classified in many ways in order to provide the answers necessary in handling the operating variables. The possible outcomes of decisions may even be tested by simulation if workable, mathematical models reducible to computer programs can be constructed. With operations planned and with systems for reporting and control mechanized, major decisions can be centrally made and quickly effected. This will cut down on the diffusion of decision making through numerous management levels now prevailing.

Automation a Stimulant to Decision Making

An automated plant will require personnel effective in decision making and users of data processing and related business-systems techniques. Gallagher[3] points out that better decision making can be achieved by giving the manager accurate and timely information with which to measure more precisely the economic and operational consequences of a decision.

The decision cannot be an automatic response to information input. The manager's judgment and the responsibility for the consequences will not be transferred to a systems group of data processors. Certainly this will never be done in the levels of top-management decision making.

Drucker cites the needs very clearly:

> In dealing with their new tasks, the managers of the 1960's will, to a large extent, have to employ the same tools they are using today. But managers will also find, increasingly, that they are expected to know, understand, and handle new concepts and tools of management. Increasingly, they will find that they are expected to use systematic methods of analysis and decision-making, supplemented by new systematic tools of communications, computation and presentation.
>
> Executives can safely disregard all the fanciful talk about the computer replacing managers and making decisions. Managers' work, it can be said with confidence, is going to be more important, and their numbers larger. But the management sciences — such as operations research or decision-making logic — and the new electronic tools and systems are going to make a difference, even to the manager of the small business.
>
> And the manager of 1970 will need all the help he can get from such new concepts and tools. For his job is going to be so complex, so big, so demanding as to require all the tools of simplification and systematization that can be possibly obtained.[4]

Factors Stimulating Technical Progress

Technically, progressive firms are those in the forefront of discovery in applied science and technology, quick to perceive and master new ideas.[5] In their study of 246 English firms Carter and Williams found that there was a sound relationship between a "technical progressiveness" rating made by the experimentalists and the scores on a twenty-four-item "general quality" rating scale. This scale assessed such characteristics as policies, communications, managerial talent, and investment. Carter and Williams also found that effective research and development is closely related to problems of manufacture and marketing. Those firms which have always been known as "innovators" will probably surmount all the obstacles of automation.

Efficient Engineering — The Rule of Integration

Drucker cites two principles pertinent to successful automation. The principle of *mechanization* applies to mechanical work; the principle of *integration* applies to human work.[6]

Both principles begin with a systematic analysis of the work into its constituent motions. Attention must be focused on each motion to make it easier, faster, and more effortless. Of course, work will have to have been laid out in a logical sequence of motions. The improvement of the entire output will depend on the improvement of the component motions.

The key is to organize motions *mechanically* so as to utilize the special property of the machine (that is, the ability to do one thing fast and faultlessly). At the same time it is essential to *integrate* operations so well that all the special properties of the human being are fully utilized, such as the abilities to make a whole out of many things, to judge, to plan, and to change.

There are vast technological opportunities for efficient production in automation — production that gives the human his dignity and at the same time gets the full price out of the machine. Automation provides the means to make fully mechanical those jobs in which the human being is used as an adjunct of the machine tool. The work that still depends on the human factor must be organized through integration. Productivity and a good way of life will, therefore, depend on the successful understanding of the principles of mechanization and of integration, linking them together and applying them systematically.

Plant Layout and the Working Environment

Originally, mechanization influenced plant layout by subdivisions of functions. An important part of the space problem was the provision for many human beings. Automated machines will be grouped according to the span of activities these machines can handle, and they have no connection with the span of activities a human being can handle.[7]

Automation requires that the whole industrial process be a complete, integrated system from the delivery of the raw material to the removal of the final product. Materials should flow through the various processes, and interruptions to this flow resulting from unnatural bottlenecks should be eliminated.

With automation, large areas of floor space will be taken up by machines working under clean conditions. The concentration of machines will be much greater per square foot than in the conventional plant. Factories of the future will then probably be, at most, a quarter of the present size.[8]

Extreme fire precautions will have to be taken, as the plants of the future will have large areas unbroken by walls, and fire can spread more easily in this type of structure. The new buildings will be primarily shells designed to accommodate the equipment, whereas conventional plants are designed to accommodate a variety of purposes. Because of personnel required, the areas for toilets, stores, and canteens will be much smaller in relation to the size of the general plant. Leisure areas for employees will be proportionately greater than in conventional plants.

Communications Important for Employee Support of Automation

With automation, new channels of communications must be established. The age of mass production did not adequately prepare the workers for the change from the smaller, more informal factory. This mistake should not be repeated. Through joint consultation with employees, decisions, new information, and new ideas should be made known to them before launching into great automated change. If management is inherently sincere, then employee committees (in a nonunion shop) or union representatives (in a union shop) will appreciate the honest approach of management.

Goodman[9] tells of a series of departmental joint productivity councils in a steel plant in England that were enlarged into a works council. This council became the means of joint consideration of day-to-day problems that arose as technological change was introduced in the plant. One of the decisions of the council was that a monthly departmental breakdown of costs and production should be explained each month to the employees by a member of the firm's accounting department. As a result of joint participation in planning change, interest in training courses grew. As Goodman says:

> Automation will provide a favorable atmosphere for a sincere attempt to better human relations in industry; for the operator in an automated plant will come into much closer contact with management, technical personnel, and maintenance staff, with whom he will work as a member of a team. He will be in charge of large expensive machines, and his responsibility, too, will be correspondingly greater; for any mistake that he might make will be very costly indeed. All this will increase his pride in his work and his status, both in his own eyes and in those of his friends.[10]

The Professional Manager

The development of an industrial enterprise depends broadly on the supply and utilization of human resources, raw materials, the availability of capital, and, of course, a progressive management — the most important factor in business survival today. The manager must be able to balance social factors against scientific ones. Often he is a representative of absentee ownership and his burden is almost intolerable. The greater the complexity of mechanization, the higher becomes the ratio of managers and supervisors to productive employees. Automation will accelerate this trend.

Management Structure

Size of organization and type of activity fundamentally affect the structure of management. Organizations suitable for batch production are not suitable for mass production. Automation requires another type of management structuring. The speed with which data are received offers new opportunities of decentralization. The greater number of levels of responsibility in the conventional plant will be reduced by automation; there will be fewer people between the top and the bottom man.

The present line and staff organizations should be carefully reviewed. If a machine breaks down, there will be some delay if information has to be passed up the traditional lines of authority, across, and then down again to the right specialist in a staff department. Under automation, the specialist may have to be called in directly, thus creating a link between the process machine operator and the technician. Everything will have to be done more quickly by management, both as to planning and implementation.

New Management Responsibilities

Management needs to understand automation and what advantages it promises and provides, and must take the responsibility for initiating research studies on the possibilities of automation — in other words, management will have to educate itself constantly about new methods of work.

A problem taxing to management will be when to make a change. If the decision is premature, substantial financial loss might result; if no action is taken, markets and volume might be sacrificed. As was stated previously, a great deal of inflexibility may occur through automation, particularly in production. Combine this factor with the high capital costs, and a mistake can be much more severe than in the conventional plant.

The Human Problems

How can management coordinate the specialists in technical application with the other employees of the company? How can they be welded together as a team and appreciate each other's problems? Production engineers must now be interested in the outlook of the electronics specialists. The new product designer must be sympathetic to the problems of the production people. Designs by normal methods might be absolutely useless under an automated system. The engineering staff will show signs of great strain. Patience and guidance are needed everywhere. In the coming integration of the various operations, one way to improve morale is to have a good system of communications, a factor so important that it requires repeated mention.

Information must be made available from top to bottom, and vice versa. Full explanations of changes must be made quickly to all employees involved. Comments should be invited on newly proposed layouts. If management can work together in an automated plant, the chances are excellent that management and labor will see eye to eye. Integration of operations will require study and planning. When the work has been defined, new courses of training should be set up and methods of filling jobs from the outside or by internal promotion and transfer should be explained to all concerned.

When the plant is fully automated and shifts are worked out, new problems will develop. The channels of authority between shift supervisors and the day management ought to be carefully worked out.

Utilization of Engineers

A measure of mechanization is the rising consumption of electrical energy by the firm. The more electrical energy purchased or used, the more the demand for engineers. Engineering talent will have to be conserved. In 1910, 1 person out of 250 in the United States was employed as an engineer. By 1955 the ratio was 1 to 100. In aircraft manufacturing it was as high as 1 to 7. The average in industry today may be approaching 1 to 50.[11]

If the trend continues, the nation will experience an alarming shortage of engineers. Engineers must be confined to technical work of the highest order, with the highest level of engineering work centralized. They should have technicians and technical assistants to aid with the routine duties. Industry and the colleges should be training technicians in two-year post high school technical institutes or community colleges.

Use of Industrial Engineering

The conception of industrial engineering as a management tool can be of great value in advancing automation. The typical functions of the industrial engineering department with respect to automation might be:

1. To advise top management on developments in automation, applicable to its products and manufacturing techniques.

2. To redesign products particularly suitable for automatic assembly or other automation techniques.

3. To implement the introduction of automation and to assist in training.

4. To maintain liaison with various branches and departments of the Company, and contacts with other research centers, research associations and universities who are interested in similar problems.[12]

Industrial engineering may be considered from two aspects, one involving the integration of the various staff services — namely, acting as a specialist to the specialists; the other requiring the individual specialist to be aware of the work going on in the other departments. The following chart (page 98), prepared by L. Landon Goodman, shows the industrial engineer's role in automation. It should be noted that eventually problems of space, materials handling, production design, heating and ventilating, mechanical handling, and other factors, all lead back to problems with individuals and unions. Hence it is important that management know something about what an industrial engineer can do, to lessen the problems with human beings as well as with mechanical processes.

Management Training Essential

Greater productivity can result only from the introduction of new methods, new techniques, and new ways of solving problems. American corporations and various business enterprises must take every step to educate, train, and develop future business leaders who will be competent to manage in an automated age. This has always been the measure of American superiority in production over European; namely, the fact that the United States has trained more and better professional managers. Now Europe, too, is pressing hard on this goal.

Decision making in an automated economy will be of vital consequence, and management will have to be of a higher standard than at present. Qualifications will be upgraded, and adaptability and versatility will be important personal characteristics in the new managerial profession. Management training will have to broaden the technical people to give them a general appreciation of industrial and social affairs, as well as human factors in industry.

Should these men be recruited from among scientists or nonscientists? Technical skill and management abilities should be present and compatible in the "new" manager.

The average engineering program has been much too narrow to provide the economic and business backgrounds now desired in managers. The curriculums at engineering schools should be revised,

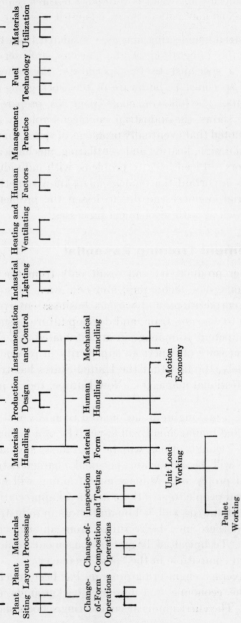

and the firm ought to carry on additional training. In some of these new jobs where computers are used, a knowledge of mathematics will be helpful. The technical man will have more of this background than the college graduate recruited from the four-year school of business. Colleges offering business administration programs are now beginning to require college mathematics as a part of the basic curriculum.* This then leads into quantitative business programs, such as operations research and linear programming.

Intuition a Requisite in the Manager

The new technology will require better performance by managers in all areas. Not only will marketing and production be important, but the location of personnel resources will assume more and more importance.

> Because the new technology requires it, and because social pressures demand it, the manager of tomorrow will have to make it possible to anticipate employment and to maintain it as close to stability as possible. At the same time, as today's semi-skilled operator becomes tomorrow's highly trained maintenance man, and today's skilled worker tomorrow's individual professional contributor, labor will become a much more expensive resource — a capital investment of the business rather than a current cost. And its importance will have a much greater impact on the performance of the whole business.[13]

The above statement by Drucker implies that the manager will have to acquire a whole new set of tools, many of which he will have to develop himself. The personnel manager must have his objectives clearly in mind and must acquire adequate yardsticks for performance and results in the key areas of business objectives. He must acquire economic tools to make meaningful decisions that will fit into the long-range planning of today's automated enterprises.

New Management Tools More Than "Operations Research"

The new tools have been introduced under the confusing name of "operations research." Drucker says they "are neither operations nor research."[14] They are the tools of systematic, logical, mathe-

*The new program at the Wharton School of Finance and Commerce at the University of Pennsylvania first made this a requirement in 1961.

matical analysis and synthesis. With any new tool it is important to say what it cannot do. Operations research and all its techniques — mathematical analysis, modern symbolic logic, mathematical information theory, theory of games, mathematical probability, and so on, cannot help in defining what the management problem is. Tools, however, can be of help in analyzing the problem and in developing alternatives. They can point out relevant factors. They can show what resources are needed for each alternative action. They can show the impact of a given action. But these tools are not without danger. If improperly used, they can help make the wrong decision. They can oversolve a problem in one small area, or "suboptimize," as the technicians call it. When this occurs, the decision is full of distortion. In essence, these aids are tools of information rather than of decision making, and they will be of great help to the manager in automation. Even if the manager cannot work each tool in person, he must be able to understand each one while it is being handled by the specialist. Decision making becomes ever so much more important in automation than in the conventional plants. No amount of skill in making tactical decisions will relieve the manager of making strategic decisions.

Demands on Management

Despite the promises of European "planners" that automation will result in further monopoly, cartelization, and other combines, the new technology "will demand the utmost in decentralization, in flexibility and in management autonomy."[15] Any society in this era of the new technology would perish miserably were it to attempt to get rid of free management of autonomous enterprise, so as to run the economy by central planning. And so would any enterprise that attempts to centralize responsibility and decision making at the top.

Several writers in the field of automation have indicated that the new techniques will eliminate supervisors and make centralized decision making possible to a larger extent. Drucker does not accept this thesis. Furthermore, if we follow his ideas, it appears that the new technology will demand many more managers — that many of the present rank and file will begin to perform a type of managerial work.

The greater majority of technicians will have to try to understand what top management wants. They will have to begin to think and act like managers. If management is found wanting in the great tasks lying ahead, then the mass-production leadership that America exercised over the world in the first half of the twentieth century will not be duplicated in the automated society of the second half.

Relationship Shifts

Just as automation has resulted in a change in factors that influence management and the workers, so does automation influence the supervisor in many ways. One way, of course, is the relationship to the workers.

The change in relationship between worker and supervisor under automation is due largely to the changes in the job responsibilities of workers. Faunce states:

> The worker in the automated [automobile] plant is responsible for a larger share of the production process. The job requires more constant and careful attention. The results of failure to attend more closely to the job are more costly and, because of the increased complexity of the transfer machinery, and the fact that it has only been recently introduced into the automobile industry, machine breakdowns are more frequent in automated departments. These factors play a major role in increasing the amount of supervision of workers on automated jobs.[16]

By and large it appears that the ratio of supervisor to workers goes up in the automated plant. Actually a decrease is observed in the number of workers per foreman, and an increase in the amount of time foremen will spend in supervising the line.

In response to the question given to workers as part of the Faunce study — "Would you say it is easier to get along with the foreman on your present job [automated] than on your old job [nonautomated]?" — the majority of the employees indicated a happier relationship with foremen on the conventional job. The principal reason given by those who stated that they got along better with the foreman in the newly automated plant appeared to be the better personal characteristics of the *new* foreman and not the change in working conditions.

Foreman Affected by Trying Work Conditions

The Faunce study of automobile plants indicated that even in those circumstances where foremen in the conventional plants were retained as foremen in the automated plant, these individuals in supervision began to change under changing conditions of responsibility. The foremen, apparently anxious to adjust to the new demands of the automated setups, could no longer relax with their subordinates. The following quotations from interviews suggest the nature of the change:

> We have 100 men in the [automated] department and we have five foremen. Before, we had 134 men and one foreman and one assistant. It was better on the old job. Nobody breathing down your neck. Over here it's altogether different, just push, push, push all the time. . . .
>
> They never say hello . . . treat you like a machine. They used to be friendly. Now they seem to be under a strain.
>
> The foremen at the new plant have too much to do and too much responsibility, and they get tired and cranky. They'll die of a heart attack, yet.[17]

Job Content of Foreman Under Automation

Increasing pressure on the foreman is responsible for his changed relationships with workers under automated conditions. In the conventional plants the foreman met his principal responsibility — that of seeing that production schedules were met — by making certain that each worker was performing his share of the operation at the required speed and by seeing that machine breakdowns were promptly repaired.

On the automated line, however, the foreman cannot keep production up by whipping the workers to greater speed or intensity of effort. The worker *does not* control the pace of the transfer machine, and the speed or production is not affected by the vigor with which a button is punched or the intensity with which the machine is watched.

When a breakdown occurs in the nonautomated plant, it is localized in one machine and does not necessarily stop the entire line. Repairs can be made by the operator or the foreman. In the automated plant a stoppage in one transfer machine can stop the entire line, and over a million dollars' worth of machinery and equipment will be idle while repairs are being made. Repairs are generally out of the domain of both operator and foreman. Complex maintenance and repairs must be handled by top-level maintenance personnel. The inability of the foreman to get more work out of the operators by his personality, leadership, and human relations skills, or by his mechanical abilities, which in the past kept the machines running, has resulted in negative changes in his relationships with his subordinates.

Planning for Job Displacement

It is the responsibility of the employer to provide stable employment. This is admittedly so. The employer generally pays his tax, based on a merit rating, to the state unemployment compensation commission. The higher the unemployment rate, the higher the tax rate. There is thus an incentive to maintaining stable employment.

On moral grounds, also, it is important to gauge carefully the effect of technological change on the plans and futures of employees. The employee's morale is important to the firm. Production is required even on days of acute change, and worried, unhappy employees are a drag to efficient production.

In the early stage of the technical planning, management should discuss the future with representatives of the union or the employees through joint consultation. This does not mean the sacrifice of managerial prerogatives — it indicates the exercise of common sense in order to avoid the pitfalls of latent bitterness and restrictive conduct by the workers.

All aspects of the coming changes should be discussed with employees and the union (if one exists). Studies should be made to minimize the effect on the individuals concerned. Discussions with the union or an employees' committee should, of course, be confidential, if possible, as news of impending technical changes would be of a great commercial advantage to a competitor.

Discussions with employees will remove much of the worry about a possible job loss. An expanding company will not often have a serious displacement problem and the workers should be so advised.

Attrition

Where fewer people are required in the new work, normal attrition or labor turnover will usually prevent "redundancy," the British term for job displacement. If normal labor turnover is about 10 percent, then advance plans of technical change should stop recruitment, and the numbers in each department should be allowed to fall to the revised figure. Overtime can be worked by the smaller work force until the new methods are introduced. Turnover by class of workers should be studied carefully to forestall the firm's falling into the error of applying turnover of stenographers to the reduced need for clerks.

Problem of Displacement

If the firm with a labor surplus is not limited in its action by a labor agreement, then the normal thing to do is to advise the employees concerned, at the earliest possible moment, of their impending displacement. They should be given the maximum time to look for new jobs and, if at all possible, be kept on the payroll for several additional weeks while they are going for interviews. The personnel department should seek the help of the state employment service in getting an employee a job elsewhere if it is not possible to retrain the worker in some needed job within the same company.

If the company retirement system is strong enough, those who are eligible for full retirement should be separated first. Even where a labor agreement does not exist, in all fairness firms ought to provide a lump-sum separation allowance. Much study should be given by the nonunion firm to such factors as seniority, age, sex, dependency, and related factors.

Where the firm is not clearly bound by a union agreement, what should be the basis for a specific amount of separation pay? Length of service should certainly be taken into account, as should previous earnings. Should earnings be considered on a basis of straight-time earnings or annual earnings including overtime? Should the allowance be graded on the basis of number of dependents? Should moving expenses and mortgage problems be considered?

The fact that displacement occurs does not mean that the employer will not be in the labor market for new workers in the near future. When he is, the chances of getting good employees will depend on the firm's reputation of fairness in the community. The company image should be a lasting one; namely, that meticulous care was given to the problem of each individual who was separated, and that no unfairness was evident.

Collective Bargaining Helpful

In every industry, collective bargaining has developed some answers to automation — some useful and effective, others mere stopgaps, none large enough for tomorrow's needs. Public utilities, breweries, offices, and chemical, auto, steel, electrical manufacturing, oil refining, and food packaging industries — all have experimented with adjustment mechanisms. Viewed intelligently, these mechanisms can be useful not only for future bargaining but also for future policy making at both the public and private levels of our society.

Generalizations about collective bargaining gains are dangerous because each problem calls for, and each adjustment results from, practical, specific, two-way negotiations for a certain purpose. These precedent-setting ideas, however, stand out as the only available forerunners of future adjustment mechanisms. The following list, paraphrased from a report prepared in 1961 by the Research Department of the AFL-CIO, includes some useful procedures already established and indicates their value as initial efforts toward solutions for problems at the work place.

1. *Advance notice.* Preparation for change can mean the reduction of unnecessary problems both for workers and for management. New machinery requires prior knowledge, and joint planning with the union can permit scheduling of the introduction of such equipment during periods of high employment. Other planning can make it possible for reduction in the size of the work force to take place gradually through attrition rather than through layoffs, and also for proper time allowances for retraining employees.

2. *Transition safeguards.* Collective bargaining and labor-management cooperation can and should provide some safeguards for employees during transitions from old methods to new. Fair and orderly procedures for layoffs, rehiring, transfers, promotions, retraining opportunities, and changes of job classifications and wage rates are essential.

a. RETRAINING. At the collective bargaining level, seniority and other procedures can be worked out to make eligibility for retraining fair and reasonable. Provisions can also allow time off for specified retraining periods, for compensation during the time of retraining, and for other aspects helpful to those who must get acquainted with new skills.

b. FINANCIAL CUSHIONS. Financial help should be provided for laid-off employees through severance pay or supplemental unemployment benefit provisions.

c. JOB CHANGES. Whether jobs are upgraded or downgraded through automation depends on the type of equipment installed and the requirements of the new jobs. Job-and-wage protection are needed in collective bargaining agreements for those whose jobs are changing. Joint negotiations are the most effective procedures for determining the rates of the new job, for the experienced worker moving to the new job, and for the newly hired workers assigned to the technological job.

d. TRANSFERABILITY PROVISIONS. Workers need to have the benefit of negotiated seniority and financial help provisions to enable them to change to a different plant of the same company when technological change causes relocation of a department or even a whole plant. The chance of change to the new job in the new area and the chance to move one's family can be enhanced by provisions for seniority and financial help.

3. *Older workers.* Special efforts are needed both in pension planning and job engineering to provide for older workers' special problems. Some workers who find adjustment to new machines difficult may not have reached retirement age. Pension plans may need to provide for voluntary retirement at an earlier age.

4. *Pension plans.* Transferring from one plant to another or from one company to another within the same industry or area may require changes in pension plans so that rights will not be lost through change in locations.

5. *Wage structures.* The new technology obviously calls for changes in job titles, wage structures, job contents and responsibilities; rising output and more expensive equipment calls for upward revision of wage rates. The new machines also call for re-examination of wage incentive systems and job evaluation plans — automation may show they need revision or even destruction in some instances, since the new technology does away with so many conditions formerly subject to industrial engineering approaches.[18]

None of these collective bargaining efforts is particularly new or startling. Each has been a practical attempt to find a satisfactory answer to a most perplexing problem. None exists in a vacuum. But these represent far more effective, original, and practical efforts than other groups in America have produced for a problem that concerns everyone.

Most of the ideas expressed above about the responsibility of management to prepare sensibly with unions for automation and its effects would appear to have come from a management expert rather than from a union. Nevertheless, many management experts agree with a majority of these points.

Conclusion

It becomes apparent that automation brings on certain inflexibilities which require more accurate decision making, or severe losses may take place. Advance planning becomes more important than is the case in conventional plants. Information systems, such as data processing, employ computers and do a good job, but are not a complete substitution for managerial skill and judgment. Professional managers are more important in an automative plant than in a conventional plant. Training in plant management requires a knowledge of proper plant layout and techniques in orienting for adjustment to change. There becomes evident a new relationship between supervisors and workers, which requires a better knowledge of human relations and organizational leadership.

References

1. Jack Rogers, *Automation, Technology's New Face* (Berkeley: University of California, Institute of Industrial Relations, 1958), p. 69.
2. *Ibid.*
3. James D. Gallagher, *Management Information Systems and the Computer* (New York: American Management Association, 1961), p. 56.
4. Peter F. Drucker, "The Next Decade in Management," *Dun's Review and Modern Industry*, vol. 74, no. 6 (December 1959), pp. 60–61.
5. C. F. Carter and B. R. Williams, *Industry and Technical Progress: Factors Governing the Speed of Application of Science* (London: Oxford University Press, 1957).
6. Drucker, *The Practice of Management* (New York: Harper & Row, 1954), p. 293.
7. L. Landon Goodman, *Man and Automation* (Middlesex: Penguin Books, Ltd., 1957), p. 113.
8. *Ibid.*, p. 114.
9. *Ibid.*, p. 135.
10. *Ibid.*, p. 138.
11. T. G. LeClair, "Engineering Futures Unlimited," *Electrical Engineering*, vol. 75, no. 6 (June 1956).
12. Goodman, *op. cit.*, p. 200.
13. Drucker, *The Practice of Management*, *op. cit.*, p. 372.
14. *Ibid.*
15. *Ibid.*, p. 23.
16. W. A. Faunce, "Automation in the Automobile Industry," *American Sociological Review*, vol. 23, no. 4 (August 1958), p. 404.
17. *Ibid.*, p. 405.
18. "The Impact of Automation — A Challenge to America," *AFL-CIO Federationist*, vol. 68, no. 8 (August 1961), pp. 19–20.

▶ ▶ ▶ ▶ **7**

Automation,
Job Satisfaction, and
Resistance to Change

As working environment changes, managers should be sensitive to the psychological responses of workers. The loss of control over the machine creates a definite pattern of insecurity, and managers of successfully automated plants must be on guard against conscious or subconscious resistance to change. Every effort and technique to assure plant harmony and the well-being of the employee group should be utilized by employers.

Even under automation ample opportunities exist for humanizing the work. Automation will bring out new "slants" on the relative importance of earnings versus job satisfaction and status. An awareness of all the factors entering into the creation of the worker's "attitude" is an essential requirement in management, particularly when the "new technology" is to be explored fully.

A New Kind of Monotony

Automation will, to some degree, reverse the trend in mechanization where the operator is exposed to increasing job monotony by his machine-tending duties. While automation may not bring a tremendous increase in the diversification of duties that keep men interested in their tasks, nevertheless the "new" operators, while relatively inactive, will have to face situations in which they must be mentally alert.

Low-grade decision-making functions will vanish and leave in their place long periods of necessarily sustained mental alertness. Management is not yet completely aware of how many of the present labor force will be able to adjust to this new job demand.

Effect on Worker Morale

Many writers have stressed the importance of interpersonal relationships and job motivation. Automation may make the formation of work groups impossib'e; on the other hand, it may re-emphasize their importance. It is known that workers satisfy their social needs through the formation of informal plant groups. If workers in an automated plant are isolated (and there is a complete absence of joking, griping, and gossiping, which generally is found in the working environment), what will happen to morale — will it droop? If, on the other hand, automation can develop work groups that will draw people together, then job satisfaction would be increased materially.

Influence on the Foreman

With fewer employees to supervise and more technical problems to contend with, the position of foreman will be subject to much change. The traditional authority responsible for the selection of certain foremen may disappear. Where previously a supervisor had to be a leader, now his principal responsibility might be to operate or "supervise" equipment. Foremen will have to possess new skills and to work alongside those skilled persons they formerly directed. There will possibly be much stress and strain among supervisors and subordinates in the new environment.

Technology and Job Satisfaction

Strauss and Sayles point out certain psychological reactions to mass-production work. Among these are fatigue and boredom, lack of opportunity to exercise skill or autonomy, inadequate sense of accomplishment, inability to control work pace, and need to apply only surface attention, with resultant daydreaming and monotony.[1]

Workers compensate for the deadliness of some of the mass-production industries by engaging in informal social activities during the time they should be working. They also restrict production, introduce new methods in the job not planned or desired by the employer, are sometimes absent from work, or lose time on any provocation. Some workers also relax by engaging in antimanagement activities.

Clever managements have attempted to solve the problem of monotony and routine jobs by job enlargement, by job rotation, by permitting a change of pace, by scheduled rest or "break" periods, by reducing working hours, by playing recorded music, by developing worker participation in setting goals providing the worker with progress information, by greater autonomy where possible, and by breaking down the job into meaningful units.[2] How much of these techniques will be possible in the automated plant is a guess. However, the automated manager can learn by what is done in the mass-production industries.

Job Satisfaction and Degree of Automation

The effect of automation on job satisfaction depends on the degree of automation produced. The problem will be academic only when the firm reaches that perfect state of complete automation where the self-regulating machine makes its own adjustments without human supervision. Even in designing the machine that eliminates the worker completely, the designer will still have to depend on the computer.

It is in the partly automated situations, where the operater must still watch and control the equipment, that a possibility of change in job satisfaction occurs. According to Strauss and Sayles, in the semiautomated plant:

> ... the job requirements are substantially different from the requirements of the non-automated processes. The work is physically easier, safer and less subject to discomfort from heat, dampness, and so forth. The manipulative skills are almost completely eliminated, except among repairmen. On the other hand the job requires responsibility and alertness [surface attention].[3]

Charles R. Walker, on the other hand, describes the changing pattern of job duties and responsibilities of steel workers in a highly automated steel mill:

> A basic skill ... is the ability to remain continually on the alert, to deduce quickly what needs to be done, and to act with split second speed and accuracy when the need arises. ... How different it is from the skill of a craftsman's job on the one hand or of an ordinary machine operator on the other.[4]

Morale and Production

Ever since the Hawthorne experiments at the Western Electric Company there has been healthy skepticism about the direct relationship of morale to productivity. Under the automated industrial setups it appears that even less of a relationship will exist between morale and productivity than existed in the conventional plants.

In the conventional work group the foreman was integrated into a cohesive group. This is no longer true. Further study of the role of foremen under automated systems is necessary. Some investigations disclose the fact that increasing output is not necessarily a goal of industrial work groups.[5]

Certain research findings have demonstrated that group cohesiveness and morale may be effective in subverting management objectives and restricting output.

> The morale of the operator who pushes a button that starts the operation of a transfer machine has no effect whatsoever upon the rate of production of that machine. Where work pace is no longer controlled by the worker, man-hour productivity becomes a meaningless measure of achievement of group goals even where cohesive work groups exist, and where they are identified with the organization to the degree that output is accepted as a goal of such groups.[6]

Opportunity for Humanization of Work

There is an opportunity to humanize work despite the development of automation. This will require attention by both management and labor unions. The meaning of industrialization, as a peculiar modern fact, arose out of the *measurement of work*. When work can be measured; when a man can be hitched to the job; when he can be "harnessed"; when his output can be measured in terms of a single piece, with payment by the piece or by the hour — then modern industrialization is observable. Unless this fact is understood, it is impossible for anyone to understand the historical impact of what automation itself imposes.

Automation in its largest sense means, in effect, the *end* of measurement of work. With automation the output of a single man cannot be measured; instead, equipment utilization must be measured.

If this idea is generalized into a kind of concept, the conclusion becomes clear. There is no longer any reason to pay a man by the piece or by the hour. There is no reason to keep up a sort of dual system of wage payments, where some people are paid by salary, with its dignity and status, while others are paid simply by the piece or by the hour.

With automation the individual piece-work incentive system goes by the board. There is no rational reason for continuation of such a system. This is a challenge to the labor movement.

If there is to be an end to the measurement of work, one can think, too, of the larger categories of work atmosphere and the whole problem of satisfaction in work. With increased dignity and status on the job, the worker in the automated plant will compare himself with the supervisor or executive on the annual salary basis. This will result in "humanizing" the job.

Phenomenology of Change

A great research area exists relating specifically not to the "new technology" but to a study of the effects of the employee's moving to greater or lesser demanding situations in terms of new work tasks.

Jacobson states the following about the "phenomenology of change":

> The phenomenology of change includes the worker's perceptions, expectations, attitudes and beliefs about his performance, his role and his relationship to himself. As the change occurs the worker will be concerned with his performance, the differences that the change makes in his task, his physical working conditions, his hours of work, his work pace. He will have and will develop attitudes that will influence his performance in the new task.
>
> A technological change quite frequently includes a change in role for the employee. He will have new relationships with his peers, his subordinates and supervisors, and with the entire work organization. Interpersonal contacts may become more or less frequent, his status may be increased or decreased, his dependency on his superiors may be more or less pronounced, his opportunities for influencing the performance of his peers may be reduced or enhanced.[7]

The fear of not maintaining work effectiveness will create concern by the worker about his adequacy, the meaning of his contribution to productivity, and the chances of upsetting his career.

Rokeach pointed out a few years ago that the current work on mental rigidity and flexibility "offers much promise in achieving greater understanding of the worker whose job must change through the new technologies."[8]

Researches dealing with personality differences resulting from adaptation to change are very difficult to come by. On the other hand the "social psychological variables of organization offer the promise of providing understanding that can lead to improved management practices that are always subject to revision."[9]

Jacobson suggests further that the organizational variables can be classified easily into six classes corresponding to recognizably separate theoretical developments in the social psychology of industry, and that their original contribution lies in the attempt to understand (1) hierarchical control, (2) role, (3) communication, (4) supervisory climate and leadership, (5) small groups, and (6) organization.[10]

Employee Response to Industrial Change

Coch and French[11] reported on studies done in the clothing industry in the forties by a number of students under the direction of Kurt Lewin.[12] Apparently there was an appreciable lag in those clothing factories which worked on short production cycles. After each production change there was a characteristic lag by each worker. The surveyors believed that by varying the methods of introducing changes, the lag might be reduced. Among the controls set up in the experiments were groups with whom management discussed what the forthcoming changes would be, and groups who were told nothing in advance.

The investigators concluded that resistance to change was less when the workers participated in group discussions in advance of making changes. In this group lags were overcome, and ultimate productivity was higher than in the nondiscussion groups. The authors also concluded that complex forces against change operated within workers.

These studies followed up the work of the Harvard group under Mayo[13] in the earlier Western Electric studies, in which Mayo pointed out the importance of group processes in the establishing, maintaining, and altering of individual worker standards of performance.

Investigations reported by Fleishman as part of the research headed by Carroll Shartle at Ohio State focused attention on factors in the group situation that tend to limit the likelihood of change taking place.[14]

At the same time Hariton's activities, at Rensis Likert's Institute of Social Research at the University of Michigan,[15] are somewhat similar in approach and results.

In the Ohio State and the Michigan studies, typical foreman-training programs were studied. Worker and foreman attitudes were analyzed before foremen went off to training school, during training school, and after training school. In both studies the training was designed to change the foreman's behavior and attitudes.

The results of both worker and foreman questionnaires tend to show that whereas the attitudes and behavior of foremen changed during the training program and immediately after, in a short time their attitudes and behavior reverted to their earlier posture because of work pressures. As students they were free to change; as workers they were captives! The conclusion is readily adapted to the expectations of what could develop through changes in a newly automated work situation.

Factors in Employee Response to Automation

Walker and his associates observed the work of steel-mill crews over a period of several years as one part of the plant learned to use more highly automated equipment. A body of data was systematically accumulated by the observers through interviews and observation that permitted interpretation in terms of time-correlated patterns of employee adjustment to technological change. In this and in subsequent reports the investigators explained the way in which employees initially respond and then adjust to change and newness.

In these instances supervision attempted to cope with the problems of changing work and changing individuals. After a time, difficulties were ironed out and standards and practices were set up successfully. This study and one later by Walker and Griffith developed certain hypotheses about characteristic worker responses over time.[16]

Mann and Hoffman studied two electric power plants, one more highly automated than the other. The authors related differences in worker satisfaction in the two plants to differences in the size of work force, training programs, shift arrangements, job definitions, supervisory climate, management philosophy, and many other factors associated with both changes in technology and variations in the quality of management.[17]

Organizational Health during Increased Mechanization

Management must be concerned about both the physical and the mental health of its employees as mechanization becomes fuller and automation is finally effected.

People are moving into and out of the work situation and moving laterally and vertically within it. Jobs and roles are being created, altered and eliminated. Supervisory styles are changing and new generations of supervisors emerge or incumbents are replaced. Communications networks are being established, used, abandoned or altered. Work processes are in flux.

Correspondingly, changes within the individual alter his relationship to the organization. The relatively new, relatively young employee just learning to perform is different from the mature, fully contributing employee who, in turn, is different from the employee approaching retirement age. An industrial psychology based on assumptions of unchanging organizations and unchanging individuals is less likely to provide understanding of the conditions for a healthy relationship between the individual and organization than a psychology concerned with change.[18]

A healthy organization is one that understands its change processes and sees to it that its employees are kept informed about prospective changes. In this way it enlists their support and understanding. All benefit as a result — ownership, management, supervisors, and workers.

Norms for Evaluating Status Not Clearly Defined

When a worker believes that his job content is changing and that the importance and responsibilities of the job are increasing, this attitude is expected to influence the way in which he looks at his job in terms of his *total* activities. Faunce points out that the newly automated worker is somewhat bewildered.

Generally accepted and clearly defined norms with which industrial machine operators might evaluate their jobs have not developed as a part of the value framework of industrial social systems. The absence of such norms is due in part to the absence of a clearly defined status hierarchy of "blue collar" jobs.[19]

A file clerk can see more clearly what his promotional possibilities are as he looks up the clerical classification ladder. Cleaners can view their chances for promotion more exactly than automated production workers. In the automated plant, where revolutionary changes in manufacturing techniques are occurring, norms for evaluating work experience have not yet become part of the general value system. There is some evidence from Faunce's studies that "the range of the status hierarchy is even more compressed in automated than in non-automated plants so that such norms may even be less likely to emerge."[20]

Importance of Economic Factor in Resistance to Change

Of all types of resistance to change, perhaps the one most commonly discussed is the resistance of industrial workers to technological change and more recently to automation. Resistance to change in industry may evidence itself in many ways: by work restriction, by aggression or regression, by emotional reaction, and by frequent union-management grievances.

A number of factors are prominent in creating resistance to change. The most obvious one, of course, is economic. Others relate to inconvenience, uncertainty, threats to traditional social relationships, resentment to increased control, and other factors.[21]

Workers resist automation because they fear they will lose their jobs. For example, they are slow to accept the argument that "in the long run the nation will be better off and it will be able to compete more easily in the European Common Market; or that 'new industries will spring up to take care of the displaced workers.' "

Strauss and Sayles warn, however, that employers should not fall prey to the misconception that all workers and all unions resist all forms of technological progress.

> The Hat Workers and Clothing Workers Union, for instance, have developed special programs designed to encourage management to introduce such changes. They recognize that only through raising productivity can wages be raised. Similarly John L. Lewis and the United Mine Workers cooperated with coal mine owners in an extensive mechanization program which resulted in substantially fewer jobs in the coal fields but higher wages for those who remained.
>
> Foreign visitors to this country express surprise at the extent to which American workers have learned that technological change redounds to their benefit and is the source of rising wages. There is, however, a significant gap between the intellectual recognition of this relationship and the acceptance of change in a particular case.[22]

Strauss and Sayles cite the garment workers as an example of acceptance of technological improvements. Actually these industries have only mild mechanization — not automation. The citing of the

United Mine Workers is not a happy illustration. This industry has gone steadily downhill. The authors also failed to mention the plight of the United Packinghouse Workers and their automation fund. With all its planning and cooperation, the union has experienced serious displacement and little redeployment after retraining programs were completed.

Reaction of Workers after Transfer to Automated Jobs

In their case studies in power plants, Walker, Mann, and Hoffman observe that workers had mixed emotions when transferred for the first time to automated work. They found that the work was more demanding but at the same time more interesting. Apparently, the nervous strain exhausted them at the end of the day, even though the physical work was less arduous than that of the former job.[23]

In another study, Faunce explained that the closer attention paid by the worker to the machine made it virtually impossible for him to carry on the normal sociability common in nonautomated plants. Apparently, with the reduction in the number of workers assigned to the automated departments in the automobile industry, the men found themselves too far apart to converse easily. Furthermore, the feeling of detachment engendered by not seeing the results of his individual effort made the worker feel quite insecure.[24] However, Faunce reported that, as time passed, most of these fears and worries were eliminated in the newly automated plant or department.

With the more complete types of automation, the machine appears to be taking over more and more of the responsibilities of the operator through self-regulation. When this occurs, the worker is reduced to the routine status of watching and feeding the machine.[25] In fact, Bright concluded that "automation often tends to reduce the skill and training required of the work force."[26] Were it not for increasingly necessary repair and maintenance, completely automated setups would have little or no requirement of "depth attention."

Aspects of Motivation Through Automation

Strauss and Sayles reveal an important difference in worker motivation in a comparison of the automated job with the nonautomated job:

On the assembly line there is no real incentive for workers to keep the equipment running smoothly. The more uninterruptedly the line runs, the more work the worker must do. But with automation, the operator has almost nothing to do as long as the equipment is operating smoothly; the only time he has to work is when it breaks down. Consequently, he is strongly motivated to keep things in good running order. And since good work is self-rewarding, such jobs are likely to be satisfying. (If the job involves feeding or watching the machine, however, this generalization does not hold true.)[27]

There is much to be learned by an investigation of whether or not automation increases job satisfaction. It appears that partial automation may bring back the time-honored dignity of the master craftsman; on the other hand, almost complete automation may make jobs even duller and more boring.

The increase in repair and maintenance work will provide interesting assignments for workers with the proper skill and training. Certain shop employees may be switched into white-collar work, such as programming, tape preparation, and the like. These positions will provide variety and interest to employees.

Interaction Patterns in a Newly Automated Plant

An additional study by Faunce[28] attempted to discover the effects of the introduction of automatic transfer machines on interaction patterns in an automobile engine plant. One hundred and twenty-five workers were selected by random sample from four large machining departments in one of the most highly automated engine plants in Detroit. These men were interviewed as part of the study. Eighty percent had been transferred from conventional plants, where they had been assigned to relatively the same job classifications. These workers averaged about twenty years seniority, and had some fifteen months' experience with automation.

Sizes of Work and Interaction Groups   Each man selected was asked to compare his previous job in the nonautomated plant with his present job. The difference in the work stations environment as between the conventional plants and the automated plants is striking. In the older conventional plants, machines were spaced on either side of a moving conveyor, usually with a worker at each machine. The average distance between work stations in the nonautomated plants was somewhat under 10 feet, and the average size of the work group about ten employees.

Interaction was generally found to occur among the four or five workers adjacent to one another or among those who worked directly across one another on the line. This finding was similar to that of Walker and Guest,[29] who determined that interaction occurred most frequently among the two to five workers next to and across from one another on the line and within a series of overlapping groups along the assembly line.

Social interaction was found to be frequent in the old plants, since the work stations were close to one another and the jobs did not require too close attention. The analysts found that 80 percent of those interviewed indicated they were able to converse often with those around them in the older plants — the majority of the social contacts reported on these jobs occurring as frequently as once or twice an hour. There was frequent interaction in the conventional plants on jobs requiring more than one worker to perform a particular operation. Most of these jobs were eliminated in the automated plants.

Control of Work Pace   To those interested in worker independence asserted through piece-rate bargaining, it comes as no surprise to find that workers like to control their own work pace. Observers of this practice always attributed a somewhat crass motive to it; namely, that fear of a subsequent cut in rate slows down the worker's current output.

It is now concluded, however, that the loss of control over the work pace, as a result of automation, also results in loss of time for a "breather" or "bull session" with one's fellows. As Faunce puts it:

> If the worker is able to vary work pace, he is able to create opportunities for social intercourse with others around him on the job. Interaction occurred significantly more frequently among workers who were able to vary work pace, and to take a break in both the old non-automated plants and among those workers in the new plant who controlled work pace.[30]

Effect of Variable Factors on Social Interaction

Faunce, in his Detroit studies, also concluded that social interaction in the automated auto engine plant differed from that in the nonautomated plant on a basis of certain variables, which have an important effect on the frequency and nature of social interaction. These were (1) the amount of attention required by the job, (2) the distance between the work stations, (3) the extent of control of work pace, (4) machine noise, and (5) number of jobs involving teamwork.[31]

The combination of these variables changed radically in the automated environment. Studies in the auto industry indicated that automated jobs required much more attention than nonautomated jobs. Bright takes a contrary view, however. (See Chapter 11, "Influence of Automation on Job Evaluation and Skill Requirements.")

The automated plant had a significantly greater distance between work stations. This averaged about 20 feet compared to 10 in the conventional auto plants, where the subjects under study worked previously. Control of work pace by the employee was for all intents and purposes practically eliminated.

A slightly larger percentage of the workers studied in the automobile investigation indicated that the automated plants were noisier, a condition adversely influencing social interaction. Also, it must be admitted that fewer jobs in the automated plants involve more than one person teaming together on an operation. A question was asked the workers: "Are you able to talk very often to the men around you while you are working?" Eighty percent of the men so queried answered "yes" on the old job, and only 45 percent answered "yes" on the automated job. As to frequency of contacts with fellow workers, 40 percent reported frequent interaction on the conventional job and only 18 percent on the automated jobs.

The data in Faunce's studies suggest that socializing is not only less frequent in the automated plant, but occurs among fewer workers.

Relationship Patterns Within Groups

Of great significance is the finding by Faunce and others that in the conventional plant each worker along the line characteristically belonged to a different interaction group than the worker next to him.

In automated plants studied both by Faunce and by Friedmann,[32] work groups were so structured that the men on each transfer line tended to form a separate and isolated group. Despite this, little teamwork was evidenced, because of the difficulty of communication. In fact, sign language was used to indicate the time of day, the approach of a foreman, and other information. The amount of discussions on nonwork matters, characteristic of the conventional plant, was almost completely cut out.

The isolation of the workers in the automated plant led to the following percentage distribution of answers to this question: "Would you say that you have made more friends on your present job [automated] than on your former jobs [nonautomated]?" Thirteen percent made more friends on the automated job; 47 percent indicated that they made more friends on the conventional job; the remainder engaged in a variety of answers difficult to categorize.

When a real effort is made, automation may help develop team-work on the job. Friedmann[33] cites the increasing use of production teams in French automated plants to foster cooperation and joint responsibility.

Workers, Masters of the Job?

Abruzzi[34] takes a rather optimistic view of what automation will accomplish in the way of freeing the working man of the drudgery of the factory. He found that workers became "external" to production activity and, therefore, became the "masters" of work. In automation, standardized and undistinguished components of work become physically separated from unstandardized and distinguished components of work. It follows that the standardized component is completed by the machine, whereas the unstandardized elements are completed by the person. Abruzzi perceived the emphasis on productive *minds*, not productive *hands*. This maturing of management and the work force has a certain intellectual characteristic.

Emphasis should now be placed on smooth functioning in areas of planning and organizing, and not on the provincial matter of production units, as in previous days. Now management can be involved in the "diagnosis" and "prognosis" of work. With this type of description of the plant to come, the author wonders whether the employees will have to pay the boss for the privilege of working in the plant. Leisure activities will be considered as dignified, and leisure will be considered as an opportunity for the work-family to develop the art of living.

Worried Workers

Bloomberg,[35] in his studies of a Gary steel plant, described the workings of a continuous annealer and its effects on the work force. He pictured the reaction of the workers as, for the first time, they become worried about a furtherance of the automated processes. Management tolerated an easier work schedule for the men with the new equipment, but the men became more worried. These men were basically production-minded and -oriented, and "would not loaf beyond a certain point." It was fairly well agreed that the new machine had removed from the worker his control over production pace, and he feared subsequent layoffs.

Burlingame,[36] in 1949, saw a reversal of the trend of man conquering the physical forces. He saw that man would lose his individuality in progress toward more automatic machinery. The only deterrent to an absolute trend in this direction would be the social scientist's ability to impress the men of industry that a better balance between men and machines would actually have money value.

Workers should favor automation because of its attendant advantages in the work environment. Unfortunately, the human problems which result when some workers remain on conventional work, while others are either displaced or assigned to automated work creates disunity. Halsbury[37], in his English studies, saw the labor movement terribly upset because whole classes of labor, such as stevedores and coal miners, were being by-passed insofar as the advantages of automation were concerned.

Automation and Minority Groups

Faunce, in his study of 125 workers in a Detroit automobile plant, found that Negroes, whether from the North or the South, were significantly more satisfied with automated jobs than were the white workers. He found that the principal reason for this overwhelming preference was the reduction or elimination of job content, which had previously involved materials handling. Negroes have always been assigned work involving the lowest forms of manual labor — and these were conceived to be low-status jobs. Any job change that reduced materials handling for the Negro was regarded as important to personal status. Most white workers would appreciate less materials handling, but not to the degree Negroes would.[38]

Rural Workers Versus Urban Workers

In the Faunce study it was found that workers with rural backgrounds were relatively more dissatisfied with automated jobs than urban workers, and preferred nonautomated jobs. However, these rural workers did not differ too much from the urban workers on the pros and cons of automation. Apparently much can be learned about the motivation of rural workers.

Intelligence and Ability to Adjust to Change

Trumbo[39] did some work on the subject of attitudes of insurance company employees toward work-related change. He found that these attitudes were positively related to intelligence scores, degree of education, and freedom from job anxiety. This finding supports the view that "changed attitudes" are related to the capacity to adjust to the stimulus of change. Trumbo also reported that informal group membership influenced the response to change. In fact, he concluded that the threat of change is an important variable in determining attitudes.

Personnel Psychology and Automation

Winthrop makes his readers very much aware of the impact of automation on the personnel administrator, the industrial psychologist, and the worker. In an interesting and provocative study he pointed out the following:

1. The first important phase to come out of the advent of automation will be a "re-adaption" phase concerned primarily with those qualities and abilities of the worker which are appropriate to the objectives of automation.

2. A second important phase will be where the practices and techniques which are inimical to automation are discarded and new practices and procedures adopted.

3. In the last stage the personnel expert, as he is known today, will have to change radically into a coordinator of high-level working teams, or he too will be outmoded.[40]

These concepts have already been partly borne out, but the idea of replacing the personnel director with a "coordinator" is startling, indeed.

Conclusion

Though automation may be the talking point in the discussion of change, the basic cause of resistance to change will always be a desire to avoid incidental hardships. Resistance to change comes from being hurt by previous change or from the fear of being hurt. Education can provide a solution to part of the problem if it can dispel the hurt or the fear of being hurt.

Technological change is vitally necessary in a dynamic economy. The faster the improvements come, within certain limits, the better will be the nation's economy. Resistance to change, either from the individual or from the union, will, however, be present and must be taken into account. If nothing is done by the firm or the nation to reduce opposition, resistance will grow. As Walter P. Reuther, president of the United Automobile Workers, once said: "The real measurement of the worth of any free society is the ability of that free society to translate technical progress into human progress, into human happiness, into human dignity for the individual."[41] A happy individual is an advantage to society; an unhappy individual is a disadvantage to society.

References

1. George Strauss and Leonard R. Sayles, *The Human Problems of Management* (Englewood Cliffs, N.J.: Prentice-Hall, 1960), pp. 33–43.
2. *Ibid.*, pp. 43–52.
3. *Ibid.*, p. 53.
4. Charles R. Walker, *Toward the Automatic Factory* (New Haven: Yale University Press, 1957), p. 195.
5. D. Roy, "Quota Restriction and Goldbricking in a Machine Shop," *American Journal of Sociology*, 57 (1952), pp. 427–442; and D. Collins, M. Dalton, and D. Roy, "Restriction of Output and Social Cleavage in Industry," *Applied Anthropology*, 5 (1946), pp. 1–14.
6. W. A. Faunce, "Automation in the Automobile Industry, Some Consequences for In-Plant Social Structure," *American Sociological Review*, vol. 23, no. 4 (August 1958), pp. 406–407.
7. Eugene H. Jacobson, "The Effect of Changing Industrial Methods and Automation on Personnel," *Proceedings of April, 1957 Symposium on Preventive and Social Psychiatry* (Washington: Walter Reed Army Medical Center, 1959), p. 237.
8. M. Rokeach, "On the Unity of Thought and Belief," *Journal of Personality*, 25:224, 1956.
9. Jacobson, *op. cit.*, p. 237.
10. *Ibid.*, p. 238.
11. L. Coch and J. R. P. French, Jr., "Overcoming Resistance to Change," *Human Relations*, 1:512, 1948; and French, "Experiments in Field Settings," in L. Festinger and D. Katz (eds.), *Research Methods in the Behavioral Sciences* (New York: Holt, Rinehart and Winston, 1953), pp. 98–135.
12. K. Lewin, "Frontiers in Group Dynamics," *Human Relations*, 1:5, 1947.
13. F. Roethlisberger and W. J. Dickson, *Management and the Worker* (Cambridge: Harvard University Press, 1939).

14. E. A. Fleishman, E. F. Harris, and H. E. Burtt, "Leadership and Supervision in Industry," (Columbus: Bureau of Educational Research, Ohio State University, 1955).
15. T. Hariton, "Conditions Influencing the Effects of Training Foremen in New Human Relations Principles," Ph.D. dissertation, University of Michigan, 1951.
16. C. R. Walker and R. Griffith, "Case History of a Steel Mill in Man and Automation, *Report of Proceedings of Conference Sponsored by Society for Applied Anthropology* (Yale University, 1956), pp. 44–52.
17. Jacobson, *op. cit.*, p. 243; and F. C. Mann and L. R. Hoffman, *Automation and the Worker* (New York: Holt, Rinehart and Winston, 1960).
18. Jacobson, *op. cit.*, p. 245.
19. William A. Faunce, "Automation and the Automobile Worker," *Social Problems*, vol. VI, no. 1 (Summer 1958), p. 77.
20. *Ibid.*
21. Strauss and Sayles, *op. cit.*, pp. 265–269.
22. *Ibid.*, p. 265.
23. Charles R. Walker, Floyd C. Mann, L. Richard Hoffman, "Case History in Two Power Plants," *Man and Automation* (New Haven: Yale University, 1956).
24. Faunce, "Automation and the Automobile Worker," *op. cit.*, pp. 68–78.
25. Harlow F. Craig, *Administering a Conversion to Electric Accounting* (Boston: Harvard Graduate School of Business Administration, 1955).
26. James R. Bright, "Does Automation Raise Skill Requirements?" *Harvard Business Review*, vol. 36 (July 1958), p. 97.
27. Strauss and Sayles, *op. cit.*, p. 54.
28. Faunce, "Automation in the Automobile Industry," *op. cit.*, p. 402.
29. Charles R. Walker and Robert H. Guest, *The Man on the Assembly Line* (Cambridge: Harvard University Press, 1952), pp. 67–72.
30. Faunce, "Automation in the Automobile Industry," *op. cit.*, p. 402.
31. *Ibid.*, pp. 402–403.
32. G. Friedmann, "Ou va le Travail Human?" *Human Organization*, 13 (1955), pp. 29–33.
33. *Ibid.*
34. A. Abruzzi, "Automation, Work and Work Morality," *Symposium on Automation*, American Association for the Advancement of Science, Atlanta, Ga., December 27, 1955.
35. W. Bloomberg, "The Monstrous Machine and the Worried Workers," *The Reporter* (September 29, 1953), pp. 28–32.
36. Burlingame, R., *Backgrounds of Power* (New York: Scribner, 1949), 327 pp.
37. E. Halsbury, "Technical and Human Problems of the Automatic Factory," *The Automatic Factory — What Does it Mean?* Report on

Conference held at Margate, June 16–19, 1955 (London: The Institution of Production Engineers), pp. 23–28.

38. Faunce, "Automation and the Automobile Worker," *op. cit.*, p. 74.
39. D. A. Trumbo, "Individual and Group Correlates of Attitudes Toward Work-Related Change," *Journal of Applied Psychology*, 45 (1961), pp. 338–344.
40. H. Winthrop, "Automation and the Future of Personnel and Industrial Psychology," *Personnel and Guidance Journal*, 37 (1959), pp. 326–333.
41. L. Landon Goodman, *Man and Automation* (Middlesex: Penguin Books, Ltd., 1957), p. 168.

▶▶▶▶ **8**

Labor Looks at
Automation

The next three chapters will provide the reader with the
union point of view about automation. It is difficult to see any difference between certain examples of union partisanship and certain
examples of the employer's blind spots. Both can be extreme, even
in the face of peril to national interest. It is important for both
managers and labor leaders to know each other's side of the story. If,
in the national interest, both labor and management must prepare for
change, then they must not work at cross purposes.

President's Advisory Committee on Labor-Management Policy

On January 11, 1962, the President's Advisory Committee on
Labor-Management Policy released a report entitled "The Benefits
and Problems Incident to Automation and Other Technological
Advances."[1] The Committee consisted of labor, management, and
public members. Recommendation No. 11 of this report dealt with
the problem of full employment and the question of maintaining the
present workweek. This recommendation stated in part: ". . . we
consider the development of programs directed at the achievement of
full employment as being more significant at the present time than
the consideration of a general reduction in the hours of work. . . ."

The labor members of the Advisory Committee presented their
own statements indicating the current anxiety of organized labor
about maintenance of full employment with present working hours.
George Meany, president of the AFL-CIO, David Dubinsky, president of the ILGWU, George M. Harrison, president of the Railway
and Steamship Clerks, Walter P. Reuther, president of the United

127

Automobile Workers, and Joseph D. Keenan, secretary of the Brotherhood of Electrical Workers, all wished to amend recommendation No. 11 of the report as follows:

> The need for goods and services must not be left unfilled, particularly in a time of international crisis. At the same time, high unemployment is intolerable. In the light of our current responsibilities to meet world conditions, and in view of our unmet needs at home, we consider the development of programs directed at the achievement of maximum output and full employment as most significant at the present time. However, if unemployment is not reduced substantially in the near future we will have to resort to a general shortening of the work period through collective bargaining and by law. In connection with such a development, consideration would necessarily be given to the extent to which purchasing power could be maintained along with a reduced work period. A reduction in the basic work period has historically been one means of sharing fruits of technological progress.[2]

In addition, David J. McDonald, of the United Steel Workers, Reuther, and Keenan had these comments:

> We agree that, in the light of the considerations stated, the most desirable solution now to the problem of unemployment is the development of programs which will achieve full employment at forty hours per week. Saying that this is the most desirable solution is not, however, the same thing as saying that we have in fact achieved that solution or that we will in fact achieve it in the near future. And only the fact of full employment — not a statement of its desirability — can properly serve as the premise for the statement that the necessity for shortening the work period will only develop "in the future." If we fail, as we have so far failed, to achieve the most desirable solution we will have to move more quickly than we are now moving in the direction of shortening the work period.[3]

Official Position of the AFL-CIO

In AFL-CIO Publication no. 21, the AFL-CIO position on automation was put forth officially:

> This is a time of remarkable technical progress. Significant new types of automatic machines and methods — symbolized by the term "automation" — are being put to use rapidly and widely. Labor welcomes these technological changes. The new techniques offer promise of higher living standards for all, greater leisure, and more pleasant working conditions. Yet, there are pitfalls as well as promises in the

new technology. There is no automatic guarantee that the potential benefits to society will be transformed into reality.[4]

Labor unions, however, cannot be expected to sit back and entrust the employers with the complete responsibility for looking out for their members. Unions are endeavoring to work their problems out through collective bargaining and thus provide with employers the necessary arrangements for the introduction of new techniques and new equipment. The most important union question is: will benefits of the new technology be shared by management with the workers? Unions want to be told in advance which specific job classifications and which pay rates are to be affected. What provisions are to be made for those displaced? What about retraining and possible reassignment of displaced workers? These are the natural questions which arise in the minds of labor leaders.

Unions likewise are concerned with the fact that, while industry may grow more efficient and produce more goods at lower unit costs, the additional products coming from the machines may never reach the consumer because of his inadequate purchasing power.

Implications for the National Economy

Labor has taken the position that the new technology may provide the tools for economic abundance. This could result in improvements in the level of living of American workers. The transition stage, however, creates fear and unrest. Long-range gains are discussed with unions, but generally the assurance of employers falls on the ears of union managers, who are sensitive to the dangers of change. These union leaders remember the Great Depression. Increased man-hour output without corresponding increases in sales volume and in growing markets is believed by many union leaders to be the formula for another great depression.

Without additional customers for the mounting output resulting by rising productivity, unions believe that unemployment is inevitable. In the years since World War II, particularly from 1946 to 1953, the economy expanded greatly. Production was the key factor, but this economic expansion was sparked by larger markets and increased demand. From 1953 economic growth slowed down, as the volume of national production averaged only 2.5 percent a year. Technology kept its upward surge, but sales demand did not keep pace and unemployment rose from 3 percent of the work force in 1953 to about double that ratio in 1961.

Labor displacement in a transition period of automation brings widespread problems. Men cannot be absorbed quickly in other job areas. Displaced textile and steel workers cannot immediately be placed in industries manufacturing automated machinery or electronics controls because these industries are likewise automating.

Labor believes that for a while displaced workers will have opportunities for retraining in clerical and service industries. This was true between 1953 and 1959, when many young persons as well as displaced workers found job opportunities in white-collar employment, retail and wholesale trade, services, and state and local governments. With automation entering the office and clerical fields, this area may not be great enough to provide for industrial displacement, and at the same time absorb the young people of America entering the labor force. In the past decade an average of 800,000 entered the labor force each year. This figure is expected to rise to about 1,500,000 a year by 1965–1966.

Government Policies Needed for High Employment Levels

Labor leaders believe that the answer to the problem of automation lies partly in governmental policies. In 1959 the AFL-CIO Research Department took this position:

> High levels of employment can be achieved by economic growth of 5 percent per year — based on growing markets — and federal government assistance to workers and businesses in distressed communities, as well as gradual reduction in working hours. Increases in the buying power of wage and salary workers are required to build expanding consumer markets. Government policies are needed to encourage economic growth and to cushion the disrupting effect of rapid technological change on working people, businesses and entire communities.
>
> Economic and social policies to cushion the effects of rapid technological change will not occur automatically. Positive measures must be taken by the government and private groups to sustain economic growth and minimize the disrupting effects of the spread of the new technology so that the creation of economic abundance can become a reality.[5]

Labor Union Recommendations to Minimize Dislocations

Unions and management are both attempting to soften the impact of automation. As unions learn what is developing, they are approaching labor agreements and negotiations with new attitudes. Unions believe that a working basis with management can generally be reached by some of the following techniques:

1. Labor displacement eased by joint consultation between companies and unions.

2. Management planning required to schedule the introduction of automation in periods of high employment.

3. Management to permit attrition to reduce the size of the work force and to allow time for the retraining of employees.

4. Labor-management planning to take place well in advance of the ordering of new and expensive equipment.

5. Workers to share in the savings resulting from rising productivity.

6. Reduced workweek and substantial protection by increased fringe benefits.

7. Guaranteed wage plans and severance pay provisions in order to cushion layoffs, and a fund permitting more planning with reference to future dislocations.

8. Contractual safeguards, such as fair and orderly procedures governing layoffs, rehiring, transfers, promotions, and changes in job classifications and wage structures.

9. Broadening of seniority areas — such as company-wide or plant-wide seniority — to assure equitable seniority protection for the union membership. This would permit the possibility of interdepartmental and interplant transfers based upon seniority.

10. Preferential hiring provisions to require all plants under contract with the union to give preference to laid-off workers in the same industry and area.

11. Senior employees considered in promotion and upgrading in order to qualify for new higher skilled jobs. Age should not be a deterrent.

12. Wage structures overhauled. The unions want new job classifications and new wage structures as manufacturing methods and job content change.

13. Jobs upgraded in automated factories, since unions claim that responsibility is increased. Many job-evaluation plans will have to be drastically altered and revised. Incentive systems may have to be thrown out altogether.

14. Special job and wage provisions for downgraded workers; downgrading occurs when semiskilled employees are transferred to other departments as a result of job elimination.

15. Pension plans reviewed and changed to permit earlier retirement as well as transfer of pension rights from one plant to another within an

industry or an area. This is to protect accrued pension rights and to provide a type of vesting that does not exist in many industries.

16. Retraining at company expense.

17. Contractual clauses to protect workers whose plants move to new locations. Unions want the workers to have the right to move with families and property at company expense.

18. Special consideration for older workers, who may not adjust to retraining or to other requirements of automated production.

Unions view the attempts of management to combine traditionally separate skills into one job, particularly in maintenance employment, as a threat to traditional jurisdictions as well as to gains made by unions in the fields of job classification and wage administration.

Unions Look to Federal Government for Legislation

With the tendency of management to shut down obsolete plants and to build others in new areas, unions look to the Federal Government for action that will aid distressed communities, soften the blow of technological displacement, and reduce unemployment.

Among the Government-sponsored laws the unions espouse are the following:

1. Relocation allowances to move workers and families to new areas, thus contributing to worker mobility.

2. Substantial improvements in unemployment compensation. This is believed necessary in order to cushion displacement. Unions want longer and greater weekly benefits.

3. Federal aid to state educational departments and local school districts to provide technical training in desired skills and improve vocational training facilities.

4. Extension of unemployment compensation benefits to workers undertaking retraining, even where the ordinary unemployment benefit has expired under state laws. (The Manpower Development and Training Act, discussed in Chapter 4, was backed by labor.)

5. Further amendment of Social Security Act to provide for earlier retirements, without substantial loss in benefits.

6. Federal laws to provide for a gradual reduction in working hours, as productivity per man rises under the new technology.

7. Special aid to low-income families and a share in the fruits of technological progress.

8. Careful observation of tendency of corporations to merge with other corporations, thus concentrating control in certain industries and negatively influencing the unemployment of workers.

Coordination of Plans and Policies of Government, Management, Labor, Schools, and Colleges

In an enlightened address in Chicago in 1955, Weiss[6] pointed out to the Brotherhood of Teamsters that unionism should have two principal objectives with respect to automation: (1) a distribution of purchasing power to balance ability to consume with ability to produce; (2) maximum protection for the workers in terms of security.

He looked to the Government to provide higher minimum wages, higher pensions and other social security benefits, more unemployment insurance, and certain public works programs. Schools and colleges, he stated, should be preparing educational programs to meet changing needs at both the technical and the managerial levels for an automated economy.

Weiss stated that unions now have the responsibility of insisting that contracts provide joint union-management committees to study automation and its effects on the company. He recommended that the influence of automation be studied with respect to possible upgrading of job classifications and the establishing of new classifications, and that production bonuses should also be considered as a subject for study because of the superior productivity expected from the new equipment. He also suggested broadened seniority clauses and preferential hiring as possible constructive action to alleviate displacement.

Organized Labor's View of the Worker

Most labor leaders would say that the reaction of workers to the effects of technological change is nothing new or surprising. Workers have seen their jobs sometimes made easier and sometimes harder. They have worked under changing conditions, sometimes better and sometimes worse. They have been credited with more skill toward the pay basis, and sometimes with less skill, but they have always resisted change where it has set up fear, uncertainty, and possibility of insecurity.

To what extent shall the worker be subordinated to the demands of industrial efficiency? The worker's role has been described in the following manner by Haire:

> Our industrial production layouts are built to utilize the production technique, the machines' characteristics, and the material's qualities to the utmost. The operator is considered the dependent variable. He is expected to (and fortunately does) bend and adjust. . . .

A new American myth is being created. High priced public relations experts are saturating us with a barrage of material that sets technology upon a pedestal and pictures man worshipping at its base. Even more than free enterprise, improved technology is cited as the cause of reduced hours, higher wages, more jobs and improved living standards. We are led to believe that technology automatically confers benefits on society. Technology is represented as the independent variable, the causal factor. But this is not true. Man is the independent variable. His customs, his habits, his desires, his needs, his ingenuity, resourcefulness and wisdom determine the shape, kind and degree of prosperity he can and does wring from the natural resources of the world.[7]

Techniques of Organized Labor to Combat Automation

Various techniques have been employed over the years by unions in combating the advances of fuller mechanization. Obstruction to change have generally included such procedures as refusal to let members operate the machines, strikes, restriction of production, and appeals to the public or to the legislators. Managements not using the new technology have sometimes been surprised by the increases in production forthcoming from the obsolete equipment — in cases where operators have tried to prove that automation is unnecessary.

In most cases where obstruction has finally ceased, the unions have attempted, through collective bargaining, to gain concessions in wages, piece rates, job classifications, or work rules in order to control the effect of change. Where the type of work in a department has become radically different, unions have attempted to organize and train the new technicians on the automated equipment. Some of this interest has, of course, been beneficial to management; not all of it has been negative.

Unions have fought strenuously against technological displacement. They have pushed for controls to limit displacement; they have demanded higher rates of pay for operators of the new equipment than for other operators; they have demanded reduced hours of work without loss of earnings; they have tried to provide for transfer of displaced workers; they have won severance pay; they have limited the rate at which technical changes could be introduced, fought for set ratios of men to machines, and attempted to control entrance into these crafts by rigid control of union membership and hiring.

In many unions the official position is not directed against automation. The following statement is taken from the records of the United Automobile Workers:

> The UAW-CIO and its one and one-half million members welcome automation, technological progress, and the promise of peacetime use of the power of the atom. We offer our cooperation to men and women of good will in all walks of life in a common search for policies and programs within the structure of our free society that will insure that greater technological progress will result in greater human progress.
>
> This goal will not be achieved, however, if we put our trust in luck or in blind economic forces. We can be certain of recognizing the great promise for good and averting the dangers that would result from irresponsible use of the new technology only if we consciously and constructively plan to utilize automation for human betterment. We cannot afford to hypnotize ourselves into passivity with monotonous repetition of the comforting thought, that in the long run the economy will adjust to labor displacement and disruption which could result from the Second Industrial Revolution as it did from the First.[8]

In the last four labor contracts negotiated by the United Automobile Workers, a strategy of control has been evident. This union has already achieved, or is now asking for, guaranteed employment through GAW (guaranteed annual wage) or SUB (Supplemental Unemployment Benefit Plan); a shorter workweek; broadened seniority units; strengthened transfer rights; preferential hiring of workers displaced from other plants of the same company or from other companies in the same industry and area; negotiation of new job classifications required by technological change, with wage rates that properly reflect increased worker responsibility for costly equipment and an enlarged volume of output; protection of the skilled trades; establishing of joint union-management plans for training and retraining of workers at company expense and without loss of wages.[9]

Automation and Union Growth

Some experts in the field of automation believe that this new technology will reduce the size and power of unions or will at least influence its activities into new areas such as politics, recreation, and community action of one sort or another. Faunce states:

> Increased leisure produced by automation may also have an effect upon the role of the local union in community power structure. If

automation reduces the size of the workforce in the automated plant, the number of grievance proceedings and other day-to-day union-management relations as well as the number of most other functions usually performed by the local union may also be expected to decrease.

It is the testimony of history, however, that power once held is only reluctantly relinquished and, that, while institutional structure may be slow to change, the function of various structural units may vary more readily. If it becomes no longer necessary for the local union to perform its traditional functions at the plant level, it may turn with increasing interest to participation in community affairs.[10]

In his study of the automobile industry Faunce indicated that a substantial number of workers in the automated plant wished to get into politics if by so doing they would be permitted an increased amount of leisure time away from their jobs.

Unions, Review: Impact of Automation on the Labor Movement

Congressman Elmer J. Holland of Pennsylvania, who chaired a Subcommittee on Automation in the U. S. House of Representatives, was very anxious to secure from the labor movement its own reaction to reports of displacement in various fields as a result of increased productivity and automation. The following information, consisting of résumés of reports submitted by each union, was prepared by Holland and his Committee on February 13, 1961. Some of the claims of unemployment resulting from automation are obviously due in part to the national recession in 1960–1961. However, the replies to Congressman Holland's query indicate the unions' position on automation. In fact, the unions seem to blame most of the nation's economic ills on it.

1. Auto Workers

> 1947–1960: Production increased 50%.
> Employment decreased 2.9%.
> Sales increased 93.4%.
> Production payroll increased 21.6%.

The first half of 1957 and 1960: Employment decreased 3.2%.
Production increased 14.9%.
An estimated 160,000 unemployed auto workers in Detroit will never return to automobile factories due to automation.

(Author's note: Unemployment in the automobile industry is better indicated by a drop in UAW membership from 1,300,000 in 1954 to 1,000,000 in 1962.)

2. *Boilermakers, Iron Shipbuilders, Blacksmiths, Forgers, Helpers*

1958–1960: 6½% unemployed.
Construction Industry:
Man hours worked — down 41.2%.
Boiler Manufacturing and Plate Fabrication:
Man hours worked — down 41.2%.
Forging Industry:
Working only 27%.
Railroad Maintenance:
Employment down 49.5%.
Majority of any of these plants are working only 3-day week.

3. *Brewery Workers (Flour, Cereal, Soft Drink and Distillery)*

1950–1960: Employment decreased 25% due to mechanization and automation in the following industries:
a. Breweries
b. Malt beverages (beer)
c. Distilled liquor
d. Soft drinks
e. Malt processing
f. Yeast processing
g. Cigar making

4. *Building and Construction Workers*

1959–1960: Unemployed — 8%, November 1960; 16%, December 1960.

NOTE: Automation effect has not been calculated in figures as yet; however, prefabrication is being felt considerably in construction industry.

5. *Building Services*

1945–1960: Automatic elevators replaced 40,000 elevator operators.
Commercial Recreation:
Bowling alleys automated — eliminating pinball boys.
Vending machines have replaced sales clerks.

Custodial Work:
Cleaning machines have replaced janitors and charwomen.
Dishwashing machines have replaced workers in hospitals, schools, institutions, hotels, etc.

NOTE: This report is from New York City only — national figures are being tabulated by Rep. Holland's staff.

6. *Chemical Workers*

1953–1960: Production increased 80%.
Employment decreased by 13,000.

7. *Clothing Workers*

Unemployment in this industry is seasonal.
Cutting work is automated to some extent.

8. *Communication Workers*

1955–1960: Telephone business increased 25%.
Employment decreased 5.5% — 33,000 jobs.

NOTE: Telephone calls increased 60% from 1946 to 1960.

9. *Electrical Workers (IUE)*

a. Electrical Machinery Industry:
1953–1960: Production and related worker employment is down — 80,000 jobs.
Production output is up 20%.

b. Electric Lamp Industry:
1950–1959: Employment down 1500 jobs.
Production up by 42%.
Productivity of worker up 52%.

NOTE: Westinghouse Electric Corporation makes a completely automated lamp-making machine — output is 32 million incandescent bulbs per year; raw material fed to machine and 100 feet later completed bulbs emerge. Machine in-inspects, rejects imperfect products, packs bulbs, boxes in cartons, conveys to trucks and boxcars for shipment.

c. Radio and Television Industry:
1950–1960: Wiring, soldering and component assembly auto-mated, with the result that 50,000 jobs elimi-nated.

10. *Electrical Workers (IBEW)*

  a. Radio:
     1953–1960: Federal Communications Commission authorized
                 1300 stations to operate automatically.
                 Result — 3,900 jobs eliminated as each station has
                 approximately 3 jobs per station.

  b. Television:
     1958–1960: Loss of 25% of jobs due to automation.

  c. Telephone Industry:
     1959–1960: Elimination of 2122 jobs.

  d. Electric Utilities Industry:
     1927–1960: Annual KWH output increased 850%.
                 Employment increased only 11%.

  NOTE: Utility plants now double size and output with no increase
        in employment.

11. *Electronics*

  1947–1956: Output in United States increased 325%.
              Employment increased 50%.

12. *Longshoremen*

  Negotiated contract with provisions to set up Mechanization and
  Modernization Fund — $5 million a year for $5\frac{1}{2}$ years to be put
  into Fund for retraining, relocating, providing severance pay for
  those replaced by machines or mechanization.

13. *Mineworkers*

  a. Bituminous Coal:
     1950–1960: Production per miner increased 100%.
     1937–1957: 45 million tons more coal produced annually with
                 50% less workers.

  b. Anthracite Coal:
     1930–1960: Elimination of 80,000 jobs.

14. *Oilworkers*

  1947–1957: Operating capacity increased from 5.3 to 8.4 million
              barrels daily.
              Production workers eliminated from jobs — 10,000.

15. Office Workers

1955–1960:   25% of jobs eliminated due to electronic machines.

NOTE: It is estimated that within the next 5 years, 4 million more office and clerical jobs will be eliminated by automation.

16. Post Office Clerks

Automation entering this field — however, those now employed have been assured their jobs will not be eliminated but they will be "frozen" and upon their departure or resignation the jobs will not be filled by others.

17. Railway and Steamship Clerks

1946–1960:   37.1% reduction in work force due to automation. Jobs were not filled when vacated by workers retiring or resigning.

18. Railroad Workers

1940–1960:   1,000,000 jobs eliminated.

NOTE: Southern Railroad Example:
Operates 6200 miles of line.
Now completely dieselized.
Operates 4 automatic freight yards.
Uses centralized traffic control system.
Has mechanization maintenance work.
Has reduced size of repair shops through automation.
Employs office automation:
Programs accounting and statistical work on electronic computer.
Saved $850,000.00 in first year.

1946–1956:   Increased gross business 6%.
Efficiency up 116%.
Profits rose from $19.5 to $40.5 million, +100%.
Employment dropped from 40,000 to 22,000, −45%.

19. Retail Clerks

1947–1960:   Output rose 150.8%.
Employment is practically all part-time, but not by preference.

NOTE: Automation has been felt here — wrapping and packing devices, meat cutting, vending machines, etc.

Serve yourself supermarkets.

35 employees in warehouse replace 150 clerks.

Elimination of independent stores.

20. *Rubber Workers (Tire and Tube)*

1947–1958: Produced 100 million tires yearly.
Employment reduced 30% — 31,000 jobs.
Work hours reduced 29%.

1958–1959: Employment remained level.
Production increased 22%.

21. *Seafarers (Maritime Workers)*

1952–1960: Employment down 27,500.
Larger and faster ships with smaller crews.

NOTE: American owned or controlled vessels registered under foreign flags — purpose of this is to avoid American wages and working conditions, American taxes and safety standards.

1946: 65% of total cargo carried in U. S. ships.

1959: 9.1% of total cargo carried in U. S. ships.

22. *Steelworkers*

1937–1959: Employment down 18.5% — elimination of 95,000 jobs.
Productivity up 121.1%.
Ingot production increased 65%.
Steel shipments increased 80.9%.

In 1941: 20 men were required to produce one ton of steel.

In 1960: 12 men were required to produce one ton of steel.

23. *Teamsters*

a. Trucking: Due to the increased weight and size of the trucks, the productivity per driver has increased as larger loads can be carried and fewer trucks are used.

b. Terminals: This section of industry is largely automated today in loading and unloading due to conveyors, hoisting devices, inclined tracks, pre-loaded carts, closed circuit TV, etc.

Automated and electronic data processing is being used to handle billing and related activities, including inventory data. Payroll processing, maintenance of personnel records, maintenance and operating cost and control, preparation of various reports, etc.

c. Dairy: Automated machinery being used to large extent in all sized dairies.
Ice cream plants, milk processing plants, frozen food, from raw products to finished boxing or bottling. Even automatic cleaning of pipelines at conclusion of operations.

d. Canning: Extensive use of automation in this industry.
1947–1958: Output per manhour increased 40%. Employment was decreased 12%.

24. *Textile Workers*

1947–1959: Production jobs decreased 38%.
Production output increased 5%.
Productivity per manhour increased almost 70%.

25. *United Electrical Workers*

1953–1960: Electrical manufacturing industry as a whole:
Employment down 10%.
Production up 20%.

1956–1960: General Electric:
Jobs lost — 40,566.
Sales increased $259.5 million.
Lamp division:
Value of shipments increased — 24%.
Hourly employment decreased — 1200.
Steam Turbine Generator Parts division:
Hourly employment decreased — 16,802.

Conclusion

The preceding material covered the reactions of twenty-five important unions in the United States. The reader will observe that regardless of the complete objectivity of these union reports, the data are nevertheless impressive in showing that unions are definitely upset by the rapid advance of technology. Every effort should be made by both management and Government to allay some of the unions' fears about unplanned and chaotic job displacement. Of great help will be the intense utilization of Government-sponsored retraining programs such as are possible under the Distressed Area Program, as well as the new program sponsored by Senator Joseph Clark of Pennsylvania and Representative Elmer Holland of Pennsylvania, which was enacted into law in 1962.

References

1. Released by the U. S. Department of Commerce, U. S. Government Printing Office 0-629224, p. 6, President's Advisory Committee on Labor-Management Policy, January 11, 1962.
2. *Ibid.*
3. *Ibid.*
4. *Labor Looks at Automation*, AFL-CIO Publication no. 21, Department of Research (July 1959), p. 3.
5. *Ibid.*, pp. 20–21.
6. A. Weiss, "Automation." Address delivered before the National Trades Conference of the International Brotherhood of Teamsters, Chicago, April 13–15, 1955.
7. Mason Haire, *Psychology in Management* (New York: McGraw-Hill Book Company, 1956), p. 177.
8. Resolution of the United Automobile Workers at their 1955 Convention.
9. Jack Rogers, *Automation: Technology's New Face* (Berkeley: University of California, Institute of Industrial Relations), 1958, p. 78.
10. W. A. Faunce, "Automation and Leisure," in *Automation and Society*, H. B. Jacobson and J. S. Roucek (New York: Philosophical Library), 1959, p. 305.

Collective
Bargaining Provisions
Resulting from Automation

There has been a growing concern among labor unions that despite the promises of employers to maintain substantial work forces when automation is introduced, the increasing threat of mass displacements through automation requires organized labor to protect the position of its members through tightened collective bargaining. Unions hope to have the support of survey commissions set up by the Federal Government, but preventive action is required, and labor unions have negotiated contracts to protect union membership and to alleviate, if possible, the effects of automation.

In some management quarters such provisions have been termed "work-rule" restrictions; in others they have been called "featherbedding." In any event, employers about to automate their plants should be aware that the union will press strongly for protective devices through the collective agreement.

As the International Association of Machinists stated in an excellent research survey:

> We regard the assumption that [automation will come slowly . . . that it will create more jobs than it eliminates] as a Maginot line of 19th century ideas. We do not believe that we can rely upon such illusory defenses to protect the interests of our membership any more than the French were able to rely upon the Maginot line to hold back the German onslaught in 1939.[1]

As a result the IAM recommended that collective bargaining techniques be applied to the problems of technological change, and that the adjustments to automation consist to a great extent of modification, amendment, and extension of existing rules and practices.

144

The following excerpts from agreements cover such contract requirements as advance notice and consultation, transfer rights, moving allowances, training and retraining, supplemental unemployment benefits and severance pay, provisions for early retirement, negotiations of new automated job classifications, and requirements for equitable distribution of the gains of productivity. The studies of the Research Department of the IAM have been invaluable in effecting these provisions.

Advance Notice and Consultation

Where unions have been highly regarded by management and bargaining is mature, in many instances in the past two decades companies have given unions advance notice of the steps management planned to take. This has been particularly important where morale of employees might be affected or the good will of union representatives sacrificed.

Those progressive employers who have contemplated fuller mechanization or automation have continued these beneficial practices with constructive results. In the collective agreements, however, unions have taken action against those employers who ran for cover behind a "management's rights" clause or behind certain waiver clauses restricting the rights of unions to bargain collectively in certain areas not specifically referred to in the collective agreement.

Unions believe that it is in their best interest to establish firmly the right of advance notice, the rights to certain kinds of information, and the obligation to bargain over necessary adjustments through clear and specific contract language. This is the sort of contractual information included in the following excerpts from six agreements and in the sample clause developed by the International Chemical Workers Union covering "technological changes."

Agreement between Brotherhood of Railway Clerks and Chesapeake and Ohio Railway Company

Notice to union of change. It was further agreed that whenever the company wants to shift more work to the new computer center, it is to notify the union, and before the work is moved, the parties are to negotiate agreement on the "manner and conditions" under which that is to be done. . . .

The notice to the union is to be given at least 90 days in advance of the change, with a statement of the number of workers affected. Negotiation with the union would then be arranged in 30 days after the notice.

Agreement between Insurance Workers of America and Golden Eagle Life Insurance Company

The employer agrees to meet with the union to discuss salary rates and classifications of those employees in the clerical force covered by this agreement who may be affected by a substantial change of job duties made necessary by a substantial mechanization of work.

Agreement between the Oil, Chemical and Atomic Workers International Union and Corn Products Refining Company

Because of the mutuality of interest, the Company agrees to give the Union notice as soon as possible on proposed installations of automation which will result in a lower number of employees required due to the proposed changes. The Company will also furnish the Union a tentative proposal of staffing for the changed department or process, and a list of those employees affected.

Agreement between Brotherhood of Maintenance of Way Employees and Representatives of Railroad Conference Committees

In the event a carrier decides to effect a material change in work methods involving employees covered by the rules of the collective agreement of the organization party hereto, said carrier will notify the General Chairman thereof as far in advance of the effectuation of such change as is practicable and in any event not less than fifteen (15) days prior to such effectuation. If the General Chairman or his representative is available prior to the date set for effectuation of the change, the representative of the carrier and the General Chairman or his representative shall meet for the purpose of discussing the manner in which and the extent to which employees represented by the organization may be affected by such change, the application of existing rules such as seniority rules, placement and displacement rules and other pertinent rules, with a view to avoiding grievances arising out of the terms of the existing collective agreement and minimizing adverse effects upon the employees involved.

Agreement between Building Service Employees and Building
Managers Association of Chicago (Local 66)

One key provision calls for *substantial advance notice* to the union.
The employer is to notify the union within 30 days of the date he contracts to have "operatorless" elevators installed. This notice is also to
inform the union of the number of such elevators and approximate date
when the conversion to them will be completed.

If workers have to be dropped, the union agreement calls for:
Advance notice of at least 30 days to the individual worker of the date
when his services may no longer be required.

Agreement between United Steel
Workers of America and Blaw Knox

When the installation of mechanical or electronic equipment will
have an effect on the job status of employees, management shall review
the matter with the local union grievance committee. . . .

Sample Clause developed by
International Chemical Workers Union[2]

Technological Changes

The Union recognizes the Company's right to control production,
to change production methods and techniques, and to introduce labor-
saving equipment. In turn, the Company recognizes that its exercise of
this right will have an effect on matters that are properly areas for
collective bargaining between the Union and the Company. In recognition of these mutual interests it is agreed as follows:

(1) Before the introduction of any labor-saving equipment and/or
modification of production methods, or before any reduction in labor
force affecting an entire department or departments or sizeable groups
of employees, the Company shall give reasonable notice of the contemplated changes to the Union after which the parties shall meet to
negotiate over other conditions of employment which may be affected by
the proposed changes. The employer shall make available to the Union
any and all information necessary for a constructive and intelligent
discussion of these matters.

(2) In the event the parties are unable to reach a mutual agreement
regarding all matters of working conditions relating to the proposed
changes, the unresolved issues shall be submitted to arbitration only

when both parties agree. Should the Company and the Union not reach agreement on the unresolved issues nor an agreement to submit the differences to arbitration, and should the Company proceed to make the contemplated changes, the provisions of Article .... (no-strike clause) shall be of no force and effect.

Softening Job Displacement

There have been many cases of conversion to automation where employees presently on the payroll were not injured. In those cases management planned its moves carefully, generally with union agreement as to future moves. Layoffs were averted through curtailing hiring and recruiting, through pool arrangements and transfers, and by permitting a normal attrition of the work force to take place to the desired levels by voluntary quittal, death, or retirement.

In a number of Federal Government agencies the heavy proportion of unmarried females created a high labor-turnover rate when the girls married; these marriages permitted a total reduction in the work force because of automation without harm to individuals.

The following memo of understanding in a Pacific Maritime Association contract specifically illustrates the use of this technique. Verbal agreements between employer and union often result in a "memo to file," which is scrupulously adhered to. It may be expected that more clauses of this type will, in the near future, actually be made a part of the labor agreement.

Memorandum of Understanding between Pacific Maritime Association and International Longshoremen's and Warehousemen's Union, August 10, 1959

Mechanization and the utilization of labor saving devices have been a subject of discussion between the parties since 1957. During the course of the 1959 negotiations the following items were agreed to on this subject.

To allow a certain amount of time (not more than one year) for the parties to further study and gain factual experience.

It is the purpose and intent of the parties, during the course and as the result of this study period, to achieve and meet the following aims and objectives:

To maintain the 1958 fully registered work force, *with allowance for normal attrition.*

Preferential Employment Rights

Technological displacement has caused unions to make bold demands for preferential employment rights. This means that when one plant of a company closes down, the displaced employee can be given preference in the filling of available jobs in the other plant. The same provision can be made to apply to a departmental shutdown. The displaced employee has to make application within a given period or he loses his rights for preference. Certain union agreements require a firm to maintain an employee "recall list," to be used by the firm when it shuts down one plant and opens a new one. By the use of such a list employees affected by the plant shutdown may be considered for jobs at the new plant.

There is a movement afoot to extend preferential employment rights to an entire industry. Following are some of the most important excerpts from contracts with American Can, Lockheed Aircraft, General Motors Corporation, Ford Motor Company, and other companies.

Agreement between International Association of Machinists and American Can Company

Employees who are to be terminated because of the permanent closing of a plant, and who otherwise are eligible for a severance allowance or single severance payment as provided in the supplemental unemployment benefit plan, will be given preferential employment rights (provided there are available jobs) at another plant of the company, provided the employee indicates at least a week in advance of the closing of his plant, the plant or plants in which he desires to obtain employment. An employee who is offered employment at one of the company plants he has selected, and then declines for any reason, will be removed from the preferential employment list.

Preferential employment rights will terminate 90 calendar days after the plant closing. Eligible employees who do not obtain employment at another of the company's plants will be paid their severance allowance or single severance payment at the end of the 90-day period.

An employee who accepts employment at another of the company's plants as a result of the permanent closing of the plant where he is employed will not be eligible for any severance allowance or single severance payment.

An employee, who, under the circumstances specified . . . above, is transferred by the company to another plant covered by this agreement will carry accredited service from the closed plant to the plant to which he is transferred.

Agreement between IUE and Eastern Container Corp.

In the event that the Company should move its plant or establish plants in other geographical areas, senior Employees who, in the opinion of the Company, are qualified to perform the work which might be available, shall have preference over all other job applicants for any vacant positions. The Employee shall carry his total seniority into the new plant *without* loss of any benefits.

Agreement between IAM (District Lodge 727) and Lockheed Aircraft Corporation Missiles and Space Division

In the event work performed at the Company is transferred to a newly established plant of LMSD outside the scope of this Agreement, the Company and the Union shall at that time negotiate with respect to which employees of the Company shall be permitted to transfer to such plant during the period of establishment of such new plant. Employees so permitted to transfer shall do so with all employee rights and benefits at the Company except where another collective bargaining agent has established collective bargaining rights at such plant. All such employee rights shall continue unless and except as restricted by a subsequent collective bargaining agreement negotiated with the collective bargaining agent representing such employees at the new plant.

Agreement between United Rubber, Cork, Linoleum and Plastic Workers (Local 207) and Cooper Tire & Rubber Co.

It is understood that if the Company shall move any of its present operations to a new location or should acquire a plant in some other location to perform operations that are performed at the present location, any or all employees affected shall be moved to the new location if the employee so desires.

Agreement between United Automobile Workers and General Motors Corporation

Employers with seniority laid off from General Motors plants in a given community and who make application will be given preference over other applicants, provided their previous experience in General Motors shows they are qualified for the job. Such application may be filed by the employee at the time of layoff at the plant from which he is being laid off. The Corporation will establish a procedure for making the applications available to the General Motors plants in the community. When employed, such employees will have the status of temporary employees in the plant where hired in accordance with Paragraphs 56 and 57 of the National Agreement.

For six months after production begins in a new plant, the Corporation will give preference to the applications of laid off employees having seniority in other plants over applications of individuals who have not previously worked for the Corporation, provided their previous experience in the Corporation shows that they can qualify for the job. When employed, such employees will have the status of temporary employees in the new plant. Such employees will retain their seniority in the plant where originally acquired until broken in accordance with the seniority rules herein.

If the transfer of major operations between plants results in the permanent release of employees with seniority, the case may be presented to the Corporation and, after investigation, it will be reviewed with the International Union in an effort to negotiate an equitable solution, in accordance with the principles set forth in the previous paragraph. Any transfer of employees resulting from this review shall be on the basis that such employees are transferred with full seniority.

Seniority shall be by non-interchangeable occupational groups within departments, groups of departments or plantwide, as may be negotiated locally in each plant and reduced to writing. . . .

When changes in methods, products or policies would otherwise require the permanent laying off of employees, the seniority of the displaced employees shall become plant-wide and they shall be transferred out of the group in line with their seniority to work they are capable of doing, as comparable to the work they have been doing as may be available, at the rate for the job to which they have been transferred.

Agreement between UAW and Ford Motor Company
— Rouge Area Local Agreement

1. Subsequent to the effective date of the Master Agreement, all employees laid off from plants in the Rouge Area with 10 or more years of seniority shall be placed on a common recall list.

2. Job openings for plants in the Rouge Area shall be filled by recall from said list, except that deviations from this provision may be made

for the purpose of recalling employees with less than 10 years of seniority who have previously performed specialized jobs as determined by the Company.

. . . .

4. The Company shall have the right to recall any of the employees referred to in Section 2 of this agreement and place them on work on any job classification (excluding skilled classifications) which they are qualified to perform in any of the plants in the Rouge Area as determined by the Company, displacing, if necessary, employees with less than 10 years' seniority. The selection of the jobs on which such employees may be placed shall be at the sole discretion of the Company. Employees so placed shall take all of their seniority to the new unit.

Agreement between IUE (Local 1131) and Louis Allis Company

If an employee's job is eliminated due to "automation" . . . and he can then show to the Company experience in a different type of work than that in which he has been employed and which is available in the Company's plant, such employee shall have the right to replace an employee over whom he has seniority. . . .

Broadened Seniority Rights

Unions have used collective agreements as a means of protecting workers against loss of jobs as a result of closing of plants or technological displacement. At the same time they have pushed to broaden seniority clauses within a plant and between plants and have facilitated transfer to new jobs in the company.

In some of the following contract excerpts will be found instances of provisions covering a desire of employees to transfer to a new plant, as in the case of the Lockheed Aircraft Missile Systems Division in California, in which there is a specific clause providing moving allowances to workers and their families. Also covered is the famous "Washington Agreement" of 1936, which covered a situation of how employees would be affected by railroad mergers. This was a rather extensive protection arrangement hailed by organized labor as a model to be followed in planning for the current problems of technological displacement.

A contract section is also taken from the Curtiss-Wright agreement, which provides for moving expenses and broadened seniority provisions.

Agreement between IAM (District Lodge 727) and Lockheed
Aircraft Corporation Missile Systems Division

Employees on the payroll of the Company upon the signing of this
Supplement who desire to transfer to the Sunnyvale-Palo Alto Plant of
the Missile Systems Division and who have seniority dates ... of or
prior to December 10, 1956, shall within a period of fifteen (15) calendar
days from the effective date of this Supplement notify the Labor
Relations Department of the Company in writing of their desire to
transfer to the Sunnyvale-Palo Alto plant. The following conditions
shall apply to such transfers:

1. The foregoing notification of desire to transfer is irrevocable by
the employee.

2. The foregoing notification shall include a statement of the
employee's preference regarding the calendar quarter of the year during
which he would prefer to transfer. As transfers are scheduled by the
Company they will be assigned to employees who have requested transfer
in the order — from the earliest period to the latest — of their requested
transfer period. Those employees within a classification who have
requested to transfer within a particular period will be moved, subject
to the other conditions of this Supplement, in seniority order, the most
senior first, etc. It is understood that the agreement stated in this
paragraph numbered 2 affects only the sequence in which employees
within a classification will transfer, and does not in any way affect the
time or any other aspects of such transfer.

3. Subject to the availability of suitable openings at the Sunnyvale-
Palo Alto plant and to operational requirements of both plants, such
employees shall for a two-year period from the date of this Supplement
be given consideration for placement ahead of promotions and new hires
at the Sunnyvale-Palo Alto plant in the same classification or in a lateral
classification for which they are qualified. (The term "opening" as used
in this paragraph 3 means an opening in an occupation in which there is
no one on the recall list for that occupation.)

4. Such employees to be transferred shall report for work at the
Sunnyvale-Palo Alto plant within ten (10) working days following the
day the Company notifies them to transfer to the Sunnyvale-Palo Alto
plant.

5. Such employees will be reimbursed, in accordance with Company
policy, for actual cost in moving household goods (up to 8,000 pounds)
from their homes in Los Angeles County to the Sunnyvale-Palo Alto area
and for transportation costs for the employee and his family. In addition
a per diem allowance of $10.00 for employee, $10.00 for spouse, $5.00 for
dependent children living in the home of the employee, for one day

travel time and for a ten (10) day period after arrival will be paid. Payment of the per diem allowance will normally be made in two installments. The allowance for one day travel and for five days of the relocation period will be given to the employee when he arrives at the Sunnyvale-Palo Alto plant. Payment of the balance of the relocation allowance will be made ten days thereafter.

6. Employee grievances regarding the selection of employees under paragraph numbered 2 above shall be subject to the provisions of Article III of said Agreement dated May 19, 1958, provided, however, that such grievance shall be deemed to be waived unless filed within five working days after notice is given to the senior chairman in the department where such selection is made. If notice cannot be given in accordance with the above portion of this paragraph, such notice will be forwarded to the main Union office.

Washington Agreement between Railroad Carriers and Several Unions, including IAM, May 1936

Section 5. Each plan of coordination which results in the displacement of employees or rearrangement of forces shall provide for the selection of forces from the employees of all the carriers involved on bases accepted as appropriate for application in the particular case; and any assignment of employees made necessary by a coordination shall be made on the basis of an agreement between the carriers and the organization of the employees affected. . . .

.   .   .   .

Section 10 (a). Any employee who is retained in the service of any carrier involved in a particular coordination . . . who is required to change the point of his employment as a result of such coordination and is therefore required to move his place of residence, shall be reimbursed for all expenses of moving his household and other personal effects and for the traveling expenses of himself and members of his family, including living expenses for himself and his family and his own actual wage loss during the time necessary for such transfer, and for a reasonable time thereafter (not to exceed two working days), used in securing a place of residence in his new location.

(b) If any such employee is furloughed within three years after changing his point of employment as a result of coordination and elects to move his place of residence back to his original point of employment, the carrier shall assume the expense of moving his household and other personal effects under the conditions imposed in paragraph (a) of this section.

Section 11 (a). The following provisions shall apply, to the extent they are applicable in each instance, to any employee who is retained in the service of any of the carriers involved in a particular coordination . . . who is required to change the point of his employment as a result of such coordination and is therefore required to move his place of residence:

1. If the employee owns his own home in the locality from which he is required to move, he shall at his option be reimbursed by his employing carrier for any loss suffered in the sale of his home for less than its fair value. In each case the fair value of the home in question shall be determined as of a date sufficiently prior to the coordination to be unaffected thereby. The employing carrier shall in each instance be afforded an opportunity to purchase the home at such fair value before it is sold by the employee to any other party.

2. If the employee is under a contract to purchase his home, the employing carrier shall protect him against loss to the extent of the fair value of any equity he may have in the home and in addition shall relieve him from any further obligations under his contract.

3. If the employee holds an unexpired lease of a dwelling occupied by him as his home, the employing carrier shall protect him from all loss and cost in securing the cancellation of his said lease.

Agreement between UAW (Locals 669 and 300) and Curtiss-Wright, Inc.

Should any operations performed at Wood-Ridge, covered by the bargaining unit represented by Local 669, be moved to any other geographical area, each employee with two or more years of seniority whose job is eliminated will be offered the opportunity to move with his job if his job is performed at the new location.

Any employee who accepts such offer will be paid at the new location at the rate of pay he is then receiving provided, however, that if such rate is higher than the top rate being paid in the new plant for such job he will be paid at such top rate.

The matter of moving expenses to the new location for such employees will be subject to negotiations between the parties beginning at least thirty days prior to job offers being made in accordance with Paragraph #1 above; however, no moving expense will be paid to any new location within a 50 mile radius of Wood-Ridge.

If the job in the new plant to which an employee is moved is included within a bargaining unit represented by the International Union, UAW-CIO, the seniority status of the employee in the new plant may be made the subject of negotiations between the Wright

Aeronautical Division, Local 669, and the International Union, UAW-CIO.

Provisions for Training or Retraining

When workers find their skills obsolete as a result of automation or new equipment, retraining will often be helpful in preventing layoff. A number of collective bargaining agreements contain features involving training on company premises at company expense. Sometimes there is joint administration of the training programs. Many of them emphasize concern for the older workers.

In 1960 a new contract between the Amalgamated Lithographers of America and the Metropolitan Lithographers Association was described as follows:

> ... the new contract calls for support by employers of a jointly administered education and training fund. This fund is not only to be used for the training of apprentices at the New York Trade School but for the retraining for other jobs of the craftsmen who have been displaced by improved methods of production.[3]

Some contracts provide special funds for provision of training, as in the Armour and Longshore agreements; others make arrangements for training in outside institutions.

Some of the following clauses are taken from such well-known agreements as Armour and United Packinghouse Workers contract, Western Union and Commercial Telegraphers, American Can Co. and United Steelworkers, and Brotherhood of Railway Clerks and Chesapeake and Ohio Railway Company.

Agreement between Commercial Telegraphers and Western Union

The Company agrees that when for any reason changes in its operating and technical methods or practices require additional knowledge and skill on the part of its employees, such employees will be given opportunity to study and practice to acquire any knowledge and skill necessary to retain their employment, provided the individual can qualify for the new work within a reasonable training period, due recognition being given to the difference in aptitude in various employees. The Company agrees to furnish the necessary instructions, at such employees' prevailing rates of pay.

Agreement between IAM (Lodge 550) and Griscom-Russell Company

In case of automation, employees with greater seniority shall be given first opportunity for training on the new machine tools insofar as possible, recognizing capabilities of such candidates for training in the new work.

Agreement between Armour & Co. and Amalgamated Meat Cutters and United Packinghouse Workers

The company . . . agrees with the unions to establish a fund to be administered by a committee of nine, composed of four representatives of management and two representatives selected by each of the two unions and an impartial chairman selected by mutual agreement of the parties. . . . This committee is authorized to utilize the company contributions to the fund for the purpose of studying the problems resulting from the modernization program and making recommendations for their solution including training employees to perform new and changed jobs . . . . The expenditures for . . . a training and retraining program may be authorized by the committee from the joint fund.

Agreement between Brotherhood of Railway Clerks and Chesapeake and Ohio Railway Company

It is further agreed that employes entitled to and making application for positions advertised to work in the Computer Center will be schooled or trained for the positions at the carrier's expense and without loss in compensation to them; also that employes securing positions in the Computer Center desiring to take promotion to other positions for which they have not been trained will be accorded similar treatment and consideration.

Memorandum of Agreement between American Can Company and United Steelworkers of America

In the event such mechanical or electronic office equipment is installed, management shall provide reasonable training arrangements for the employees who were displaced from their positions by such installation in order that such employees may have an opportunity to become qualified as required for newly established jobs on such installations.

The balance of the employees whose jobs are discontinued will be given reasonable training in order that they may become qualified to take other jobs in the unit to which their seniority entitles them.

Provisions for Income During Layoff

The Supplemental Unemployment Benefit (SUB) in contracts of the steel, auto, and glass industries illustrates a provision under which workers in those industries maintain income in time of temporary layoff, by payments from the employers; such payments are not in legal conflict with unemployment compensation.

As these plans can be costly to employers, to prevent unemployment they have concentrated on liberalization of transfer rights, at the same time planning production more carefully in order to stabilize employment.

Some contracts provide for rate retention on a full or permanent basis. The following clauses are taken from the contracts of Commonwealth Edison, Central Hudson Gas and Electric, Niagara-Mohawk Power, and Armour & Company. These contracts go so far as to guarantee freedom from layoff for employees with specified seniority and no rate reduction during the life of the contract.

Agreement between International Brotherhood of Electrical Workers and Niagara-Mohawk Power Corporation

While this agreement is effective, no regular employee with five (5) or more years of continuous service shall be laid off because of lack of work, nor shall his rate of pay be reduced thereby. In the event of a reduction, elimination or reassignment of work, the Company will offer to an eligible employee affected thereby a job that may then be available within the division in which he is employed and for which he is qualified. It is understood, however, that such job offer to an eligible employee shall not displace another employee with five (5) or more years of continuous service. If such affected eligible employee declines the job offered, his services shall be terminated and the Company shall have no further obligations of any kind.

Agreement between IBEW (Local 320) and Central Hudson Gas and Electric Corporation

No employee who has been continuously in the employ of the Company for three years or more will have his pay reduced during the term of this contract by reason of lay-off or demotion due to lack of work. The Company shall have the right to transfer any employee who but for the provisions of this paragraph would have suffered a reduction in pay by reason of lay-off or demotion and such transfer may be made without the necessity of complying with paragraphs E and F of Article IV hereof. The Union may establish rules subject to the approval of the Company governing the seniority of employees so transferred.

Agreement between IBEW (Local 1427) and Commonwealth Edison Company covering clerical employees

Employees not required for the computer operations will retain their job classification titles and will be assigned to such other work as may be available either in their own or in another department. *Personnel not required in the computer operation shall not be laid off or suffer a reduction in rate of pay by reason of reassignment in accordance with this memorandum.* Such employees will be eligible for time step increases in accordance with their respective job classification schedules until the schedule maximum is reached.

Agreement between United Packinghouse Workers and Amalgamated Meat Cutters and Armour and Company

If, as a result of an agreement or an arbitration award, a job rate is reduced on a changed job, the employees who remain on the changed job at the time of the rate reduction shall not have their hourly rate reduced to conform to the new rate, but all future employees on the job shall be paid the reduced job rate.

Partial and Temporary Guarantees

The Western Electric Company agreement includes a cushioning allowance for a temporary period for an employee who is downgraded or transferred for lack of work. The contract goes into great detail on what happens to the worker's pay, week by week until he reaches the new or reduced base rate.

The American Can agreement with the IAM provides that a man who has worked at least 500 hours in a certain mechanical classification will keep the rate even in a lower classified job. The situation is reviewed periodically, and the employee can ultimately be downgraded in rate. These clauses and those in other agreements are reproduced on the following pages.

Agreement between IBEW (Local 1898) and Western Electric Company

Reduction in earnings due to lack of work

7.1 When an employee would suffer an immediate reduction in BASE RATE because of downgrading or formal transfer as a result of lack of work, he shall be paid a cushioning allowance for a maximum of twelve (12) weeks that will be gradually reduced so as to result in reduction in BASE RATE within his standard work schedule as follows, starting from the effective date of transfer:

(a) During the first four payroll weeks a cushioning allowance equivalent to the difference between the employee's former rate as determined in Paragraph 7.2 and new rate at time of transfer.

(b) At the beginning of the fifth payroll week, the cushioning allowance shall be reduced by an amount up to

    (1) $.06 per hour, or
    (2) If the reduction amounts to $.18 per hour or more, one-third of the total reduction.

(c) At the beginning of the ninth payroll week, the reduction in cushioning allowance shall be:

    (1) for the full amount of the balance if $.06 or less,
    (2) a reduction of $.06 per hour if the balance is less than $.12 per hour, or
    (3) one-third of the total reduction if the balance is $.12 per hour or more.

(d) At the beginning of the thirteenth payroll week, whatever further reduction is required to reduce to the new rate or level of earnings.

7.2 The cushioning allowance shall be determined as follows, and shall be applied to all time paid for including absences approved for payment.

(a) For employees transferred from one hourly-rated daywork job to another hourly-rated daywork job, the cushioning allowance shall be the difference between the employee's former and new BASE RATE.

7.3 Night work Bonus and 7-Day Coverage Bonus shall not be applied to the cushioning allowance, nor shall they be used to affect any such allowance.

Agreement between International Association of Machinists
and American Can Company

After an employee has been classified in one of the mechanical jobs listed above and when work in his classification is not available so that he is assigned by the company to a lower-rated job, he will keep the rate of his mechanical classification provided he has worked at least 500 hours in that mechanical classification within the twelve months preceding the change in assignment. Thereafter, as long as he continues on the lower-rate job, his work assignments will be reviewed four times a year (January 1, April 1, July 1, and October 1). When a quarterly review shows that the employee has worked at least 500 hours in his mechanical classification during the preceding twelve months, he will continue to keep the rate of his mechanical classification until the next review. However, if a quarterly review shows that the employee has not worked at least 500 hours in his mechanical classification in the preceding twelve months, he will then lose the rate of his previous mechanical classification and will thereafter receive the regular rate of the job to which he is currently assigned.

Washington Agreement between Railroad Carriers and Several Unions, including IAM, May 1936

No employee of any of the carriers involved in a particular coordination who is continued in service shall, for a period not exceeding five years following the effective date of such coordination, be placed, as a result of such coordination, in a worse position with respect to compensation and rules governing working conditions than he occupied at the time of such coordination so long as he is unable in the normal exercise of his seniority rights under existing agreements, rules and practices to obtain a position producing compensation equal to or exceeding the compensation of the position held by him at the time of the particular coordination.

The protection afforded by the foregoing paragraph shall be made effective whenever appropriate through what is hereby designated as a "displacement allowance" which shall be determined in each instance in the manner hereinafter described. Any employee entitled to such an allowance is hereinafter referred to as a "displaced" employee.

Each displacement allowance shall be a monthly allowance determined by computing the total compensation received by the employee and his total time paid for during the last twelve (12) months in which he performed service immediately preceding the date of his displacement (such twelve (12) months being hereinafter referred to as the "test period") and by dividing separately the total compensation and the total time paid for by twelve, thereby producing the average monthly compensation and average monthly time paid for, which shall be the minimum amounts used to guarantee the displaced employee, and if his compensation in his current position is less in any month in which he performs work than the aforesaid average compensation he shall be paid the difference, less compensation for any time lost on account of voluntary absences to the extent that he is not available for service equivalent to his average monthly time during the test period, but he shall be compensated in addition thereto at the rate of the position filled for any time worked in excess of the average monthly time paid for during the test period.

Provisions for Early Retirement

Organized labor believes that one solution to technological displacement would be the liberalization of policies involving earlier retirement. So far the problem has been that early retirements generally result in a reduced annuity. The first two following plans, however, are unusual in that they allow early annuitants full retirement pay based on separation under certain prescribed conditions (plant shutdown and other reasons). The third contract permits double the amount of normal annuity under certain circumstances. The contracts covered are those of Continental Can, eleven basic steel companies, and Ford Motor Company.

Memorandum of Agreement between United Steelworkers of America and Eleven Basic Steel Companies

Provide full retirement pension for employees terminated on or after 1/1/60 at or after 55 with at least 20 years of service, by reason of a permanent shutdown or by reason of a layoff or sickness resulting in a break in service, provided that any such employee must have attained age 53 with at least 18 years of continuous service on the date on which he ceased work for the Company on account of the shutdown, layoff or disability. The company in its sole discretion may grant a pension prior to the date, absence due to layoff would otherwise result in a break in service if in its judgment there is little likelihood that the employee will be recalled to work. Under mutually satisfactory conditions, permit early retirement with full pension upon attainment of age 60 with 15 or more years of service.

Agreement between International Association of Machinists and the Continental Can Company

Any present Employee who upon permanent shutdown of his plant shall have had at least 15 years of continuous service and shall have

attained the age of 60 years, and who at such time shall be in the
bargaining unit specified in the Master Agreement, will be retired with
a lump sum retirement allowance and, after 3 months, a *normal pension,
or an early pension without reduction* if he shall not have attained the
age of 65 years. . . ."

Agreement between the UAW and Ford
Motor Company

Article IV, Section 2. *Early Retirement.* On or after September 1,
1958, any employe (not retired prior to such date) who shall have reached
his 60th birthday but not his normal retirement age and shall have 10
or more years of creditable service, (i) may retire at his option or (ii) may
be retired at the option of the Company or under mutually satisfactory
conditions, and, upon making due application therefor, shall be eligible
for an early retirement benefit as provided in Article V, Section 2, of
the Plan.

Article V, Section 2. *Early Retirement Benefits.* The amount of the
monthly retirement benefit payable out of the Pension Fund for an
employe who shall be retired on or after September 1, 1958, *at the option
of the Company or under mutually satisfactory conditions under the provisions of Article IV, Section 2, of the Plan,* and who shall make application
to the Board therefor, shall be an amount equal to (i) $4.80 for each year
of his credited service based on service prior to January 1, 1958, plus
(ii) $4.86 for his credited service based on service in the year 1958, plus
(iii) $5.00 for each year of his credited service based on service subsequent
to December 31, 1958; provided, however, that for any month after the
retired employe attains age 65 or becomes eligible for a Primary or
Disability Insurance Benefit under the Federal Social Security Act,
whichever occurs first, his monthly retirement benefit payable out of
the Pension Fund shall be an amount equal to (i) $2.40 for each year of
his credited service based on service prior to January 1, 1958, plus (ii)
$2.43 for his credited service for service based on service in the year 1958,
plus (iii) $2.50 for each year of his credited service based on service
subsequent to December 31, 1958.

Special Automation Fund

There has recently been much discussion about special funds
being set up by labor agreements to alleviate the burden of technological unemployment. In Chapter 10 the Armour agreements with
the United Packinghouse Workers, setting up an "automation Fund"
and other funds, are described in some detail.

The American Federation of Musicians set the pattern, at one time, for "taxing" technological developments in the entertainment world.

The most recent contract worthy of note in this regard is the one negotiated by the Pacific Maritime Association with the International Longshoremen's and Warehousemen's Union in 1960. This follows in detail:

> Contract Provisions taken from 1960 Mechanization and Modernization Agreement between International Longshoremen's & Warehousemen's Union and Pacific Maritime Association Information Sheet, issued by ILWU

I. *The Agreement.* The memorandum of agreement, reached and initialed October 18, 1960, runs from the time of ratification to July 1, 1966.

II. *Summary of Provisions.* The mechanization and modernization agreement provides that for the regularly employed work force, i.e., fully registered longshoremen and shipclerks, there shall be no layoffs, a guaranteed weekly minimum wage to be annually computed, early retirement or a lump benefit at normal retirement and additional death and disability benefits.

Benefits will begin after ratification at a date to be set by the Trustees.

The employing stevedoring and steamship companies, through their association for collective bargaining, agree to establish a Mechanization and Modernization Fund at the rate of $5 million per year for five and one-half years in order to provide the benefits mentioned above. This fund, running to July 1, 1966, will amount to $27.5 million of itself, and there will be added to it $1.5 million which was negotiated as a pilot fund in 1959, bringing the total fund available for benefits to $29 million.

III. *Benefits.* The Fund will be used to put a floor under earnings, to permit retirement as early as age 62, to provide a lump sum amount upon retirement to men who do not retire before age 65, and graduated death benefits. All benefits apply only to the basic work force, i.e., fully registered men. Actual benefit amounts will be determined by the Trustees after the Fund has been set up. The benefit amounts given here are those proposed by the Union and estimated to be feasible within the limits of the Fund.

The men's share in cost savings resulting from the use of machines will finance the early retirement and vesting benefits. Elimination of make-work practices add enough more to finance the floor under earnings.

IV. *Floor Under Earnings.* Whenever work opportunity declines to the point that men cannot earn the equivalent of 35 straight time hours of work per week, their earnings will be supplemented from the Fund up to the level of 35 straight time hours. This means a guarantee of $98.70 per week at present wage levels ($2.92 × 35). The guarantee applies whenever hours fall below 35 due to mechanization and improved efficiency; it does not apply to a drop in hours due to economic recession.

Men will have to make themselves regularly available (unless sick or injured) in order to be eligible. It is planned to work out provisions for shifting them from areas of low work opportunity to areas of high work opportunity. Since registration is on a coastwise basis, this can be managed with a minimum of difficulty.

V. *Early Retirement.* Provision for voluntary early retirement permits withdrawal from the industry with a guaranteed income for life, plus substantially complete medical and hospital coverage for the men and their families. There is thus the basis for an orderly decline in the work force if work opportunity declines.

Men who have worked 25 years or more in the longshore industry will be eligible to retire at any time between the ages of 62 and 65 with a monthly pension of $220 (the normal industry paid pension of $100 plus the equivalent of present maximum social security). This amount will be payable until a man reaches age 65 when he will go on the regular $100 per month pension and will be eligible for his social security benefit.

If work opportunity falls drastically, early retirement may be made mandatory by a joint determination of the parties. In this event the men forced to retire shall receive an extra $100 from the present pension plan, or a total of $320 per month (plus medical and hospital coverage) until age 65 when each would pick up his normal pension.

VI. *Vesting.* After 15 years of service in the industry each fully registered longshoreman becomes entitled to a vested share in the Fund. After 25 years his right is fully vested and amounts to $7920 which is the amount he would receive in 36 monthly payments if he retires at age 62. If a 25 year man does not retire early, he receives the full $7920 upon normal retirement at age 65.

Men who become unable to work in the industry because of disability are entitled to their vested share in the Fund upon leaving the industry. The amount varies from $2640 for a man with 15 years' service up to the maximum of $7920 with 25 years. The 25 year man is also eligible for the regular disability pension irrespective of age, and to medical and hospital coverage.

In the case of a man who dies before receipt of his vested share, his beneficiary receives the amount to which he is entitled on the basis of length of service, up to a maximum of $5000.

VII. *Other Death Benefits.* Beneficiaries of registered men with 5 to 15 years of service are entitled to a death benefit of $2640. This is in addition to a regular death benefit provided under the ILWU-PMA Welfare Plan of $2000 or $4000 in case of accidental death.

Continuation of Fringe Benefits During Layoff Periods

At issue these days is a demand by unions that fringe benefits such as accident and sickness benefits, hospitalization and major medical programs, and other benefits, be continued on behalf of the employee during layoff periods. The following data are taken either from company memorandums or from clauses in bargaining agreements of Continental Can Company, basic steel, General Electric Company, Lever Brothers, and the Washington Agreement of 1936 on railroad mergers.

Memorandum of Agreement between United Steelworkers of America and Eleven Basic Steel Companies

Effective January 1st, 1960, the companies . . . shall provide, without any contribution by the employees, the present program of insurance benefits with the following changes:

Life insurance to be continued during layoff up to 2 years, with employees paying 60¢ per month per $1,000 after the first six months of layoff.

Hospitalization, surgical and related coverages under the present program to be continued during first six months of layoff for employees with 2 years or more of continuous service at date of layoff.

Agreement between IAM and Continental Can Company

For lay-offs commencing on or after . . . all Group Insurance except Weekly Sickness and Accident Benefits will be continued following lay-off for employees with at least two years of continuous service at date of lay-off for up to six months following date of lay-off provided that an employee who fails to return upon recall shall cease to have such continued coverage. The provisions in paragraph 1 for continued coverage in excess of the foregoing shall continue in effect.

The Washington Agreement of May, 1936, between a number of Railway Carriers and Unions, including the IAM

An employee affected by a particular coordination shall not be deprived of benefits attaching to his previous employment, such as free transportation, pensions, hospitalization, relief, etc., under the same conditions and so long as such benefits continue to be accorded to other employees on his home road, in active service or on furlough as the case may be, to the extent that such benefits can be so maintained under present authority of law or corporate action or through future authorization which may be obtained.

Memorandum to All Employees at Cambridge Plant of Lever Bros.[4]

Any employee who at termination is at least 55 years of age and has completed at least 5 years of service, or who has completed 30 years of service regardless of age, will have his company-paid group life insurance continued until he obtains other employment in which group life insurance is made available to him or in which his rate of pay exceeds 50 per cent of his final Lever base rate. Contributory insurance will remain in force under the same conditions, if the employee continues his contributions toward its cost.

Memorandum describing the Offer made by General Electric Company to IAM and Other Unions during Negotiations in 1960[5]

In addition, for employees with 3 or more full years of service who are on layoff, the Company will assume Insurance Plan contributions for both personal and dependent coverage during the first 12 months of layoff so as to assure protection during this period of reduced income.

Sharing Gains of Greater Productivity

Unions take the position that workers have the right to share in the gains of productivity as it increases through technological change. This sharing may be reflected in wage increases, shorter hours of work, or additional fringe benefits. Management is not always ready to admit that it should share profits with its employees. In many cases firms have been driven to automation in order to survive in a competitive market. This situation, however, does not lessen the intensity of the union demand for some sharing of the gains.

A profit-sharing agreement was recently negotiated between UAW and American Motors. The UAW at a special collective bargaining convention in 1958 had previously approved a profit-sharing principle. The UAW resolution stated:

> Collective bargaining demands must take into account the unevenness in the distribution of profits. Excessive profits represent gains from technological advances unfairly withheld from the workers and consumers with whom they should be shared.[6]

The Kaiser Steel Corporation has been a leader in developing a joint committee chaired by George W. Taylor of the University of Pennsylvania. The committee includes representatives of the public, labor, and management and is dedicated to the equitable sharing of economic progress.

In recent negotiations over which the question of technological change hovered, the Kaiser Steel Corporation and the United Steel Workers of America agreed upon the following language:

Committee to Develop a Long Range Plan for the Equitable Sharing of Economic Progress

The parties shall establish a joint committee, consisting of Dr. George Taylor, Chairman, David L. Cole, and Dr. John Dunlop, and three representatives designated by each party to recommend for the consideration of the parties the establishment of a long range plan for equitable sharing between the stockholders, the employees and the public, of the fruits of the Company's progress. The formula shall give appropriate consideration to safeguarding the employees against increases in cost of living, to promoting stability of employment, to reasonable sharing of increased productivity, labor cost savings, to providing for necessary expansion and for assuring the Company's and the employees' progress. The Committee shall report its recommendation to the parties prior to July 1, 1960, and the parties by mutual agreement may incorporate an agreed upon plan in substitution for the wage and cost of living provisions in this Memorandum, which would otherwise become effective on or after July 1, 1960.*

*This language was finally ratified in the agreement between the United Steelworkers of America and the Kaiser Steel Corporation, October 26, 1959.

In addition to the Kaiser Committee, other committees have been set up from time to time through collective bargaining agreements to make studies, establish automation funds, change or modify contracts during the contract period, and provide consultation to union and management on technological or economic problems and other matters.

The best-known committee is the one set up by Armour and Company in the meat-packing industry. In the following paragraphs will be found provisions from the Armour agreement, the United Steelworkers and the eleven basic steel companies, Sylvania Products. The steel clauses are of great interest in that they set up a Human Relations Research Committee, which appears to have interest in many problems besides human relations; for example, job classifications, seniority, and other problems.

There is pressure in the maritime industry for the formation of a similar committee to solve the problem of the "foreign-flag ships." Such a committee may be expected as a result of contracts signed in 1961 by NMU and SIU with American shipowners. Incidentally, automation offers one possibility of increasing the number of American-flag ships, for at present the owners believe that the American-flag ships are uncompetitive with the ships of other nations as well as with those owned by United States companies but flying the foreign flags of Panama, Liberia, and Honduras.

The several clauses follow:

Agreement between IUE (Local 352) and Batavia Plant of Sylvania Electric Products, Inc.

Automation Committee. The Company and the Union agree that a joint committee on which the Company and the Union shall have equal representation (not to exceed five (5) members each) will be set up on the effective date of this contract to deal with automation. The Company will furnish the Union Representatives with complete information on the application of automation wherever it might affect the employees of the Batavia Plant.

The committee will be commissioned to study and, if necessary, modify the present job evaluation system in order to adopt a job evaluation system that will cover automation. This committee will study the problem of employee displacement and will recommend methods to be adopted to minimize this effect.

Agreement between Amalgamated Meat Cutters and United
Packinghouse Workers and Armour and Company

Mechanization and new methods to promote operating and distributing efficiencies affect the number of employees required and the
manner in which they perform their work. Technological improvement
may result in the need for developing new skills and the acquiring of
new knowledge by the employees. In addition, problems are created
for employees affected by these changes that require the joint consideration of the Company and the Unions ... it is recognized that these
problems require continued study to promote employment opportunities
for employees affected by the introduction of more efficient methods
and technological changes.

The Company, therefore, agrees with the Unions to establish a fund
to be administered by a committee of nine, composed of four representatives of Management and two representatives selected by each of the
two Unions and an impartial chairman selected by mutual agreement
of the parties. The Management and the Unions shall each pay for
the expenses of their respective representatives on the committee and the
fees and expenses of the impartial chairman shall be paid by the fund.
This committee is authorized to utilize the Company contributions to
the fund for the purpose of studying the problems resulting from the
modernization program and making recommendations for their solution
including training employees to perform new and changed jobs and
promoting employment opportunities within the Company for those
affected.

The committee should consider for appropriate action a program
of training qualified employees in the knowledge and skill required to
perform new and changed jobs so that the present employees may be
utilized for this purpose to the greatest extent possible. The expenditures
for such a training and retraining program may be authorized by the
committee from the joint fund. The committee should also consider
other programs such as transfer rights to plants covered by the Master
Agreements where job opportunities remain or are increasing, and should
consider any other methods that might be employed to promote continued employment opportunities for those affected. It is agreed,
however, that the fund shall not be used to increase present severance
pay benefits.

The findings and recommendations of the committee shall not be
binding on the parties but shall be made to the Company and to the
Unions for their further consideration. The final report and recommendations by the committee is to be made no later than six months
prior to the termination of the contract.

The fund to be utilized for the purposes set forth above shall be created by Company contributions made in accordance with the following formula:

The contributions shall be in an amount equal to one cent for each hundred-weight of total tonnage shipped from slaughter and meat packing plants covered by the Master Agreements. Such tonnage figures shall be based upon the periodical Food Division financial statements and a monthly list of such tonnage for the covered plants shall be presented to the joint committee. The company's tonnage figures shall be final and binding upon the parties. Contributions shall terminate upon the total of the Company's contributions reaching $500,000.

Agreement between United Steelworkers of America and Eleven Basic Steel Companies

Human Relations Research Committee

The parties shall establish a Human Relations Research Committee to plan and oversee studies and recommend solutions of mutual problems in the areas of:

a. Guides for the determination of equitable wage and benefit adjustments.
b. The Job Classification System.
c. Wage incentives, including development of appropriate guides for determining fair incentive compensation.
d. Seniority, including maximum practicable protection for long-service employees against layoffs and for recalls after layoffs.
e. Medical care.
f. Such other over-all problems as the parties by mutual agreement may from time to time refer to such Committee.

The Human Relations Research Committee shall be composed of an equal number of representatives designated by the parties (the number of which by agreement of the parties may be changed from time to time), and shall be under the co-chairmanship of two persons of outstanding qualifications and objectivity, one each to be designated by the Company and the Union.

The Human Relations Research Committee shall be empowered to retain, by mutual agreement of the co-chairmen thereof, qualified experts and services in the various fields of study for the purposes of consultation and advice.

Expense of the Human Relations Research Committee work shall be shared equally by the parties.

Conclusion

The trade unions are conscious of the problems developing from automation or fuller mechanization. They are confident that union structure is sufficiently solid to weather the storm and that they have the flexibility through collective bargaining to respond constructively to the problem. For this reason more and more provisions will be demanded in collective agreements to protect the rights of workers in danger of losing their jobs because of automation.

The change in the character of work under automation will make the union's work more difficult. Union contacts may be more welcomed, however, because of the increasing isolation of the workers in the automated plants. In any event the unions are pressing for an extension of the area of collective bargaining so that their views may be taken into account in the transition toward increasingly automatic production.

References

1. "Meeting the Problems of Automation Through Collective Bargaining," International Association of Machinists, December 1960, page v.
2. *Ibid.*, p. 4.
3. Editorial, *New York Times*, April 5, 1960.
4. "Meeting the Problems of Automation Through Collective Bargaining," *op. cit.* p. 32.
5. *Ibid.*
6. "Recommended UAW 1958 Collective Bargaining Program," *Daily Labor Reporter*, January 14, 1958.

▶ ▶ ▶ ▶ **10**

Attitudes and
Experiences in Six
Leading Industries

Labor unions have been fortunate in the last two decades in securing generous fringe benefits for health, welfare, and pension plans. They have, for the most part, wiped out regional differentials in important industries in the South. Each year, whether one of recession or recovery, they have been able to negotiate annual wage increases, together with improvements in other benefits. At no time have general wage reductions been attempted, even with a 7 percent unemployment rate in 1958.[1]

Certainly, the derivative gains to the economy as a whole, as a result of collective bargaining, cannot be ignored. What is the unseen hand that guides the bargaining demands of these "private" negotiations into socially desirable channels? It does not follow that what is good for union members is automatically good for America in all cases.

Certain economists, concerned with structural unemployment, have come up with solutions in the public area, which are much the same as those arrived at privately by unions in their bargaining proposals.[2] These experts have testified on the need for severance pay, retraining, relocation, and further extension of unemployment benefits. Also cited by the economists are the Longshore and Meatpacking plans, discussed later in this chapter, which provide funds for solutions to displacement. Despite the fact that this nation prefers to work out its own problems without Government interference, every effort should be made to give substantial credit to these private bargaining agreements.

The following material about the experiences of labor unions in the automobile, oil refining, meat-packing, electrical, and electronics, steel, and longshore industries, with respect to problems of automation, rising productivity and unemployment, should be of value to managers who contemplate further utilization of automated or laborsaving devices.

On the record, labor does not appear to be blocking technological change entirely, but appears interested only in cushioning its impact. Does labor give lip service to automation on one hand, while secretly developing a vast whispering campaign against it? Often what appears on the record is the national endorsement of improved technology by the union headquarters or research group, while at the same time the locals are exasperating the employers with every possible type of obstructionism. For example, the international unions and the AFL-CIO itself have had to sustain the free trade position in the face of attacks by local unions.

Effect of Automation on Union Treasuries

One of the most vulnerable spots in the union defense against automation is the state of the union treasury, and the locals realize this. When members lose jobs through automation, they stop paying dues. Unions then scramble for new members and begin to raid one another, causing weakness and consternation at the national union level.

AFL-CIO economists figure that from 1954 to 1961 1,500,000 industrial jobs had withered away, and they believe that automation was greatly responsible for this loss. Membership in the United Automobile Workers union fell from a high 1,300,000 to less than 1,000,000 in 1962. The United Steelworkers Union charge the steel companies with lopping off 200,000 jobs in the last five years despite increased production. The man-hours now required to turn out a ton of finished steel has fallen to 12.1, a drop from 18.4 at the end of World War II.

Automobile Industry

Union Position on Automation in 1954   In 1954 the United Automobile Workers examined the subject of automation and made a statement about the union's growing fears and the future demands the union would have to make on employers as a result of automation.

Included in the objectives of the 1954 Economic and Collective Bargaining Conference on Automation were achievement of guaranteed employment; broadening of seniority units, strengthening of transfer rights; preferential hiring of displaced workers within the same company or in other companies in the same industry and area; negotiation of new job classifications required by technological change, with wage rates properly reflecting increased worker responsibility and increased volume of output; protection of the integrity of the skilled trades and the establishment of programs under the joint control of labor and management to train and retrain workers at company expense and without loss of wages — for new jobs that would permit improved earnings during a period of technological change.

The UAW placed high on the priority list the attainment of a shorter workweek, after the guaranteed annual wage was achieved. A form of guaranteed wage (SUB, mentioned in Chapter 9) has now been achieved in the automobile industry. With this out of the way, the UAW is now ready to push to the shorter workweek. This matter is under discussion in current bargaining.

Reuther on Automation   In the 1955 hearings on automation in Washington, D.C., Walter Reuther foresaw the vast possibilities of employee displacement, the need for training and retraining, and the lack of capital of some businesses to survive the competition of the period.[3]

Reuther suggested earlier pensions and accelerated social security eligibility for those workers who could not adjust to the new technology. He stated that the minimum wage should be increased and the length of the workweek further reduced.

Petroleum Refining Industry

Strikes Ineffective at Automated Plants

A struck plant where production continues at a fast pace. A vigorous union organizing drive that brings in fewer members than leave. A contract settlement in which the employer wins an almost complete victory.[4]

This is what the Oil Workers (OACW) found when they engaged in a seventy-two-day strike at Gulf Oil Corporation's huge installation at Port Arthur, Texas. Management has learned that union tactics and procedures which once worked against the conventional plant are no longer to be feared in the automated plant. The OCAW's experience at Port Arthur has revealed the threat to union survival. Union leaders know that automation is a threat to their total membership, but they have never realized how easy it is becoming to lose a strike under automation.

At Port Arthur, although not a single worker out of the 3,700-odd production and maintenance workers crossed the picket line, yet the firm continued to turn out gasoline, fuel oil, and other products at a rate of 130,000 barrels a day, or 65 percent of the prestrike pace, with 600 supervisors working in the automated plant.

Security Versus Insecurity   In the Gulf strike the issue was job security in the face of automation. The OCAW sought restrictions on the contracting out of maintenance work and protection against layoffs. All the union got was a promise from Gulf that it would give workers a sixty-day warning on layoffs due to pending technological change, but no warning on layoffs due to reduced business volume.

Furthermore, Gulf won from the union permission to be more flexible on job assignments, an important factor in an automated plant.

Increase in Union Organizing Costs   The Oil Workers have been trying to recoup their losses in membership at such plants as Gulf by trying to organize the independent refineries. They have discovered a side effect of automation; namely, that while automation is shrinking the size of plant employment, organizing costs are not declining proportionately. E. C. Mattern, organizing director of the OCAW, indicated that "it costs just as much to organize 100 men as it does to organize 500. . . . as a result the cost of bringing in new members (to offset losses) has at least doubled over the past six years."[5]

Contract Strategy   Mattern went on to point out that contract strategy must change because of automation; that "the OCAW is now pushing for company-wide contracts to replace the individual plant contracts currently in effect . . . . When we sign many similar contracts with various plants in the same company, the contract dates are different. The strike threat is weakened, because we are able to strike only one plant at a time. Now, because automation enables a plant to produce in spite of a strike, and because many companies have interlocking facilities, we know we must meet the company at the very highest level in order to bargain effectively."[6]

Shift in Bargaining Goals Resulting From Automation   The Oil Workers have had to shift bargaining goals. Job security is now the paramount issue rather than wages. Says O. A. Knight, president of OCAW:

We can usually get together with employers on wage terms, but job security is a different matter and it has become the top issue. If a man doesn't have job security, then wage hikes, health insurance, pensions, and other benefits don't mean anything to him . . . .

Unlike the question of wages, many companies don't even want to talk about job security (management wants to manage its own affairs) . . . the result is that the area of compromise, on which all labor negotiation depends, is growing narrower and narrower. This leads to increasing conflict.[7]

Meat-Packing Industry

United Packinghouse Workers Attitude on Automation The Packinghouse Workers look with pessimism on the opportunities for jobs for displaced personnel in the meat-packing industry despite the $500,000 Automation fund and the studies of the Automation Committee, headed by Clark Kerr. Their fears go beyond the meat-packing industry and are directed to the national problem. The union filed a supplemental statement to the June 19, 1961, report of the Automation Committee.

Every year in the immediate future, the nation's labor force will increase by 1,250,000 workers. And every year automation will wipe out 250,000 jobs — at the present level of the Gross National Product. Accordingly, if we are content to keep unemployment from rising above present levels, we need 2,500,000 jobs per year, or about 50,000 new jobs per week. This would require a national growth, year in and year out, averaging at least 5% every 12 months. The alternative to so organizing the giant power of automation for the creation of abundance at home and alleviation of misery abroad is certain and shattering economic disaster in the years ahead.

For the meat industry to carry a proportionate share of such needed national growth, it must raise its volume of output at a rate sufficient to create 5,000 new jobs per year. Currently the industry is losing 7,000 jobs per year. Currently per capita meat consumption is falling and meat exports are insignificant.[8]

The union looks to the Federal Government to provide the growth rate necessary to create the new jobs required for full employment. It believes that a governmental program is necessary to meet immediate human needs and at the same time to stimulate the required level of economic growth. Technological progress can then be welcomed without the negative side effects that "threaten disruption to the economy." The union wants a combination of private initiative and public policy to win and maintain full employment. It believes that the ways to achieve the required growth rate demand attention to the following items:

> A massive increase in the public investment for schools, homes, medical care, education, city rebuilding, and a wide range of other national needs. Certainly government investment to meet such urgent social needs is no less sound economically or right morally than private investment for the production of bubble gum or slot machines.
>
> Creation and expansion of private consumer purchasing power which is basic to the rate of investment, the level of production and even the profit return of private initiative. This can be accomplished through a variety of means including, for example, earlier retirement under social security with increased benefits, tax revision to reduce the benefits on low income levels, increases in the amount and duration of unemployment compensation, and immediate effective increases in the minimum wage levels above the new defined level of $1.25 and to extend coverage to millions of workers now excluded.
>
> Arrangements to gear this nation's productive capacity more realistically to the grave needs of peoples in the other nations through foreign trade.[9]

It may be difficult for a businessman to appreciate the effect of government costs on increased investment. It will also be difficult for him to understand how raising the minimum wage is going to prevent unemployment. In fact, the higher the minimum, the greater the chance of the marginal worker's being displaced by a machine.

Union Support of Shorter Workweek Despite the fact that employers are using automation as a way of reducing direct-labor costs, the union persists in the idea that a shorter workweek will permit more effective buying power and will aid in full employment. This attitude is difficult to understand, particularly when the United States stands on the threshold of keener competition with the European Common Market. Any reduction in hours but with the same take-home pay and without a corresponding productivity increase will raise the cost of manufacture. The Union states its position as follows:

> The shorter work week offers an immediate move to restore purchasing power and jobs to millions of unemployed and an offset to the continuing attrition by automation of the national total of available jobs. If a choice ever comes between more leisure and needed increase in national output, then a rational choice may be made.[10]

Electrical and Electronics Industry

Union Attitude Toward Automation The attitude of the IUE is an interesting one, because the members of this union are employed in the manufacture of electrical components for computers and automatic devices. In general, this union is in favor of automation. Following is the attitude of IUE:

> Perhaps the most significant novel feature of automation is that it makes it possible to do many things and to produce many goods and services which were simply not feasible in the past. Atomic energy research could not have possibly reached its present stage without automatic devices and controls. The huge oil refinery, chemical plants and steel plants of today could not be operated without automatic controls. Compounds of ingredients formerly too toxic to be handled safely can now be used. Many new products have come on the market as a result of refinements of precision work made possible by automation. With advanced computer technology it is possible to assemble and analyze information that was once prohibitively expensive to collect. Too often this novel aspect of automation is overlooked. Yet it is certainly the distinctive contribution of the new technology.[11]

Reasons for Union Membership Fear of Technology The impact of automation on employment of workers in the light-bulb industry is severe. Fourteen glass-blowing machines, each operated by one worker, now produce 90 percent of the glass light bulbs used in the United States and all the glass tubes used in radio and television sets, except the picture tubes.

Another example is the automatic manufacture of equipment for attaching standard electronic components to printed circuit boards. Machines now print or etch or stencil on a board that which at one time was a hand-wired circuit, soldered at all contact points. Today, machines make the components, attach them to the printed circuit boards, make the parts, and assemble them. Once the components are fed into a machine, complete radio sets can be produced — and on a one-body radio assembly line, turning out one thousand radios a day. Today two workers produce more than two hundred workers did under the old methods.[12]

Blessing or Curse? James B. Carey, president of the IUE, has from time to time clarified the position of his union with respect to automation. While, on the one hand, he believes that the nation progresses through automation, on the other hand he points out:

Automation has been responsible for the loss of 3 million jobs in mining, manufacture, agriculture and other industries in less than eight years. . . . What is more important is that the majority of workers displaced by automation will never be able to return to jobs in their own industry, and probably will never be able to find jobs in any industry.[13]

Carey points out that labor applauded the introduction of mechanization except in those cases where employers or industry flatly refused to discuss plans whereby mass unemployment could have been avoided. As to automation today, the IUE president states:

Why shouldn't we welcome automation? Why shouldn't we favor any new technology or devices that will help us to avoid hard physical work, that will reduce the workday to six or seven hours or the workweek to four days? . . . The answer is, of course, that automation, properly planned and surrounded with intelligent safeguards, should prove more of a blessing to working men and women than any other stratum of society. It is the underprivileged of this country . . . who should benefit by the vastly increased production of essential goods, at constantly lower prices.[14]

The union leader presented facts showing that the electrical industry has been one of the most severely hit by unemployment, much of it caused by automation. "In the last eight years," Mr. Carey stated, "employment has plunged from 925,000 to 836,000, a drop of 89,000 jobs, or nearly 10%, while production has soared by 21%."

The IUE recently discussed a plan before the Holland Committee studying automation's influences on employment. Carey met with the Congressional Committee on March 22, 1961, and presented the following plan to help solve the problems of automation:

1. Retraining programs should be set up to equip the displaced workers with new jobs and for new kinds of production. Provision should be made for supplementary schooling.

2. The tax provisions of the 1954 law which have encouraged corporations to close down plants and remove them to remote and rural areas should be abolished.

3. Supplementary unemployment benefits and termination pay should be provided on a liberal basis to help workers until they find new jobs.

4. Employees should be provided with a fair share of the increased production created through automation in order to enable them to buy back the goods they have produced.

   a. For example, between 1955–59, man-hour productivity in the General Electric Company soared 34%, or nearly 7% a year, but hourly wages progressed 17%, or a little more than 3% a year.

   b. Between 1954–59, the increase in man-hour productivity in Westinghouse Corporation reached 25%, or 5% a year, yet hourly wages rose by 16%, a little more than 3% a year.

   5. A government tripartite Committee on Automation should be established to study the problem and its effects upon the nation and to recommend long range solutions.[15]

Steel Industry

1960 Steelworkers' Convention   As a prelude to the steel negotiations of 1962, the Steelworkers Union, late in 1961, brought out its own study entitled, "The Impact of Technological Change and Automation on the Basic Steel Industry."[16]   This was in response to a strong resolution on automation adopted at the Tenth Constitutional Convention of the union in Atlantic City, September 19–23, 1960. The resolution called attention to the gross human and social problems of worker displacement, unemployment, widespread relief, and an increasing spread of depressed communities, all being created, the union claimed, by automation.   It called for a series of remedial actions by business, Government, and labor to remove or ease the impact of automation.   The resolution closed with:

> It is vital to our well-being as a nation that the problems of automation be solved, not in the distant future, but now and each day as they arise. Automation must not be allowed to develop into a headless monster destroying more than it creates. It must be guided for the betterment of mankind.[17]

Mixed Blessing   The Steelworkers took the position that they were aware of the many potential benefits which might be derived from automation.   But they believed that automation was not an unmixed blessing — that it means fewer workers producing more goods.   They pointed out that they did not want to obstruct progress, but felt that their responsibility as a union was to minimize the problems arising from the new technology.

Steel Facts, published by the Iron and Steel Institute, was quoted by the union as having brought out some sixty cost-saving developments in twenty-five years of progress. Among the items cited were the following: oxygen injection in open-hearth furnaces, oxygen enriched blast for blast furnaces, vacuum melting and vacuum pouring, continuous casting, ultrasonic testing, punch-card control of mills, direct reduction of iron ore to iron, continuous galvanizing of sheets, electronic devices for continuous measurement of thickness of sheets and strip, electrically welded pipe and continuous welded pipe, basic oxygen process for steelmaking, and continuous annealing.

Increase in Average Furnace Size and Production Between 1938 and 1960 the number of blast furnaces in the United States increased by only 8 percent, but the average capacity per furnace increased by 56 percent. During the same period the number of open-hearth furnaces dropped 9 percent, but the average capacity per furnace increased by 94 percent.[18]

The union claimed that the increased size and efficiency of the iron and steelmaking furnaces did not bring about a corresponding increase in labor use, primarily because of the greater productive capacity of each furnace in current years. For example, *Steel Facts*, in June 1959, reported the following experience:

> A few months ago, one steel company set out to learn how fast an open hearth furnace equipped with roof lances could produce steel under ideal conditions. Oxygen was poured in through three lances at the rate of 693 cubic feet per ton of steel. The result was a production rate of 105 tons per hour, far above the 30 or 40 tons produced per hour in a furnace of similar size under normal conditions.

Only 10 percent of the open-hearth furnaces were equipped with oxygen roof jets in 1958; today this number has increased 25 percent and by 1962–1963 it will rise to 70 percent.

In addition, the basic oxygen furnace has been a new breakthrough. In 1957 annual capacity was only 540,000 tons. A year later it was 1,100,000 tons, and in 1960 4,200,000 tons. Average annual capacity of each of these new furnaces is two and one-half times greater than that of the open-hearth furnaces.[19] The oxygen converter process will lower labor, maintenance, and other costs.

Effect of Organization and Automation on Employment The union is concerned about unemployment and mass job displacement because of progress in two items — oxygenation and automation, coupled with a stabilizing demand for steel. Unless markets can expand, union leaders fear technological unemployment.

Automation first made its advent in steel with the start of data processing. Now computer-control systems have moved in to control production operations. At least six steel companies have given computers control over rolling mills, sintering plants, and annealing lines. The steel industry appears to be made to order for supervision by computers, says *Business Week*.[20]

Control of Rolling Mills by Computers   The union claims that the rolling mills under construction will be controlled by computers. These machines will be fed information on the composition of the alloy and the size and gauge of the coil or sheet. From this point on, the machine will be completely self-regulated, taking temperature, weight, and measurement readings. It will compute roll settings and the number of passes through the rolls — and even print tickets identifying weight, dimensions, and other characteristics of the coil of metal. It will perform faster and more efficiently any of the operations performed by the present rolling mills using human labor.

Eventual Automation From Ground Up   Several steel company executives agree that the industry now has the hardware — the computers and the controls — to go to automation of mills from start to finish.[21] Already blast-furnace yields are up 15 percent through computer control of the sintering process, which conserves the ore, reduces coke rates, and provides laborsaving. With present knowledge the charging operations of the blast furnace can be completely automated; instruments and controls are already in use to regulate the furnace at critical points in the process. Experiments are under way to automate the open-hearth system. Automatic programming and control techniques are available to regulate the charging of the furnace. If the researchers come up with a way to eliminate the blast furnace by a direct reduction process, the techniques will alter the economics of steelmaking.[22]

The effect of all this research will be to automate the steel plant completely within the next decade. What will happen to the employees of these plants? Unless markets can continue to expand (which they are not doing at present), the rise in productivity will keep pace — not with an increase in sales, but with a drop in direct labor.

Attitude of Steel Mills on Job Displacement   In December 1961, the Iron and Steel Institute published a report entitled "The Competitive Challenge to Steel." This report answered in great detail the contentions of the Steelworkers Union in the studies previously referred to. The steel companies attempted to place the matter of job displacement in the following perspective:

1. Major changes in steel employment have resulted from changes in the demand for steel — not from technological change . . .

2. Job openings resulting from normal employee turnover exceed any possible losses from technological change . . .

3. Most technological change takes the form of modifications to existing facilities or replacement of existing facilities by new ones.

4. Existing seniority arrangements tend to protect the longer-service worker against loss of his job where the operation is not entirely eliminated.

5. Most employees who lose their jobs are protected against a total loss of income through state and supplemental unemployment benefits, severance pay or pensions, all paid by the employing company.

6. Except in periods of recession, it is frequently possible to assign displaced workers to other jobs in the same locality. While that may result in a reduction in earnings at the time, it is also quite likely to put workers into jobs from which they can advance as they gain experience.

7. The advance of technology in steel, insofar as it has affected employment, has been somewhat slower during the postwar period than it has in other industries. This is shown by the fact that output per manhour in steel has increased less rapidly than output per manhour in the entire private economy or in manufacturing.

8. Changes in the composition of the population over the next five or ten years portend a considerable increase in demand for housing and consumer durables, and in public and private capital spending. Any appreciable increase in steel demand tends to eliminate the adverse effects of technological displacement.

9. It is sometimes overlooked that the manhours displaced as the immediate result of technological change exaggerate the impact of such change, since such manhours are in part offset by the manhours required to build, service and replace the new equipment. Additional manhours may also be required for scheduling, supervising and otherwise insuring the most efficient utilization of such equipment.[23]

It appears that the steel mills have done their best to make a case for automation. Some of the arguments may appear theoretical in the face of the jobless individual or the man receiving unemployment compensation. Yet, in all fairness, the steel industry must have technological progress for survival. Dislocations from technological change might be managed if it were not for the fact that they are in phase with unemployment, compounded by cyclical influences and foreign competition.

Joint Planning With Management Desirable The union advocates a thirty-two-hour week as a possible answer to changing technology. It claims that a thirty-two-hour week would have created
45,300 more jobs in 1958; 65,400 more jobs in 1959; and 56,600 more
jobs in 1960. The shorter workweek would have put back to work
the majority of the unemployed steelworkers.[24]

The union states that certain steps proposed by it in the 1959
negotiations would have been helpful in meeting the problems caused
by technological change. These steps include:

1. Careful advance planning and advance notification by management to unions and workers should be the universally accepted rule
concerning all innovations in machinery, methods of production, and
other adjustments that involve displacement or transfer of workers.
Details of the adjustments required should be negotiated.

2. Transfer rights of employees to new jobs and to other plants
should be guaranteed on a preferential basis before new hirings are made.
Too often a single, new plant with enlarged capacity results in the shift
of production from older, less efficient plants, and complicates the
seniority status and transfer rights of laid-off employees. Rapid changes
in technology bring about such problems. Safeguards are required
against the loss of jobs and job rights under these circumstances.

3. Retraining programs are needed to qualify employees for new
jobs, along with transfer rights. Retraining and transfer costs should
not be at the employee's expense, or even primarily at the Government's
expense, but should rather be included in the investment costs of new
or modernized facilities. Workers who are transferred to new jobs should
be guaranteed their former earnings.

4. Seniority systems must insure maximum security for long-service
employees when technological change produces layoffs. This is particularly important in the Steel Industry where the average length of service
is high. Hardships of untold proportions occur among permanently
laid-off Steelworkers, because age often prohibits a fair change for
re-employment elsewhere. Revision of the basic seniority guides of
our Steel agreements is urgently needed.

5. Negotiated fringe benefits must be re-evaluated to take account
of the seriousness of unemployment in the Steel Industry. For example,
many laid-off workers have suffered drastic reductions in SUB when
such benefits are most needed; that is, when all other sources of funds
are no longer available to them. The objectives of SUB benefits are
negated when they no longer provide the intended protection to unemployed workers. Clearly, more money must be put into our SUB pro-

grams. Earlier normal retirement on adequate pensions is clearly required.

6. Substantial improvements in wages and fringe benefits are needed to assure workers and their families a fair share of the gains of advancing technology.

7. And, a negotiated reduction in the workweek or in annual hours of work of each employee without loss in pay must be made in order to assure full employment and the maintenance of purchasing power in an economy whose productive efficiency is so rapidly increasing. Only thus can we preserve employment opportunity in Steel.[25]

Sensitive Steel Negotiations in 1962 Desiring to avoid repetition of the steel crisis of 1958–1959, unions, management, and Government approached the steel labor issues in 1962 with sensitive and sensible treatment. The White House was interested, of course, in a noninflationary settlement, one that would hold the line on wage gains at the same time that the companies would hold the line on prices.

One of the major labor issues was more job protection and job security to offset the progress of automation in the steel industry. Management appeared willing to give some wage increases, but indicated early in the sessions that the offer should not exceed labor's contribution to increased productivity. With automation, this share is very difficult to identify. It was suggested early in the bargaining that the steel companies could give labor an annual wage increase of 2 to 3 percent without raising prices. This was the theory coming from the dicta of the President's Council of Economic Advisors early in 1962.

The final 1962 steel industry settlements were generally in line with the Administration's goal of "noninflationary" settlements.

Neither the company nor the workers had the same appetite for a strike in early 1962 as in 1959. Although the companies moved rapidly early in the year to build inventories in order to forestall the economic effects of a possible strike, nevertheless the workers went cheerfully to work, for they needed the income.

Despite early national planning by the Steelworkers president, David J. McDonald, a great deal of dissatisfaction was evident among the locals, resulting from the fact that since 1959 the companies had introduced an improved industrial technology accompanied by downward manpower adjustments. This problem requires a national review of job protection and work rules. McDonald's original demands included a thirty-two-hour week at the forty-hour pay. This demand was obviously impossible in view of the costs of production in United States mills compared with our vigorous foreign competitors.

Efficiency Reduces Need for Employees Despite the building up of inventories in late 1961 and early 1962, the rapid gains in steel-making efficiency made it unlikely that employment in the steel mills would climb back to prerecession levels. The Steelworkers claimed the work force had declined from 540,000 in 1950 to 462,000 in 1960. The union said that, in 1959, 418,000 employees turned out as much steel as 545,000 in 1949, and 65 percent more steel than 513,000 workers did in 1937.[26]

The Lukens Steel Company was quoted as saying that "it can now turn out more steel with the same number of workers,"[27] as a result of three new developments: (1) new system of planned preventive maintenance of furnaces, which allows a reduction in the number of workers in repair crews; (2) use of forced-draft smokestacks on furnaces; and (3) introduction of "lances" to blow oxygen into open-hearth furnaces and cut down the time needed to refine a batch of molten iron into steel.

Need for Lower Production Costs to Meet Foreign Competition Lower production costs and not high tariffs are the answer to increasing competition from steel imports,[28] according to Roger M. Blough, chairman of the U. S. Steel Corporation. Blough indicated that the United States imports one and one-half tons of steel for every ton it exports, whereas the ratio of imports to exports was one to three or five. He foresaw keener competition in the future from nations in the European Common Market.* He pointed out that steel in the United States is produced at a daily labor cost of $32, as compared to $10 in Europe. Hence United States steel firms must be more efficient or pass out of existence.

Meanwhile, the unions, concerned with falling employment in the face of rising production due to automation and improved manufacturing techniques, have been motivated into asking for a thirty-two-hour week in the early days of the 1962 negotiations:

> "We say," Blough declared, "we are talking about a reduced work-week as a share-the-work plan. When pinned down, we admit we are talking about more pay for less work; or putting it in another way —

*This appraisal now appears more likely in view of the Trade Expansion Act, enacted into law in 1962.

more cost for the same work. And what we are really talking about is more unemployment because buyers are already reluctant to buy such products as steel, aluminum and machinery at the prices which must be charged for these products to cover costs."

Blough pointed out that foreign companies are constantly improving their plants and equipment — the implication is that automation in American plants must go on for the welfare of the nation.

Longshore Industry

Mechanization and Modernization Fund Agreement The Pacific Coast Longshoremen in 1960 took the position that they might as well profit by automation rather than obstruct it. In an agreement with the Steamship and Stevedoring Employers on the West Coast, which was signed October 18, 1960, and which will not expire until July 1, 1966, the union recognized that the maritime industry was on the threshold of a major technological revolution.

The agreement permitted the union to share in the benefits and savings resulting from new methods, from new machinery, and from the lifting of restrictions and of work rules, which new machines had made obsolete. One and one-half million dollars was paid by employers into a mechanization fund. This fund is to put a floor under earnings, to permit retirement as early as age 62, and to provide a lump-sum retirement payment to men who do not retire before age 65, as well as providing for graduated death benefits. All benefits apply only to the basic work force; that is, men who are fully registered.

The cost savings resulting from the use of automated machinery will finance early retirement and take care of the vesting of benefits. This is the first time that any organized labor group has been guaranteed against onerous physical labor. In effect, what the agreement says is: If more or faster production is to be obtained, it shall be by means of more men or machines or of more efficient utilization of men and machines.

The language of the document is precise on this point.

> Speedup shall be understood to refer to an onerous workload on the individual worker. It shall not be construed to refer to increased production resulting from more efficient utilization and organization of the work force, introduction of labor saving devices or removal of work restrictions.

Changes in Methods   Under the agreement the employer will be under no obligation to perform work with an unnecessary number of men — "witnesses," as they are sometimes called. The men necessary to any longshore operation will be based on a determination to be made in accordance with the agreement. Necessary men are all the men required to do the job. Whereas the old contract required that men be on hand at all times, even if there was no work to be performed by them at the moment, the new agreement sets forth rules under which the necessary number of men can be determined.

Past practices requiring the unnecessary handling of cargo — practices resulting in overstandard loads being "skimmed" or in cargo being removed from pallet boards and placed on the skin of the dock while in transit to or from the ship's hold — are now eliminated. These jobs are thus eliminated from the industry — the employer may now bring machinery into the holds of the vessels.

Recapitulation of Gains   Because the employers set up a $1,500,000 automation fund, certain gains were achieved by the longshoremen in the Pacific Coast contract. These are as follows:

(1) Guarantee against layoff; (2) Guaranteed weekly minimum wage of 35 hours ($98.70 at present hourly rate); (3) Contractual provisions defining and prohibiting speed-up; (4) Rigid enforcement of safety rules; (5) Voluntary early retirement at age 62, at $220 a month, with transfer to regular pension plan at age 65; (6) In the event of mandatory retirement before age 65, a pension benefit of $320 a month paid up to age 65, after which the pensioner transfers to regular pension plan; (7) Full prepaid, noncontributory medical coverage for the individual and dependents during early as well as regular retirement; (8) Individuals who do not retire early accumulate vested rights and early retirement benefits amounting to $7920 at age 65 and with 25 years service. (Full benefit is payable upon normal retirement.)

Automation   In the longshore industry, where ships have been loaded and unloaded by the same method for years, a new development has emerged, known as "containerization." This is the principle whereby products to be transported in ships are loaded in large, fully enclosed containers at the factory or warehouse and moved by cranes to the dock and into the vessel. They are then unloaded by the same method without the use of manual labor. Adoption of this method eliminates the dockside loading and unloading and reduces costs, a factor that has made American ports noncompetitive with the rest of the maritime world. Up to 1960 only a small amount of the traffic has been "containerized," because of union opposition and the fact that ships for the most part have not been modernized sufficiently to use this method.

Displacement Fears The employers were most anxious to get the 1960 agreement because the West Coast longshoremen were very much against reducing the size of the regular work force. The agreement went far in principle, but not far enough in effect. Principally, the union agreed in this contract to eliminate casual workers and those who leave the work force. But in the main it kept the basic group at work, regardless of methods improvements.

In effect, the West Coast agreement provides a "permanent bonus to employees to refrain from opposing technological progress."[29] Involved in this provision is what amounts to a dismissal compensation concept, by providing payments for employees to seek work elsewhere.

The fund could have bad effects in practice. The maintenance of the existing labor force, except for attrition, will undoubtedly raise the average age of the employees, thus reducing efficiency, particularly in an industry requiring so much physical effort. In addition, overmanning will possibly continue. The automation bonus may further accentuate the high hourly earnings possible for casual workers in stevedoring. When longshoremen are partially unemployed, the bonus may bring their total earnings to an amount equal to a regular wage. This situation may restrict mobility of these workers and keep them tied to longshoring for even a longer period than before the automation fund.

Other Trade Union Attitudes Toward Automation

Craft Unions Versus Industrial Unions Sol Barkin, research director of the Textile Workers Union, made an important point at an Industrial Research Association meeting in 1951. He indicated his belief that craft unions were more interested in maintaining job control over a specific technology than were industrial unions. He pointed out that industrial unions have already accommodated workers to industrial change, secured a more satisfactory distribution of benefits of change, and have even stimulated change itself.

European Unions The attitude of European unions toward automation is shown by the conclusions reached at an international seminar of trade unions held in London in 1956. A central clearinghouse was set up, following decisions reached at this conference. The purpose was to collate information on the development of automation. The delegates had agreed that information and statistics on the subject of automation were very inadequate. It was determined that European unions should be in a position to assess trends. They accepted the fact that automation would cause displacement, or "redundancy," and concluded that society can only develop by a changing labor force, industry by industry.[30]

The conferees also agreed that the period of notice to workers about to be discharged should be extended and that more emphasis should be given to payment of unemployment compensation. There was some support for a form of guaranteed annual wage. Other recommendations set forth at the convention were: improvement and extension of schemes for vocational training to fit the workers for new roles in industry; early consultation with employees and unions about coming changes. It was also agreed that government should be responsible for providing full employment; and that trade unions must retain full right of negotiation on changes and of sharing in the benefits of automation. The delegates recognized that unions must give special attention to equipping themselves for their new responsibilities.

Conclusion

It has been noted that technological advance has certain clear implications for management and for labor, and that each party to the industrial economy in the United States has its own responsibilities and problems. Over a very wide area, however, the two groups must cooperate if change is to be made in an orderly and efficient manner and with a minimum of hardship. Such cooperation is imperative, moreover, if *minimum* government intervention is desired.

Unions are particularly anxious to assure serious joint consultation. Labor leaders regard such consultation as an essential feature of industrial policy, and in most cases, consider it as a prerequisite of union cooperation in technological improvement and change. No special machinery is needed for advance consultation. Only the absence of it will impel the union leaders to require formal machinery in the collective agreement.

Although joint consultation is desirable in principle, in practice, both sides show some resistance to it. Quite a few employers believe that advance consultation will deprive them of managerial prerogative and management initiative. A number of union leaders hesitate to participate in a meeting or joint consultation, when the subject to be discussed is likely to involve unpleasant consequences for some of their members. Some union leaders hesitate to dictate to management, and would rather let problems take their natural course.

Joint consultation is simply one means to the end of developing a full understanding of the nature of the problems. To quote from the report of the Director-General of the Fortieth Session of the International Labor Conference at Geneva in 1957:

> Solutions cannot be found as long as problems remain unidentified. It has already been noted that automation and other developments are having far-reaching effects on management and trade union policy in all the main areas of collective bargaining: job evaluation and wage determination, hours of work and holidays, safety, seniority and status, training, welfare and human relations. In each of these areas, labor-management cooperation is needed to make possible the rethinking of policy and practice which is required if industrial relations is to be effective and smooth.[31]

References

1. Russell Allen, "Educational Implications," *Labor's Public Responsibility*, p. 46. Symposium sponsored by the National Institute of Labor Education, Madison, Wis., 1960.
2. See papers by Neil Chamberlain, William Haber, Philip Taft, and Merton Stoltz on "Structural Unemployment," before the Joint Economic Committee (October 2, 1959).
3. Walter P. Reuther, *The Impact of Automation*, Detriot, UAW-CIO Solidarity House Publication, December 1955.
4. *Wall Street Journal*, January 19, 1962, p. 1.
5. *Ibid.*, p. 19.
6. *Ibid.*
7. *Ibid.*
8. "Automation: Report of the Armour Committee," Bureau of National Affairs, no. 419, June 23, 1961, 16:621, p. C-15.
9. Bureau of National Affairs, *op. cit.*, p. C-17.
10. *Ibid.*, p. C-17.
11. *Automation — Modern Sorcerer's Apprentice or Passport to Prosperity*, Special Report from ILO UNESCO Courier, November 1959, pp. 1–7; distributed by IUE Education Department.

12. *Ibid.*
13. James B. Carey, Paul Abelson Lectures, City College of New York, May 1, 1961, p. 2.
14. *Ibid.*, p. 4.
15. James B. Carey, testimony before Subcommittee on Unemployment, U. S. House of Representatives. Committee on Education and Labor, March 22, 1961, page 10 of reprint.
16. Pamphlet no. PR-129, United Steelworkers of America, Pittsburgh, 1961, pp. 1–15.
17. *Ibid.*, p. 1.
18. Hans Matthofer, "A Forecast of Technological Change in the Steel Industry," Trade Union Information no. 28, 1960.
19. *Ibid.*
20. *Business Week*, November 5, 1960.
21. *Ibid.*
22. Pamphlet No. PR-129, United Steelworkers of America, *op. cit.*, p. 7.
23. *"The Competitive Challenge to Steel,"* New York: The American Iron and Steel Institute, December 1961, p. 51.
24. Pamphlet no. PR-129 United Steelworkers of America, Pittsburgh, *op. cit.*, p. 12.
25. *Ibid.*, p. 14.
26. *Wall Street Journal*, December 27, 1961.
27. *Ibid.*, December 19, 1961, p. 1.
28. *Ibid.*, January 14, 1962, p. 11.
29. G. F. Bloom and H. R. Northrup, *Economics of Labor Relations* (Homewood, Illinois: Irwin, 1961), p. 259.
30. *Trade Unions and Productivity*, published by the British T.U.C., Smith Square, London, SW 1, 1950.
31. Report of the Director-General, "Part I: Automation and Other Technological Developments," International Labor Conference, Fortieth Session, Geneva, 1957; printed by the International Labor Office, 1957, Report I (Part I), p. 95.

▶ ▶ ▶ ▶ **11**

Influence of
Automation on Job Evaluation
and Skill Requirements

Automation and other technological developments are exerting considerable influence on the level and structure of wages and on conditions of work in general. They are raising a number of problems and forcing reconsideration of many traditional industrial practices.

This chapter is concerned primarily with the findings of a number of job-evaluation experts with unusual points of view, not always in agreement with one another, as to whether or not automation results in upgrading or "de-skilling." Also covered will be the experiences in certain industries that have had to adjust their classification systems away from conventional problems to automated problems. Prominent in the discussions will be the union's point of view on problems of job evaluation and wages. The following chapter covers the specific problems of wage administration in a number of industries which have had to change from the operator's controlled pace under the traditional incentive system to other means or measures of payment.

Wages have to be determined, of course, in relation to the work done. The changes occurring in the occupational and industrial world have to be recognized in any systems evolved for evaluating and classifying jobs for purposes of wage determination. For example, in 1955 the term "automation tender" began to creep in the occupational vocabulary. At Ford's Cleveland plant this new classification was said (in 1957) to cover about one third of the workers in that bargaining unit. In the breadmaking industry, where 7,000 to 10,000 loaves are produced within an hour with little human labor, the Bakery and Confectionery Workers Union has contracts classifying bakers as "electronics engineers."[1]

194

Both management and labor will have to consider the new situation. Existing job classification schemes cannot simply be extended to apply to automated and semiautomated jobs. Job reclassification is an important area for Government study and particularly for labor-management cooperation. Management ought to take the initiative and not let the union think the firm "is using job evaluation as an even more dangerous management technique than it already is."[2]

Job Evaluation Evolved Under Manual Production

Trade union people, both in factory and office automation, will have to pay close attention to the changing content of established job descriptions as they are applied under the new technology. Under many collective bargaining agreements, job descriptions are written and then evaluated according to varied factors of work required from the employee. These are the major ingredients of job description: physical effort, mental effort, training and experience, responsibility for machinery, nervous tension, dirt and noise, and responsibility for the safety of others. These and many other factors are assigned unit values generally in points, which are added to determine the worker's hourly wage rate.

The traditional job evaluation system has grown up under the old-fashioned manual system of production. Under automation there will be radical changes in job content, so that factors previously having high ratings and factors having low ratings may decrease or increase, respectively, under the new work patterns.

Unions have a new concept of "preventive maintenance." The old concept that production ensues only by the hardest physical effort and mental application is giving way to the one that the worker may be most profitable to his employer when he is doing nothing. In the latter concept the workers attending the machines are responsible for seeing that they do not stop working. This is, indeed, a new concept of preventive maintenance.

Traditional Job Evaluation Systems Disappearing

James B. Carey, president of the International Union of Electrical, Radio and Machine Workers, sees little hope for maintaining the present systems of job evaluation during this new period of changing technology. Says Carey:

One of the intricate collective bargaining questions, the dimensions of which are just beginning to appear, is the change which automation will make in the wage rates as they are determined by established job evaluation systems. Over the last couple of decades, a multitude of job titles and job descriptions have been worked out, with a system of factors carrying unit values, the total of which make the wage rates.

These traditional job descriptions will be substantially altered. Things like physical effort, the handling of raw materials and unpleasant surroundings will — under the new technology — become less significant, while such elements as mental skill, mental effort and responsibility for operations will become more significant. Does this merely mean reevaluation of tens of thousands of jobs? Yes it does and it means much more.[3]

Changing Job Content

One of the major problems of management under automation will be that of enabling the worker to broaden his horizons and to get away from the traditional job content of the conventional skilled-trade classifications. Drucker says:

> The worker under Automation will no longer do the repetitive routine chores of machine feeding and materials handling. Instead, he will build, maintain and control machines that do repetitive routine work. To do this, he must be able to do many operations, must have the largest rather than the smallest content to his job, must be able to coordinate.
>
> This, as the IBM story shows, does not mean that he must be again a manually skilled worker as the worker of yore. On the contrary, every one of the operations should be analyzed by means of Scientific Management to a point where they can be done by unskilled people. But the operations must be integrated into a job — otherwise the work needed under Automation cannot be done. In the new technology we have no choice but to say *cat*. We must learn how to put together — now that Scientific Management has taught us how to pull apart.[4]

A perfect illustration of what Drucker means is the job of the telephone maintenance man in the new automatic-dialing exchange. This man is no longer the skilled mechanic. Everything he does is by a "manual," in which his job has been reduced to simple elements, which can be mastered in a relatively short time. The "book" is more important than the manual skill acquired throughout the years. The job, however, does have a variety of operations requiring a good deal of thought and judgment and necessitating muscular and mental coordination.

Union Point of View

Ted Silvey, one of the most articulate spokesmen on automation, who is employed by the AFL-CIO headquarters, has this to say about the influence of automation on changing job classifications:

> I think job descriptions and job classifications will undergo change. I just copied a list from the Steelworkers contract. There are eight different items in the job description and twelve different items in the job classification. As you know, we set up these job classifications in order to rate or value jobs and if each one of these classifications is worth so many points, the total determined the rate of the job.[5]

At this point Silvey, without going too much into the technique of job evaluation, voices the uncertainties of the unions about the future of traditional ratings.

> According to our old system, we rated some of these things high, but they are soon going to be rated low. We have rated some of these things low that are soon going to be rated high. All of these contents of job classifications are going to have to be re-rated under the new technology.[6]

He then goes on to explain some compensable factors under the old and the new ways of doing things: pre-employment training; employment training and experience; mental skill; manual skill; responsibility for materials, for tools and equipment, for operations, for safety of others; both physical and mental effort; surroundings; and work hazards — a fairly complete list. Silvey apparently has been exposed to most of the common plans. He then goes on in a humorous way to explain the topsy-turvy of it all:

> There are going to be lots of changes. Surroundings are going to be more pleasant. A worker gets a rate value of pay for a dirty, noisy, filthy job. So many points were added because of the inconvenience of noise and dirt. Physical effort — well, it's not going to be so hard. Mental effort is going to be tremendously greater. Responsibility for safety — not so much because there are going to be built-in safety devices. Responsibility for tools and equipment in operation — very much increased! See how these values are going to have to change in the job description? That is the only point I want to make there.[7]

UAW and "Creeping Job Changes"

A great deal of animosity in the old automobile contract negotiations resulted from the use of arbitrators in job classification disputes. According to Silvey, the United Automobile Workers insist on barring umpires and arbitrators in classification disputes in the current agreements, because of the developments in the newly automated plants. Silvey makes the point that "new" ideas about wage and job classification structure will be needed for the "future" factory. The unions are now saying: "Umpires will have nothing to do with this, we will settle this by collective bargaining."[8]

The UAW won the point that, although an umpire had previously ruled that "creeping" changes do not make jobs different enough to call them new jobs, in the new UAW contracts there be a recognition of the changed work done by press operators on the major lines and by workers in other classifications such as die setters, merry-go-round welders, and machine welders. According to Silvey, the union now says:

> We won't let you umpires and arbitrators get into the act and say what the jobs are. You have already decided that creeping changes are not new jobs. . . . Well, it depends on how long they creep . . . how far the changes go![9]

Acceptable Definition of "Job Content" Change

Semantics plays a great part in the complexities of job evaluation and wage administration in the newly automated department or factory. "Upgrading" may not be a result of acquiring greater skill or responsibility — it may be a result of changing the scope of an operator's duties. For example, if an operator gives less attention to a particular machine, he may be given several machines to supervise. He, therefore, has a change in "responsibility," because of the possibility of greater monetary loss if the "system" he is now watching should be damaged.

If the worker becomes responsible for more machines, he may have to learn some additional technical knowledge, approximately on the same level as that he possessed on the former conventional job. For example:

> A milling-machine operator might be required to master a broaching machine and a drilling-tapping machine if they are integrated by automation in his work station. While these skills might not be more difficult

in degree, they definitely are additional requirements. They may or may not call for additional training.[10]

In some of the newly introduced automated jobs, individuals formerly responsible for a portion of the production line now often become responsible for setup work or insepction.

Bright recounts his experiences:

> I encountered an instance in which a maintenance man was "manning" an automated line. On another line where pistons were milled in weight automatically, the "operator" combined the remaining conventional operator duties with those of a setup man. He put the system into operation, verified performance and made adjustments. He had to have a knowledge of machinery distinctly above that of machine operator.... Clearly, an upgrading of the job has resulted.[11]

Skill in Maintenance Force

It is popularly assumed that maintenance will increase substantially under automation. It is also assumed that all maintenance workers will require increased skill, although this assumption has not been borne out by the facts. There has been no evidence that carpenters, welders, tinsmiths, and pipe fitters require increased skill as a result of automation. The introduction of control circuitry, however, does require that hydraulic and pneumatic repairmen receive better training.

The startling fact is that, under automation, the electrician is greatly in need of retraining. Electronic circuitry is a brand-new area, requiring training in the theory and practice of electronics. The ordinary electrician from the conventional plant would be as lost in electronics as a household electrician who tried to repair a radarscope. It has been concluded that, to upgrade the electrician to an "electronics circuitry man," about two thousand hours of retraining are required, in addition to the regular journeyman electrical training program of three years.

Each electrician does not need to be upgraded. In one study it was found that of seven hundred men on maintenance, approximately eighty were electricians, and the plant engineer estimated that only three or four needed the electronic training per shift. This meant that about 10 percent of the electricians needed the required skills, which amounted in absolute number to only 1 percent of the maintenance work force.

Other studies made on the maintenance problem showed that it was not always necessary to increase the maintenance force because of automation. If automation increases production to a point where less equipment is necessary, then gross maintenance payroll is decreased. When automation eliminates certain pieces of equipment necessary under the conventional system, then maintenance costs are reduced. In the intermediate stages, however, as production workers are dropped, maintenance workers are often added; hence, although there are about the same number of total employees, production is substantially increased.

Automated Job Descriptions in Electronics Industry

The reader may not be familiar with the fact that the electronics industry has already faced to some degree the issue of rewriting job descriptions for newly automated jobs. Many industries cling to traditional classifications, and misunderstandings with unions continue because the facts at issue are not being faced. A Congressional Committee in 1955 studied this problem and reported on some of the newer job descriptions in the electronics industry, which uses printed circuit and automatic assembly machines.

1. *Automation Machine Operator*

Operates radio or television automation machines to insert and fasten production parts on circuit boards. Requisitions and expedites production parts to maintain production schedules. Receives production orders for required number of circuit boards and allocates machine time to produce required units. Tabulates production records and arranges for lot shipment to designated production areas or locations. Requests machine adjustments to correct substandard work.

2. *Automation Assembler*

Loads prepackaged or bulk-packed supply of production parts into automatic feed channels of radio and television automation machines. Checks completed circuit boards for missing or loose parts and makes insertions or repairs as necessary. Matches color codes, reads production part numbers, and uses simple hand tools.

3. *Automation Machine Tender*

Operates radio or television automation machines to insert and fasten tube sockets, resistors, jumper wires, and condensers on circuit boards. Clears operating mechanisms, removes jammed part, and restarts machine, making simple adjustments as required. Re-threads machine with jumper wire. Uses simple hand tools.

4. *Stager*

Checks prepared plates for bubbles, blisters, and unexposed areas prior to etching operation. Touches up imperfections, using paint and brush. Scrapes excessive printing as necessary.

5. *Sprayer*

Sets up and operates a spray gun to spray lacquer on prepared surfaces with commercial type finish. Cleans and adjusts spray gun. Assists in other production operations as required.

6. *Machine Operator — Printed Circuits*

Operates a variety of short cycle machines to prepare, expose, and etch production parts for predesignated lengths of time. Scrubs, sensitizes, and etches parts with solutions of prepared strengths. Assists in other printed circuit operations as required.[12]

Effects of Mechanization on Skill Requirements

Originally it was thought that certain jobs in the automated plant would require increased skill and knowledge. The job of "setup man" worried management several years ago. Today, new and highly automatic machines are coming out in which the setup is performed by pressing a button. The "Milwaukee Multimatic" is an illustration of this development. When this mechanization takes place, the skill requirement is further reduced.

Programming appeared to be an insurmountable difficulty in terms of retraining and upgrading present employees. Recently MIT and Boeing Aircraft each developed an English-like language (APT and WALDO) for blueprint translation into computers. Numerical control tapes can now be prepared by the average draftsman through his own computer instructions. Here again the anticipated educational and training requirement is disappearing. The maintenance task itself is being simplified and mechanized.

One study by I. Hoos confirms the fact that the work force supporting the computer is being affected by a reduction in skill requirements and amount of training anticipated five years ago.[13]

Will Automation Upgrade the Labor Force?

It has been suggested that automation will result in a massive upgrading of the labor force. Killingsworth[14] has doubts about this. In testimony before Congress in 1960, he indicated that although job requirements have increased in some instances, the increase has usually been so slight that short in-plant training programs have met the need adequately.

The need for certain types of skilled maintenance workers has increased in some automated plants, though not all. It is true that completely unskilled jobs usually decline considerably when a plant or office is automated. But, generally speaking, the jobs that remain do not seem to have a markedly higher skill content. In fact, we have made so much progress in developing "reliable complexity," as Vannevar Bush terms it, that skill content is actually reduced in a surprisingly large number of cases.[15]

Personnel analysts are beginning to discover more about the effects of automation on job change, but admit that they know next to nothing about the fates of the displaced workers. Perhaps many of these semiskilled factory workers are winding up in some lower skilled service jobs. Government help is required to obtain this information before the entire picture of automation and its effects can be put together.

Perhaps jobs which will best resist automation are those not worth automating. In any event the much-talked-about shortage of engineers may be partially wiped out by the advent of the computer. Numerical control may rapidly eliminate the need for the much-desired skills of today's craftsmen. College graduates in business administration may find that their jobs have been taken over by the decision-making machines.

Indeed, [says Dr. Killingsworth] one of the students of automation is willing to assume that in ten years we will have the technical capacity of building machines to perform any productive function that is performed by men today. Economic feasibility will retard the realization of this technical capability. But it would be a great mistake to think that it is only the low-skilled jobs that can be mechanized.[16]

Does Automation Make the Operator's Job Easier?

Responsible persons in both union and management believe that the average worker is unemployable in an automated plant. Studies in a number of cities and the attention of the Federal Government are directed to possible retraining programs so as to avoid long-run unemployment for many workers "displaced" on the job by virtue of a boost in the skill requirements.

Bright took issue with this point of view as a result of a study he made in thirteen plants. He concluded that "to the extent that employment opportunities are available operators' jobs often are easier and more quickly mastered in the automated plant and the impact on the quantity and quality of maintenance skills required *may* be much less than expected."[17]

In this study Bright found that a prime management error in several plants was an unwarranted assumption that higher skills were required on certain operating jobs than was actually required.

It is true that in certain situations knowledge, responsibility, education, and mental effort (old job evaluation "friends") actually do increase in demand under automation, but Bright found that in most instances this was *not* true.

> ... analysis of many machines has preponderantly demonstrated that the higher levels of mechanization gradually or rapidly reduce the contribution of the operator.[18]

"Hump in Skill Requirements"

Bright finds that the impact of higher levels of mechanization leads to what he terms the "hump in skill requirements."[19] Although the job and the worker's contribution embrace more than just "skill," nevertheless, skill is one of the most important factors in operator job analysis. Bright uses "skill" as meaning a combination of the necessary experience, dexterity, and requisite technical knowledge. In his analyses Bright found the following levels:

1. The substitution of mechanical power for manual effort took some of the burden off the worker.

2. As degrees of fixed control resulted in desired machine action, Bright found the workers less and less guiding the tool.

3. When the machine developed to the point where measurement was added to the machine, the operator discovered that much of the control-decision information was obtained for him by the machine.

4. When the machine finally leaves the conventional stages and becomes almost fully automated, Bright sees the following division of work as between machine and operator:

> As the machine is given the higher levels of automaticity, more and more of the decision-making and appropriate follow-up such as the selection of the necessary production-action, control of the production-action and correction of performance is done by the machine. The more superbly automatic the machine, the less the operator has to do.

INITIATING CONTROL SOURCE	TYPE OF MACHINE RESPONSE	POWER SOURCE	LEVEL NUMBER	LEVEL OF MECHANIZATION
FROM A VARIABLE IN THE ENVIRONMENT	RESPONDS WITH ACTION — MODIFIES OWN ACTION OVER A WIDE RANGE OF VARIATION	MECHANICAL (NONMANUAL)	17	ANTICIPATES ACTION REQUIRED AND ADJUSTS TO PROVIDE IT.
			16	CORRECTS PERFORMANCE WHILE OPERATING.
			15	CORRECTS PERFORMANCE AFTER OPERATING.
	SELECTS FROM A LIMITED RANGE OF POSSIBLE PREFIXED ACTIONS		14	IDENTIFIES AND SELECTS APPROPRIATE SET OF ACTIONS.
			13	SEGREGATES OR REJECTS ACCORDING TO MEASUREMENT.
			12	CHANGES SPEED, POSITION, DIRECTION ACCORDING TO MEASUREMENT SIGNAL.
	RESPONDS WITH SIGNAL		11	RECORDS PERFORMANCE.
			10	SIGNALS PRESELECTED VALUES OF MEASUREMENT (INCLUDES ERROR DETECTION).
			9	MEASURES CHARACTERISTIC OF WORK.
FROM A CONTROL MECHANISM THAT DIRECTS A PREDETERMINED PATTERN OF ACTION	FIXED WITHIN THE MACHINE		8	ACTUATED BY INTRODUCTION OF WORK PIECE OR MATERIAL.
			7	POWER TOOL, SYSTEM, REMOTE CONTROLLED.
			6	POWER TOOL, PROGRAM CONTROL (SEQUENCE OF FIXED FUNCTIONS).
			5	POWER TOOL FIXED CYCLE (SINGLE FUNCTION).
FROM MAN	VARIABLE		4	POWER TOOL, HAND CONTROL.
			3	POWERED HAND TOOL.
		MANUAL	2	HAND TOOL.
			1	HAND.

FIGURE 1.[22] LEVELS OF MECHANIZATION AND THEIR RELATIONSHIP TO POWER AND CONTROL SOURCES.

Courtesy of James R. Bright and *Harvard Business Review*.

By its very definition, the truly automatic machine needs no human assistance for its normal functioning. Patrolling becomes the main human contribution. The operator, if he is still there, becomes a sort of watchman, a monitor. We might call him the liaison man between the machine and operating management.

Thus, the progressive effect of automation is first to relieve the operator of manual effort and then to relieve him of the need to apply continuous mental effort. At times the mental effort is increased, because of the alertness and overall responsibility required. Yet the evolution of machinery shows that eventually safety devices and various recording and signalling systems are added to reduce or eliminate this demand.[20]

Levels of Mechanization

Figure 1* provides the details of the levels of mechanization and the character of power and control in machinery. It will be observed that levels 1 and 2 are manual levels; levels 3 and 4 introduce the power hand-tool and hand-control. Levels 5–8 are mechanically controlled, starting with a fixed-cycle power tool with a single function.

The tools then have a sequence of fixed functions through program control, next through remote control, and in level 8 are actuated by the introduction of a work piece or material. In levels 5–8 the control mechanism directs a predetermined pattern of action and is fixed within the machine.

Bright obviously finds automation reducing the demand for skill and knowledge *on the part of the operator* after reaching level 5 — because the automated equipment absorbs more and more of the elements in the task.

In levels 9–11 the machine is stimulated by a variable in the environment and responds with a signal. Level 9 measures the characteristic of work; level 10 signals preselected values of measurement, including error detection; performance is recorded in level 11.

In levels 12–17 the machinery responds with action selected from a limited range of possible prefixed actions in levels 12–14, also from a variable in the environment. Level 12 changes speed, position, and direction according to measurement signal; level 13 segregates or

*Several illustrations in this chapter have been drawn from the Bright studies appearing in the *Harvard Business Review* and are a result of the excellent work done in this area by Professor Bright and the Harvard Graduate School of Business Administration.

rejects according to measurement; level 14 identifies and selects appropriate sets of actions.

Levels 15–17 respond with action and modify their own actions over a wide range of variations. Level 15, in this sector, corrects performance after operating; level 16 corrects performance while operating; level 17 anticipates the action required and adjusts to provide it.

An examination of Figure 1 would lead the observer to conclude, with Bright, that:

> Automation does not tend to make people unemployable because they lack skill and specialized education. On the contrary, many (and perhaps most) *operator* jobs can be mastered more quickly with less job experience, special skill and education as mechanization increases past level 4 and provides increasing degrees of automaticity.[21]

Job Evaluation Inferences

What inferences with respect to job evaluation problems can be drawn from the Bright studies? Certainly all unions would not graciously accept *all* Bright's findings. Labor leaders would order their own analyses so as to protect the membership. Labor can always learn from management, and vice versa. There are many tricks to job evaluation.

In a given situation, one must look for those factors which may increase skill requirements. More and more responsibility may be assumed over the production sequence (that is, a number of different kinds of machines); or there may be an assumption of responsibility for higher caliber functions, such as setup and inspection; or new jobs may develop, such as preparing or setting up tapes for programming.

Figure 2 suggests the changing contribution required of the operator as a result of advances in the level of mechanization as defined in Figure 1. Figure 2 deals with the traditionally accepted factors in job analysis and job evaluation, which result in job classification and wage administration. The higher the degrees of factors involved, the higher the hourly pay.

Skill   *Skill (knowledge of the art).* Under the Bright analysis, skill requirements are found to increase through levels 1–8 (the hand controlled and mechanically controlled levels). Here, skill, defined as "knowledge of the art," begins to decrease somewhere between levels 9–11, where "variable control — signal response" is introduced.

Worker Contribution* or Sacrifice Traditionally Receiving Compensation	Mechanization Levels			
	1–4 (Hand Controlled)	5–8 (Mechanically Controlled)	9–11 (Variable Control, Signal Response)	12–17 (Variable Control, Action Response)
Skill (Knowledge of art)	Increasing	Increasing	Increasing, Decreasing	Decreasing, Nil
Skill (Dexterity)	Increasing	Increasing, Decreasing	Decreasing	Nil
Education (Knowledge of the theory)	Increasing	Increasing, Decreasing	Decreasing	Nil
Practice, (Experience, awareness, comprehension)	Increasing	Increasing, Decreasing	Decreasing	Decreasing, Nil
Physical Effort	Increasing, Decreasing	Decreasing	Decreasing	Decreasing, Nil
Mental Effort (Concentration, attention)	Increasing	Decreasing	Decreasing	Decreasing, Nil
Productivity**	Increasing	Increasing, Decreasing	Mostly (but not always) Decreasing	Nil
Exposure to Hazards	Increasing	Decreasing	Decreasing	Nil
Acceptance of Undesirable Job Surroundings	Increasing	Decreasing	Decreasing	Nil
Responsibility***	Increasing	Increasing	Increasing, Decreasing	Increasing, Decreasing, or Nil
Seniority	Not affected	Not affected	Not affected	Not affected
Decision Making (Alertness, judgment)	Increasing	Increasing, Decreasing	Decreasing	Decreasing, or Nil

*Refers to operators and not to setup men, maintenance men, engineers or supervisors.

**Ability to influence amount of output.   ***Safety of equipment, of the product, of other people.

FIGURE 2.[23] SUGGESTIONS FOR CHANGING CONTRIBUTION REQUIRED OF OPERATOR WITH ADVANCES IN LEVELS OF MECHANIZATION (Courtesy of James R. Bright.)

In levels 12–17, where "variable control action response" takes place, skill continues to decrease.

Skill (dexterity). This contribution increases in levels 1–4, but begins to decrease much earlier than (skill, knowledge of the art). In fact, it decreases in levels 5–8, continues to decrease in levels 9–11, and finally is eliminated altogether in levels 12–17.

Education (Knowledge of the Theory)   Educational requirements increase through stages 1–4 (hand controlled) and continue increasing through the first stages of the (mechanically controlled) levels; they drop in the latter part of the mechanically controlled levels and continue to drop through the variable control levels (9–11), finally disappearing as a contribution in stages 12–17.

Practice (Experience, Awareness, and Comprehension)   The practice factor follows those previously described, increasing in the hand-controlled mechanization levels; increasing for the first few changing levels of the mechanically controlled levels; then beginning to decrease. The decrease continues through the variable control stages (signal response) and to a "nil" point in the variable-control, action-response level.

Physical Effort   Bright makes the point that physical effort increases only through the first stage or two in the hand-controlled levels, and then decreases steadily through the rest of the levels, finally becoming "nil" in the last few stages.

Mental Effort (Concentration and Attention)   Mental effort follows much the same pattern as physical effort, except that the decreasing stages do not begin until a few mechanization levels, beyond which physical effort drops off.

Productivity   Productivity is defined as the ability to influence the amount of output. The operator makes a positive contribution through the hand-controlled stages, 1–4. This contribution continues through the early levels of the mechanically controlled levels, then begins to drop off at about level 6. In most cases it then decreases steadily through levels 9–11 (variable control, signal response) and finally becomes "nil" in the action-response levels, 12–17. In other words, it is almost impossible for the operator or observer to influence positively the productivity of the equipment.

Responsibility   Responsibility refers to the safety of the equipment, of the product, and of other people. This factor increases steadily through the hand-controlled mechanization levels, 1–4, and

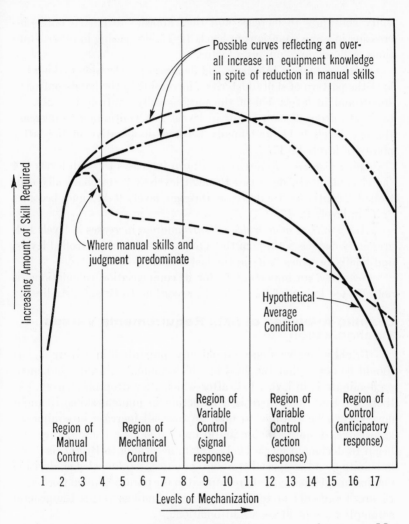

FIGURE 3.[25] SUGGESTING HOW SKILL REQUIREMENTS OF OPERATORS MAY
VARY WITH LEVELS OF MECHANIZATION.

Courtesy of James R. Bright and *Harvard Business Review.*

through the mechanically controlled levels, 5–8. In this development,
it is somewhat parallel to the experience with skill (knowledge of art).
In levels 9–11 the variable-control–signal-response levels, responsi-

bility continues to increase and then appears to flatten out — increasing in some situations in levels 12–17, decreasing in other situations or becoming "nil" as a factor.

Decision Making (Alertness and Judgment)   Decision making follows the pattern of skill (dexterity), increasing in the hand-controlled stages and in levels 5–6 of the mechanically controlled stages. It begins to drop off as a factor in levels 7–8, continuing to decrease through levels 9–11, and finally becomes inoperative in the latter phases of levels 12–17.

Other Factors   *Exposure to hazards* increases through levels 1–4 (hand controlled), decreases through levels 5–8 (mechanically controlled), continues to decrease through levels 9–11, and becomes "nil" in levels 12–17.

Acceptance of undesirable job surroundings increases in levels 1–4, gradually decreases through the more mechanically controlled levels, and finally becomes "nil" in the last levels.

Seniority, an important factor in compensation calculations, is not affected in any of the 17 levels, according to Bright's studies.

Graphic Analyses of Skill Requirements Versus Mechanization

Bright's analyses are graphically presented in Figure 3. It should be noted that the level in which manual skills and judgment predominate is in levels 1–4, after which they drop off sharply. At the same time that there is a reduction in manual skills, it might nevertheless be possible to note an over-all increase in equipment knowledge, despite a reduction in manual skills. These curves also begin to decline in levels 11–17. Skill, according to Bright, is "that indefinite blend of special training, practice, job knowledge, decision making and dexterity that are implicit in the phrase "skilled worker."[24] Figure 4 presents in total the research findings versus the general assumptions on skill versus automation.

A. N. Turner[27] made a series of studies on human adjustment to automation. Some of his cases showed little need to upgrade workers; in fact, in some cases less skill was required to work on the automated equipment.

On the other hand, manufacturers of electronic data processing equipment pointed out that the effect on clerical jobs was to raise the skill requirement, but research studies made in computer installations refuted this position.

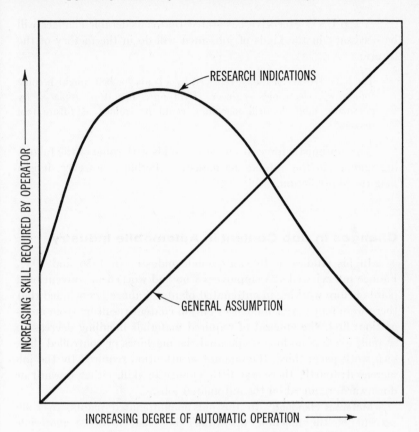

FIGURE 4.[26] SKILL VERSUS AUTOMATION AS SUGGESTED BY ACTUAL EXPERIENCE.

Courtesy of James R. Bright.

In a study made in a steel mill, Turner found that most jobs required different skills and less physical effort.

Future Upgrading Necessary in Automobile Industry?

Automation often changes the nature of the skill and training needed on individual jobs. The former single-spindle drill operator or press operator now tends a battery of machines, which perform boring, reaming, drilling, milling operations or blanking, forming, piercing, and flanging operations.

A top UAW executive has stated that considerable changes will be necessary in the kinds of jobs men will do in the factory of the future:

> The hand-trucker of today, replaced by a conveyor belt, might become tomorrow's electronics engineer. Drill press operators, replaced by automatic multiple drill machines, could be trained as future tool makers.[28]

This optimistic forecast appears at odds with some of the following findings in the automobile industry. Perhaps, however, it is a long-range prediction.

Changes in Job Content in Automobile Industry

In his studies of the automobile industry in 1956 and 1957, Faunce interviewed 125 employees who had worked in conventional plants before working in automated plants. Faunce[29] concluded that there were four major influences on job content resulting from automation: first, the amount of required materials handling decreased; second, workers no longer operated the machines or controlled their own work pace; third, the amount of attention required by the job increased; fourth, there was little change in skill, either upward or downward, required on the automated jobs.

Materials Handling   In the old nonautomated plants, over 80 percent of the machine operators' jobs had involved materials handling. In the new plants, only 44 percent of the workers queried indicated that their jobs involved materials handling. Most of the workers in the 44 percent group were in departments where smaller parts were machined or where automatic loaders were made adjunct to the transfer machinery. Materials handling involved only the feeding of small parts into a loader. Whereas, in the conventional plants, it had been necessary to handle such important items as cylinder blocks or crankshafts, under automation this phase was eliminated in all the assignments.

Control Over Work Pace   In the Detroit studies it was observed that the workers no longer operated the machines; hence, they lost all control over setting the work pace. Whereas, in the old plants there had been actuating levers to hasten the action of the machines, under automation this was eliminated. In the old days, a worker was able to speed up voluntarily, and then slacken off and rest — still meeting the production quotas. Under automation he no longer had such control, so that he no longer could keep his individuality through "negotiation."

Attention Required by Job   In the old conventional plants of the automobile industry, it was found that most jobs consisted of a series of repetitive operations. Most of these were manual and required surface attention. The worker controlled his own work pace.

In the automated plants of today, constant attention is required of the gauges and panels of lights. When something goes wrong in the automated department, the breakdown is much more costly than in the nonautomated departments, and the employees worry about this constantly. Whenever there is an expensive breakdown, it is normal procedure for the "top brass" to assemble with the workers and find out what went wrong. Many workers do not like the idea of these conferences with engineers, plant superintendents, general foremen, and repairmen.

Skill Requirements

The opinion of the management in the automated plant was that no new or greater skill was required of machine operators. Accordingly, there was no special training program set up for these workers. The responses of the workers were generally consistent with this view.[30]

The workers in this study agreed that training time on the automated job did not have to be longer than on the nonautomated job. They also agreed that the new jobs permitted them to use their abilities at about the same level as did the nonautomated jobs.

However, there was an amazing reaction to the question, "Which job, your old job or your present job, requires more skill?" A majority indicated that the present jobs in the automated plant required more skill, but management did not agree. In answering the questionnaire, the workers could have been quietly negotiating for better wages.

Faunce concluded that, although no greater skills were required by *machine operators* in the automated automobile plant, the skills were somewhat different. Once the classification of machine operator is left, a different picture is presented in the Detroit studies. A greater number of skilled workers in proportion to the semiskilled was required in the automated plant, but these were maintenance workers.

Responsibility a Job-Evaluation Factor

Does automation increase the amount of responsibility of the industrial worker? The Faunce study, as well as others, appears to emphasize the fact that the worker believes his responsibilities are increased under automation. In the first place his work now accounts for a larger share of the total production process. Also, a mistake is much more costly. Furthermore, the workers know that the investment in machinery per worker is constantly increasing with continued progress in automation. In the Faunce studies, the majority of the workers interviewed believed that their jobs were *now* more important and that their responsibilities had increased substantially. These attitudes are, of course, communicated regularly to their union representatives.

Fatigue

Faunce agrees with a finding of Bright that the newly automated jobs do not add to physical fatigue. Faunce's findings would disagree with Bright on the mental factor, however. In the Faunce studies, workers overwhelmingly stated that they felt more fatigued at the end of the day, working in the automated plant, but this fatigue was described as the "result of the constant attention required on the job, and not as a result of physical effort expended."[31]

Working Conditions

Bright points out in his studies that working conditions appear to improve under automation. Faunce does not agree with this observation in his findings. He stated:

> Working conditions appeared to vary from department to department in the automated plant and, while they were improved on some jobs by the introduction of automatic machinery, they appeared to have actually become worse in others.[32]

Job Satisfaction

Automation seems to bring new tensions into the plant. This does have considerable influence on the process of job evaluation. Wage payments in American industry generally recognize that tension is a work factor, for which there must be adequate compensation. The factor may not be called "tension" — it may be called "undesirable working conditions" or "mental energy" expended; in any event, when it is present, it costs the employer more. It is often expressed in the following ways:

[I don't like] the lack of feeling responsible for your work. The feeling that you're turning out more work, but knowing that *it's not yours really* and not as good as you could make it, if you had control of the machine, like before.

It's a completely different feel of work. On my old job I controlled the machine. On my present job the *machine controls me.*

You are very rushed on automation. You are *under pressure all the time.* That's why it's so hard to learn and some can't do it — can't stand the pressure.

[Automation is] just different all the time. You've *got to be aware all the time* and push the right button. If you push the wrong one, it could cost around $13,000, and is very dangerous. I pushed a wrong button and stuff flew all over. I was lucky, but it cost the company $13,000 to fix the machine.

Job Status

A number of studies appear to indicate that a number of nonproductive jobs in automated companies, such as "repairman," involving high skill and less physical effort are regarded highly by workingmen. This is not much different from the status of these jobs in the conventional plant. However, in Faunce's studies the workers seemingly regard the productive jobs in the automated plant as having more status than the productive jobs in the nonautomated plant. Faunce describes a new "high status" job in the automobile industry, much admired and much talked about; namely, the job of "console" operator, "which involved no more physical effort than is required to stand and watch a panel of lights for eight hours."[33]

Automation and Education Levels

A very interesting question, to be examined in greater detail later in this book, is: "What is the influence of varying degrees of education on the worker?" Faunce makes the point that, irrespective of race, workers with more education tended to be less satisfied with automated jobs. He concluded:

... while the range in the number of school years completed was not large, it may be that more highly educated workers were more perceptive of the discrepancy between the complexity of the automated machinery and the simplicity of the operations performed by the machine operator and felt more acutely the alienation from their work . . . .[34]

Survey of Skill Requirements in Metal Trades

A McGraw-Hill survey of a sample of metalworking firms with automation experience disclosed that:

> ... only 27% of the firms felt that machine operators needed more skill on automated equipment than on the old equipment; 30% reported no change in skill requirements; and 43% felt that the new operation required less skill.[35]

Many plants with newly automated systems have hired relatively inexperienced operators and, without too much training time, have managed to keep production moving. Some reported that increases in skill are actually due to the establishment of combination jobs, which require operators to perform duties such as "setup," and certain types of maintenance responsibilities, which were previously assigned to separate classifications.

Job rotation has seemingly raised skill requirements. Machine pacing and great physical efforts appear to have been eliminated, but have been replaced by a new type of monotony and fatigue. Also, where some manual operations are mixed with highly automated operations, the demands of a manual nature appear to be much more intense than they seemed to be in the previously conventional plant. (At least this seems so in the minds of the workers.)

"Job enlargement" was to be the expected result of automation. The operator has not really been given too much of job enlargement. True, he pushes buttons and watches dials — and has a sense of importance in being the guardian of valuable machinery — but, after a while, this too, becomes dull and monotonous.

Conclusion

A look at the industrial world today suggests that a redefinition of "skill" is long overdue. The classical concepts of "unskilled," "semiskilled," and "skilled" workers were largely inherited from a static, medieval guild society. Do these classifications meet the needs of today's dynamic, fast-changing industrial society? The skill of one technological era is dead and the skill of a new era is just emerging. There appears to be a need for a new concept that makes room for the broader background knowledge of the "maintenance man," the "planner," and the "automatic machine supervisor" in highly automated production.

References

1. Report of the Director-General, Fortieth Session, Geneva, 1957, International Labor Conference, Report I (Part I, "Automation and Other Technological Developments"), printed by ILO, p. 71.
2. *Report on Automation:* International Metalworkers Federation, Geneva, June 1956, p. 17.
3. James B. Carey, *The Impact of Automation on Production and Employment* (Columbus, Ohio: The Religion and Labor Foundation, 1957), p. 9.
4. Peter F. Drucker, *The Practice of Management* (New York: Harper & Row, 1954), p. 286.
5. Ted Silvey, Speech made at AFL-CIO Convention May 8, 1956, p. 7.
6. *Ibid.*
7. *Ibid.*
8. *Ibid.*
9. *Ibid.*
10. James R. Bright, "Skill Requirements and Wage Aspects of Automation." Paper presented at the University of Pennsylvania Labor Relations Council Conference, November 18, 1960, in *Industrial Relations in the 1960's — Problems and Prospects*, vol. I, George W. Taylor and Edward B. Shils, eds., p. 16.
11. *Ibid.*, p. 17.
12. *Automation and Technological Change*, Subcommittee on Economic Stabilization of the Joint Committee on the Economic Report, Congress of the United States. Hearings October 1955, Reported November 1955, Washington, D. C.: U.S. Government Printing Office, 1955.
13. I. Hoos, "When the Computer Takes Over the Office," *Harvard Business Review*, July–August 1960.
14. Charles C. Killingsworth, "Effects of Automation on Employment and Manpower Planning," Michigan State University, Reprint Series no. 37; Statement before the Senate Subcommittee on Employment and Manpower of the Senate Committee on Labor and Public Welfare, June 14, 15, 1960, p 7.
15. *Ibid.*, p. 8.
16. *Ibid.*, p. 8.
17. Bright, Presentation before the Society of Automotive Engineers. New York City, January 14, 1957, p. 8.
18. *Ibid.*, p. 9.
19. *Ibid.*
20. *Ibid.*
21. *Ibid.*, p. 10.
22. Bright, "How to Evaluate Automation," *Harvard Business Review*, July–August 1955, p. 101.

23. Bright, Presentation before the Society of Automotive Engineers, New York City, January 14, 1957 (originally Figure 4 in Bright's speech).
24. *Ibid.*
25. Bright, "Does Automation Raise Skill Requirements?" *Harvard Business Review*, July–August 1958.
26. Bright, *op. cit.*, Exhibit 4.
27. A. N. Turner, "A Researcher Views Human Adjustment to Automation," *Advanced Management*, vol. 21, no. 5, May 1956, pp. 21–25.
28. In a letter to the author from a UAW official, December 16, 1961.
29. William A. Faunce, "Automation and the Automobile Worker," *Social Problems*, vol. 6, no. 1, Summer 1958, pp. 67–78.
30. *Ibid.*
31. *Ibid.*, p. 70.
32. *Ibid.*, p. 71.
33. *Ibid.*, p. 74.
34. *Ibid.*, p. 76.
35. *American Machinist*, October 21, 1957.

►►►► **12**

Problems of
Wage Administration
in an Automated Era

Automation and other technological developments raise many questions — how should wages be paid? why should they be paid; and others. It is hoped, of course, that the general level of real wages will improve along with continued technological improvement and increased productivity. Such has been the experience of the United States over the years, and there is no reason to expect a change. In fact, the goals of greater productivity are being directed to an improvement in the standard of living.

Automation will, without a doubt, lead to quite startling increases in labor productivity. A doubling — or even tripling or quadrupling — of productivity in the plant is not impossible. The potential of the machines is there; what must be watched carefully is the short-run effect on social organization, social policy in general, and, of course, wage policy.

The unions, of course, favor wage rises proportionate to a rise in labor productivity. The difficulty lies in the short run, in measuring of productivity, or in the worker's contribution to it. Employers do not oppose wage increases as productivity increases; but they do not, however, want to be tied down, in the short run, to arrangements made through collective bargaining, which are not based upon a realistic appraisal of current production difficulties, but instead are set on the prospects of future abundance of product.

Many economists, in and out of Government, believe that increases in productivity should be shared with the general population, not just with the workers, by lower prices to consumers. This, it is said, would indicate the contribution that automation is making to society by raising living standards.

Wages Commensurate With Performance

Wages have to bear a relation to work accomplished. Automation is forcing a reappraisal of present job-evaluation and -classification techniques. How appropriate are the methods used today with respect to automated jobs?

If the workers' suspicion that something is being put over on them through automation can be dispelled, then a more reasonable cooperation can be expected. Proper wage determination can do a great deal to assist in this objective.

Automation will probably mean the end of piece-rate payment methods, and possibly of group incentive plans, since the pace of work on the automated processes will not be under the control of workers or work groups. The rate of output will be controlled by the "technician" rather than the operatives. Moreover, the contribution of one worker can rarely be isolated from the contribution of another.

Time Payment Versus Piece

Case-study materials currently available show that, in general, workers on automated processes are paid on straight time rates rather than on piece rates. Many of these rates were fixed first by job evaluation and after consultation with union representatives. Subsequently, many were revised as a result of periodic review, the revisions agreed to by the union. In certain instances, practical experience has dictated changes necessary to the successful operation of the pay plan.

In some cases, time payment has been coupled with a group bonus. This practice has been followed in those plants where the receipt of bonuses was traditional, or where nonautomated departments continue to draw bonuses in the historic manner.

Workers' Fears

The unions and the workers both fear that wages may be reduced as a result of a redefinition of the job and subsequent downgrading under a classification system. This has already occurred in some automated plants, where job analysts recomputed the value of the job "downward" as a result of "easier" working conditions under automation.

Other unions are concerned that even when the job is upgraded, the change-over from "incentive" pay to "time" payment will reduce take-home pay, despite a new higher base rate.

Demands are being made for new kinds of bonuses to replace the traditional ones. For example, certain locals want "lonely" money to compensate workers in isolated work stations for the loss of human company on the job. Other unions want "tension" money, because the worker, as observer over the new automated equipment, is subjected to added strain by having to be "alert" for long periods.

Many workers in automated plants expect downgrading, since they lack the formal education or technical training to aspire to some of the newly created jobs in the automated plant. Intelligence as well as training is demanded in many of the new jobs, which require the "integrating" knowledge so requisite to an automated plant.

For the most part, the fears of workers have been groundless, since the unions have kept a fairly tight rein on management action in terms of reclassification or displacement. Collective bargaining by the unions in these areas has become firmer than ever! Transfer of workers from one job to another has generally been accompanied by union demands for a maintenance of the guaranteed rate of the old job.

Relationship of Wages and Management Salaries

It is unlikely that the present relationship between workers' wages and management salaries will survive. The new technology will change job content and the composition of the labor force. Will there be a distinguishable difference between the supervisor and the former production worker in the new automated plant? There may even be a widening of the gap between the better paid workers and the worst paid workers. This situation will result in continued union pressure to raise once again the Federal minimum wage.

Shorter Workday and a Shorter Workweek

The history of industrial advance shows that the principal contribution of the machines has been a reduced workday and workweek and improved wages. Unions are already anxious to "spread the work" and thereby cushion the effect of technological improvements on job displacement. This solution could be only a temporary one, because competition would ultimately lose this country's position in the economic world. The more positive approach is simply that more rapid increases in productivity will permit savings in labor, the benefits of which may be paid partly in the form of greater production and partly of shorter hours.

Employers can generally bargain with union in this way: shorter hours must be earned not only by higher labor productivity, but also by a clear willingness by the union membership to accept and welcome technological improvements, thus making for increased productivity.

Reductions in hours do not necessarily have to result in a shorter workday or workweek. They can be effected through longer vacations, more frequent vacations, more holidays, and certain leaves of absence.

One aspect of automation, which is sure to have disagreeable connotations, is that of shift operations. The fully automated plant must operate twenty-four hours a day. One of the challenges will be to eliminate irregular shifts and to pay extra for shift work so that the worker and his family will have something pleasant to think about. Dividing the weekends in a novel way is often a help to a shift worker. In some firms, for example, the worker may have four consecutive days off, perhaps twice a month. The question of the amount of each varying shift differential must be studied scientifically and worked out with the union, if a union shop exists.

Incentive in Lieu of Piece Rate

With automation, the operator does not control his own output. He works as part of a team, and his contribution cannot usually be separated from that of his fellow workers.

Many schemes in lieu of the direct piece-rate incentive have been tried out and have worked well. One, designed specifically for indirect workers in a conventional plant, might be valuable in an automated factory. It rewards employees, who cannot be included in the normal incentive scheme, on the basis of assessments of reliability, initiative, attitude, safety, economy, and production (indirect).[1] Of course, even the rough assessment of production, which is used in this case, might be applicable to automation.

"Time Span of Discretion"

A new book by Elliott Jacques[2] is well worth reading in respect to the time span of discretion. He points out that wages are often set by intuition rather than by rational inquiry. New jobs under automation will require evaluation, and techniques like merit rating, job evaluation, or time span of discretion may prove to be a basis for payment.

The time span of discretion is a basis for job evaluation roughly defined as the "length of time during which a person exercises discretion without any supervision;" that is, his capacity to discharge responsibility over an extended period without review. Level of responsibility can thus be defined in terms of maximum time span of discretion.[3]

Wage-Administration Mistakes in Automation

A number of experts in both automation and wage administration, among them Bright, point out that unions present the argument — acquiesced to by certain employees — that base wage adjustments ought to be made around the "increased skill requirement" of the newly automated job. These facts are in error, and overhasty decisions will be regretted later on. This type of upgrading can lead only to hopeless inconsistencies.

There has been no evidence of the general upgrading effect of automation. In fact, it has been shown that automation has reduced the skill requirements of the production forces — and often the same is true of the maintenance department. Managers admit from time to time that, after the "breather" period, substantial errors may be made in assigning of high wage rates to some automated jobs. In terms of job difficulty, these new rates are not only out of line, but are very unfair in comparison with wages paid to operators of conventional machinery. Even the training time on certain key jobs has been reduced drastically compared to time allotted for conventional jobs.

Wage Policies

It is not enough for management to know that automation will possibly require changes in thinking about job evaluation and wage policies: what it will do to the composition of the work force — production workers versus clerical and maintenance workers. The major issue to be faced is, what to do about the dilemma of the "compensation basis"?

Since the operators no longer control quantity and quality — if they exert less physical and mental effort, if working conditions improve by automation and chance of accidents lessen, if fewer production decisions are made by the operator, and if less skill, knowledge, and experience are required on certain jobs — then what should be the criteria for wages? Should employees be paid less because they contribute less; or more, because production is rising as a result of automation? If more, then on what basis?

Wage Administration Axioms Under Automated Conditions

1. Do not jump into a union contract without reviewing all the factors entering into automation. Many unions prejudge the influence of skill on the automated job.

2. It makes good sense to share some of the production gains with workers, keeping in mind, of course, that management has to pay for the extensive new plant and equipment. However, cooperation of the workers and the union must be secured to install and operate the new equipment effectively. Some sharing is necessary. It might be possible to split the gain in output and to increase wages proportionately, almost as though the piece-work basis were continuing. Generally, the firms already affected by this problem have limited the "reasonable" increases from about five cents an hour to about 10 percent in take-home pay.

3. It is important that every increase be negotiated with the union. If the workers get these increases without union intercession, it would appear as though the union leader was not ably representing his constituents. Rest assured, however, that the union will be around in time to negotiate for an increase, regarding what the workers received without negotiation.

4. In negotiating the contract, the union would be wise to base the increases on some productivity factor as part of an annual wage-improvement program, rather than an independent wage increase. This type of clause permits management to keep stressing productivity and makes it easier for it to install new and better equipment each year without too much union "hassling." These "annual improvement" increases should be possible for all employees — a policy that will force management to keep increasing productivity.

5. The increases given should be those called for in the job-evaluation system. It is not wise to ignore job evaluation simply because new complexities have developed. If anything, the need for a systematic pay plan is even more important than ever under automation.

6. Some firms have taken the position that rather than negotiate specific increases, gains should be taken from a kind of "reserve fund" tied to the new profits coming from more efficient production, a matter of serious consideration.

7. The principal union position is, as it has always been, simply this:

> ... new classifications and rates should be established in recognition of the changed nature of the jobs in which increased responsibility offsets by far any reduction in physical effort and manual dexterity accompanying automation. This increased responsibility, in most cases, flows from the much larger investment represented by the equipment under the individual worker's control. . . .[4]

Higher Wages Because of Increased Responsibility

Unions make the claim that workers in automated plants have greater responsibility. The basis for this contention is, of course, the heavier investment in machinery per worker as compared to the conventional plants. In negotiating on this issue, managers take the position that "responsibility is the control of equipment by the worker." Management can now claim that the worker has less control over the equipment than he did in the conventional plant and, hence, has less responsibility. The quarrel here rests on the meaning of "responsibility" — and "investment per worker" is a poor formula to use in any plant, automated or nonautomated. Can you imagine what this would mean in a conventional plant, where one worker would be luckier than the next because he has more expensive machinery to run? Toolmakers and diemakers would lose pay status enormously, as would maintenance personnel. The "investment" basis in the conventional plant or department would serve to discriminate against those with the highest degrees of skill and training.

Another aspect of responsibility that might be truly "compensable" under automation is the "responsibility of the operator to prevent machinery stoppage or to lessen downtime." This might be a very important cost item and might justify additional wages. Eventually, however, more automatic controls will be introduced and this aspect of worker "responsibility" eliminated for all time.

Abandon Present Job-Evaluation Plans?

The installation of an automated system under union conditions is difficult enough without having to set up new problems of working out complicated upgrading under traditional job-evaluation plans. Unions do not see such re-evaluation as too much of a problem, and they see most jobs upgraded. They believe this is only fair, for under automation unions can only visualize *fewer* jobs. "Let's trade better jobs for more jobs" seems to sum up the union point of view — a defensive position against the march of progress under the new technology.

Let's ask the question "can we apply the best of job-evaluation techniques to the automated job"? Will our problems be solved, or will there be additional ones? Actually, few job-evaluation systems are applicable equally to automated jobs and to conventional jobs. In the traditional systems, manual skill may receive a higher weighting than responsibility. If these factors are reweighted, will the re-evaluation continue to be fair for the conventional system as well? Should two systems be developed for use in the same firm? Although this is possible, such a practice will lead to endless and seemingly contradictory complications, which the unions discover soon enough and then use as an argument in their bargaining.

At present, no single rule seems to provide the desired and equitable wage procedures, required under the ever-changing technology. Management would not be wise to abandon conventional systems of job-evaluation techniques. When management is pressed by the union or employees for wage increases as a result of upgrading, if it is convinced that distortion will result and be harmful to both the conventional and the automated departments, then it would do well to suggest a survey of the job-evaluation system. However, overhauling of the job-evaluation plan will eventually take place after sufficient experience with the new technology is gained.

Will Automation Depress Wage Rates?

It is generally held that automation will not depress wage rates. In those industries where technological change has been rapid, wage rates have risen. Even though the general effect will be a rise in wages, real wage problems will develop. The wage-payment method will undoubtedly have to change; the incentive systems and piece-rate programs in use will clearly be inappropriate under automation. The piece-rate philosophy is that the worker can control his output within limits and that the more efficiently or harder he works the more he can earn. In the highly integrated and mechanized operations, where the worker neither works on direct production nor controls the production rate, it becomes impossible to identify output results with individual efforts.[5]

Group Incentives Still Possible

Incentives may still be possible, but only by a shift to a group basis. Team operations should be compensated for through group incentives, where it is demonstrated that joint participation contributed to the success of the performance, and results may be measured. Automation implies a generally higher degree of process integration than is now found in production, and integration will sound the death knell of present incentive systems.

Bonuses

While it is possible to conceive of negative incentive methods, which penalize production interruptions, or incentives based on percentage utilization of equipment capacity, no one knows how effective these measures might be. Equipment performance, primarily, will dictate what earnings will be, and whether mechanical failures due to human fault can be separated from other failures, is a large question mark.

Market Surveys of Wages

With standard job-evaluation plans, it is generally possible to find a common job content and then survey wages paid in the industry for these similar duties and responsibilities. The problem of fair compensation, for those jobs in an automated plant that have no counterpart in a nonautomated plant, is a difficult one to solve. It will be easy to create wage inequities. Unions, which have bargained traditionally for consistent wage structures throughout the industry, will find industry-wide comparisons warped and distorted, as firms automate and change the content of jobs. Wage structures previously stabilized may be upset, as the guideposts of the "customary wage relationships" are obliterated.

Skill and Wage Payment

Job-evaluation and other measurement systems commonly take into account mental and skill requirements, physical factors, responsibilities, and working conditions of jobs, classifying them for purposes of wage payment. Automation will lay new stress on mental requirements and responsibilities, and there will often be little basis of comparison between existing job factors and the novel requirements of jobs under automation.

How will the new positions be fitted into existing classifications? How will job classifications be revised to encompass them? Regardless of the techniques involved, those who expect that automation will soften up unions in so far as wage demands are concerned are in for a surprise. Higher wages and equitable wage structures — and even bargained rates — will continue to be prime objectives of unions.

Automation and Wages

In a study of the effects of automation on wages in the automobile industry, no appreciable change seems to be noted in the general structure of the automated versus the nonautomated plant. Faunce stated:

> In automated departments a larger proportion of the workers were given job classifications with higher hourly wage rates, and higher rates for some machine operators' jobs were negotiated, but no major wage changes were made. There were also few changes in job classifications or descriptions. Only one new job classification attributable to automation was established. . . . Although there appear to have been major changes on some jobs on automated lines, job descriptions of existing classifications were not changed, and are still in use.[6]

In the company under study by Faunce, negotiations regarding new classifications were generally initiated by the labor union, not the employer. The union apparently determined that increased wages could be attained by reassignment of workers to existing classifications with higher wage rates, rather than by opening to negotiation proposed new classifications.

Union Attitudes Toward Incentive Systems

With few exceptions unions have been opposed to wage-incentive plans, because they claim that they have had damaging experience of abuses under such plans, and because of the difficulties and ill-effects of the plans — all of which they believe are inherent in incentive plans. The unions have found that the presence of an incentive system invariably means special problems of education, representation, and protection of workers, and puts a strain on the entire collective bargaining process. Employers, on the other hand, want to know what they pay wages for and to have some standard for hourly output. Accountants also like to be able to figure the direct cost of labor in each unit of output — to simplify the setting of a selling price.

Regardless of how the reader feels about industrial engineering and incentives, unions believe that the problem will disappear with automation. To quote from the December 1957 Collective Bargaining Report of the AFL-CIO:

> There is one bright spot on the incentive horizon. Most experts agree that incentive systems may well be on the way out due to technological improvement and automation.
>
> As production becomes more and more automatic, workers have less and less control over output. The supposed gains to management of incentive systems will decrease and presumably many of these plans will be eliminated.[7]

The union article also made a favorable statement on automation:

> Some companies lacking newer automatic equipment may try to cut costs through incentive systems in order to compete with their better mechanized or automated competitors. Workers in such companies will be forced to work faster and harder, but they will not be able to win a race with automatic equipment. Workers cannot produce enough to save incompetent or inefficient management.[8]

Impact of Automation at Ford Motor Company

In 1946 the Ford Motor Company began installing transfer machines as the forerunner of the automated factory. These transfer machines were placed between presses to move materials automatically from one stage in production to another. The machines were simple, consisting of gravity or roller-type chutes, activated when the materials touched an extended arm or bar, which in turn was connected to an electrical limit switch. The tripping of the switch put in motion iron hands or an air mechanism, which placed the material in the next production step. The operator who controlled each machine in the productive process was classified as an "in-line machine operator." The wage rate paid this new classification was equal to that paid an operator running a similar machine without a transfer mechanism.

Ford Expansion in Automation

After World War II, the Ford Motor Company embarked upon an unprecedented expansion program, investing $2,581,000,000 in new plant and equipment within the period from 1947 to 1957. In the main, Ford moved in the direction of new processes, which employed automatic devices, then in their most advanced stages. At present, the automation in these enlarged or new facilities includes (1) automatic movement of materials and parts from one operation to the next; (2) replacement of men in the operation of machines by devices called "mechanisms" (servomechanisms); (3) replacement of inspectors by control devices, which automatically inspect products; (4) use of mechanisms which count, fill orders, maintain inventories, reorder, give instructions, and designed with never-failing memories or memories lasting at least as long as machinery is kept in repair; (5) automatic preventative maintenance, which not only provides automatic lubrication whenever oil and grease are needed, but in addition signals the need for repairs.

This type of automaticity was a far cry from the crude transfer machines of 1946. As a result, the productivity of Ford workers increased at an average rate of 5.7 percent a year from 1948 through 1955.[9]

All the changes in machinery affected the manpower requirements of the company, and the UAW had to consider the many problems that arose in respect to rates and classifications, changing skills, seniority adjustments, and effect of automation on the most highly skilled trades classifications.

Rates and Classifications

The union was concerned because many of the changes adversely affecting the workers as a result of automation were at variance with speeches and promises made by Ford officials. For example, Del S. Harder, vice-president in charge of manufacturing, in a speech at Davenport, Iowa, on August 27, 1954, said "automation would act as a prod on the economy in several ways, one of which would be that of enabling labor to increase its earning power." Harder also stated at this time: "Automation is the key to less human effort in the future and an increase in our standard of living tomorrow;" further: "Production processes have become more complicated in departments which use automation and our production people must be more highly trained."[10]

In addition to Harder's comments, Ray H. Sullivan, another Ford vice-president, in a speech at Cleveland, January 25, 1955, was quoted as saying:

> From the standpoint of the worker, automation will supplant heavy, vigorous and unpleasant jobs with easier, better paid, more pleasant and interesting jobs. . . . (the) whole labor force is being upgraded in technical skill. . . . Automation is more than a manufacturing method or an economic necessity. . . . it's a magic key to creation or a better life for all of us. . . . Like the atom, its potential is unlimited, but we must learn to understand it, control it and direct it into avenues of increasing human betterment.[11]

The UAW was in sympathy with this position, but found it difficult to pin down the Ford negotiators on certain classification reassurances — at least this was the position, as the union describes it.

When automation began piecemeal, the Dearborn and the Buffalo plants were already in operation. The Cleveland plant, however, was brand new. In 1955 the union began a wage survey of the existing stamping plants. The survey disclosed that the average hourly earnings in the new Cleveland plant, where automation was to be made more effective, was 11 cents less than at Dearborn. The reasons for this differential were as follows: (1) rates for the same classifications at Dearborn were $4\frac{1}{2}$ cents higher at both ends of the range; (2) most of the workers in Cleveland, having little prior service, were nearer to the minimums of the ranges than workers in Dearborn; (3) similar jobs were often classified differently at the two plants. The union believed that, in many instances, the identical job bore a lower classification in the new Cleveland plant. Union representatives believed that automation and downgrading, as a result of job dilution, had gone hand-in-hand at the Cleveland stamping plant.

At the Cleveland plant the UAW decided to negotiate a new classification structure, specifically drawn up for an automated stamping plant. It requested the company to draw up this plan, but the company objected and requested the union to submit a plan. Meetings were held between the negotiators and employees were interviewed. The union finally proposed to management a new classification structure but without wage rates. The company claimed that the new structure was not valid, since, despite automation, job duties had not changed substantially enough to justify sharp revisions in classification. The arguments centered on upgrading, rather than on automated classifications.

After about three months of negotiations, Ford would not concede the principle of upgrading, and a strike authorization and a strike vote were taken; 2,240 members voted in favor of a strike on the issues, only 159 opposed. A few days after this vote, the negotiators reached an agreement, which was, in fact, a compromise. For the first time and on such a broad scale, a labor contract recognized the impact of automation on the job classifications it covered.

The new 1955 agreement in Cleveland did not achieve the application of such new classifications as "automation attendant" or "controller" in all the job situations requested by the union; but the union did win a basic principle; namely, the new agreement recognized the changed work done by press operators on the major lines and by workers in other classifications.

Furthermore, it was determined that arbitrators should have no role in the determination of new classifications resulting from automation, because no objective criteria were available. Arbitrators had previously ruled that "creeping changes" did not make jobs different enough to be called "new jobs."

In the Cleveland plant, the union was successful in blocking automated classifications, warning the workers skilled trade standards would deteriorate if the automated classifications were adopted. In any event, a common rate was established for the entire maintenance department, despite the retention of the old classifications. Apparently, what the union also wanted here was upgrading rather than automated classifications.

In the Buffalo plant of Ford, in view of the complexity of the equipment, management believed that it should be mandatory to break down the lines of demarcation between the traditional skilled trades. Before the union was recognized, the company had set up a classification called "automation equipment maker and maintenance man." This new classification cut across the traditionally recognized trades of diemaker, machine repairman, millwright, welder, hydraulic and pneumatic operator, pipe fitter, and tinsmith.

When the UAW was designated as the bargaining agent in Buffalo, the union showed its disapproval of the new classification program by attempting to abolish it. It could not accomplish this objective, because the company had already set the rate for the classification of "automation equipment maker and maintenance man," at a rate of pay equal to diemakers, which is the highest rate of any of the skills involved.

In the 1955 master agreement, Ford management would not agree to a continuation of the regular classification structure at Dearborn. The company wanted all skilled tradesmen to agree that the title "automation equipment maker and maintenance man" covered their jobs. The skilled workers refused and were supported by the production workers. At the time, the union fought this elimination of trade classifications because it believed that inevitably the basic skills of men would be undermined, and hence the members who would be "jacks of all trades and masters of none." Such was the rather confused issue on job classifications in the automobile industry. Today, automated classifications are being accepted by the UAW with more readiness.

Seniority groupings have since been broadened in the auto industry. For example, in June 1956, when Ford opened a new stamping plant in Chicago, the union immediately negotiated for a wage and classification agreement. As an illustration of the broader exercise of seniority, in the Dearborn plant, which has always been a stamping plant, there are 315 negotiated classifications of work. On the other hand, in the newer Chicago plant, there are only 101 classifications of work.

At the current time, in metropolitan Detroit, an area-wide seniority agreement has been negotiated for UAW's members. Preference is given to rehiring workers laid-off by other Ford plants before new hiring takes place in any Ford plant. This has served to complicate job classifications.

United Rubber Workers on Incentives in Changing Technology

The rubber industry has witnessed tremendous technological advances in the last few years, which have affected the incentive system. As long as men paced machines, there was no problem; but full mechanization and finally complete automation did present a problem. An agreement negotiated in 1957 with B. F. Goodrich represents substantial progress in re-evaluating the problem of wages in the rubber industry as a result of automation.

The union sees new machinery daily replacing older machinery. The new machine is always more automatic than the old machine. In some cases the obsolete equipment is continued in operation side by side with the new automatic machines — a situation that makes wage bargaining very difficult. New work standards are always being contested, and the disagreement revolves around the work load for the new equipment, rather than the attained earnings. The earnings level is practically a fixed figure in a given situation, since it is based on past earnings, which the union believes can be consistently maintained by employees without endangering their health or safety.

The rubber workers have found that as new equipment is introduced, the physical effort decreases and the machine replaces hand operations. In the new agreement with B. F. Goodrich the union recognized that the jobs were being made eaiser, but that this condition was limiting the employee's earnings. In this setting the union negotiated a maximum or "cap" on earnings, so that rates between jobs would stay in line. They also negotiated procedures in which the worker would be compensated for machine-controlled time at a level approximately equal to the maximum he would *attain if the job were entirely paced by his own skill and effort.*

The union believes that something substantial was accomplished in the Goodrich agreement in protecting membership. It points out, however, the ever-present danger that the employer could introduce a new machine and attempt to establish a base rate for the machine, which is lower than the base rate in effect for the same job classification (on conventional machinery). But the 1957 Goodrich agreement does offer some protection of pay classification for those employees affected by the introduction of automatic machinery.

Goodrich Incentive-Pay Agreement

While it is common to think of an incentive system providing unlimited earnings opportunity, the generalization does not apply to rubber plants, according to Childs and Bergmann.[12]

In the Goodrich contract for each job classification and each standard, there developed a general understanding between management and employees as to quantity of production that can be expected during the shift. This level of production yields a certain level of earnings. Despite the fact that job contents on the shift may differ, if the men have the same classification, they will tend to receive the same earnings for each hour worked. The rubber workers' contracts provide also for special wage payments for unusual conditions. If a machine breaks down or if there is a stock delay, the employee receives a rate guarantee, which could be as much as 100 percent of past earnings.

Under the Goodrich modified Bedeaux incentive-pay system, there is a base rate representing sixty units of work. At the end of a shift, it is possible the total number of units of work for which the employee receives credit may be multiplied by the unit value, to determine incentive earnings. The union does not question the company's definition of "normal." The engineering staffs of both parties use the same assumptions.

Provision for New Standards

The new master agreement at Goodrich permits the company to establish new standards "when there are changes in method, products, tools, materials, design, or other production conditions." Any revision resulting from such changes must be confined to the element or elements of work in which the work requirements or occurrences have changed since the prior labor standard was established. This clause, in other words, guarantees elemental time as long as the work for the element remains unchanged.

Conclusion

Piece-rate payment, based on the outputs of individual workers, rarely applies to automated processes. The rate of output will be decided by management on technical grounds and will be controlled by technicians rather than operatives.

Moreover, the contribution of one production worker can rarely be isolated from the contributions of others, so that payment will tend to reflect the performance of a team or a factory, rather than of an individual, and it may be based on criteria other than output — for example, machine utilization. In so far as piece rates have historically been a source of grievance and dispute, automation will confer some benefit to labor-management amity, by narrowing their scope.

The techniques of job evaluation will have to be reviewed, because compensable factors in the automated jobs will be quite different from those in their conventional counterparts.

It is probably fair to conclude that, in regard to the level of wages and hours, automation and technological improvements will strengthen the long-run trends toward higher wages and shorter working hours, as well as increase the amount of shift work. These factors will raise many short-run problems in wage administration.

References

1. L. Landon Goodman, *Man and Automation* (Harmondsworth, Middlesex: Pelican Books Ltd., 1957), p. 164.
2. *Measurement of Responsibility*, London: Tavistock Publications, 1956.
3. Goodman, *op. cit.*, p. 164.
4. *Automation* (Detroit, UAW-CIO Education Department, 1955) pp. 16–17.
5. Jack Rogers, *Automation: Technology's New Face* (Berkeley: University of California, 1958), p. 83.
6. William A. Faunce, "The Automobile Industry, A Case Study in Automation," from *Automation and Society*, H. B. Jacobson and J. S. Roucek, eds. (New York: Philosophical Library, 1959), p. 47.
7. "Wage Incentive Plans," *Collective Bargaining Report*, AFL-CIO vol. 2, no. 12, December 1957, p. 76.
8. *Ibid.*
9. Ford Department of United Automobile, Aircraft and Agricultural Implement Workers of America, AFL-CIO.
10. From information received from the UAW.
11. *Ibid.*
12. Joseph W. Childs and Ralph H. Bergmann, Wage Determination in an Automated Rubber Plant," Conference of the Industrial Union Department, AFL-CIO, held in Washington, D.C., April 26, 1958.

▶ ▶ ▶ ▶ **13**

Introduction of
Automation in Face of
Restrictive Work Practices

Because of historic restrictive work practices by unions and employees, management is often hampered in its attempts at introducing fuller mechanization or automation. This chapter describes some of the problems current in the industrial society relating to work rules, issues, seniority, grievance procedures, demands for shorter workdays and workweeks, and other related items. Special note is made of experiences in the maritime and railroad industries.

In this day of automation, the quality of management must be "top level" to convince the unions and workers that the preservation of the American system of free enterprise depends on efficient and competitive production. The Kaiser Steel Corporation has shown wisdom by relying on "informed neutrals" to help break the work-rules deadlock. The issues of automation and local working conditions were turned over to a special joint committee, empowered to explore problems and to negotiate settlements. In addition, the parties created a special "Tripartite Committee to Develop a Long Range Plan for the Equitable Sharing of the Fruits of Economic Progress." This body was asked to devise nothing less than a formula for dividing future profits* among employees, stockholders, the public, and internal growth, with special protection to the employees against rising living costs and the inroads of technological change. Other major companies are attempting to explore the same techniques.

The structure of our economic society is premised on the assumption that top management will make every effort to do away with waste. Growing competition from abroad makes management an increasingly serious responsibility. The workers, however, many of

*In December 1962, the Committee released a profit-sharing formula, considered to be a major breakthrough in the elimination of restrictive work practices. Profits arising from new productivity are to be shared among workers, corporation, and the public.

whose jobs are eliminated when new technology develops better methods, are part of a nucleus of complex social and industrial relationships which make the safeguarding of their *status quo* a necessity.

Adherence to Traditional Work Practices

"The manager is committed to change. The worker is committed to the preservation of the *status quo*. The result is the work-rules issue! It is an issue which is built into our society. I suspect it is built into any society,"[1] so stated Neil W. Chamberlain, professor of economics at Yale, in a speech at the University of Pennsylvania, November 18, 1961.

Many managers believe that the worker's resistance to change is derived from an inherited, profitable privilege; it is easier to make a living on his present job than it is to make the effort needed to find another job. Sometimes management suspects the union of resisting technological change because of its jealousy of its jurisdictional authority. Management often attributes to a particular union the desire to hang on to jobs (as in production) rather than see these jobs go elsewhere, under the jurisdiction of some other union (as in maintenance or clerical jobs).

It is not a matter of pure selfishness on the part of workers and union leaders. They wonder, fearfully, when the erosion will stop. It is not a question of who is right, manager or leader of the union — it is a social clash between individuals involved in a consistent social role. Head-on differences in attitudes need not go on indefinitely; constructive compromises and moderations are possible. The Canadian railroads appear to have the situation more realistically in hand than do the American railroads.

For example, firemen are no longer necessary on diesel engines. The Canadian solution is to keep these firemen on the payroll until they retire and then not replace them with new workers. This is a practical approach, where it is possible; but in certain situations it would be impossible to finance new equipment and technology if the total current work force had to be retained. This factor would serve to act as a deterrent to investment that otherwise might easily be raised, to the consuming public's benefit. The net result of this obstruction would be to end the present drive for cost reduction, product standardization, and work simplification. The many in-efficiencies in American industry attributable to union jurisdictions and limiting the work a man may do, regardless of his qualifications, would not be overcome if all workers had to be retained until normal attrition took place. The workers in such a firm would have little real security, for, while the competitive firm would be free to innovate and become more efficient, their employer would slowly go bankrupt, thus terminating employment for the *status quo* workers.

"Past Practices" Clauses

One contractual clause appearing in steel contracts is the "past practices" clause wherein "the parties have made a definite and affirmative assertion of the company's right to change or eliminate any local working condition, if in the exercise of its recognized managerial rights, it has changed or eliminated the basis for that local working condition, and thereby made its continuance unnecessary."[2]

The companies have claimed that the purpose of this clause has been to freeze past inefficiencies. Realistically, it has been impossible for the companies to review all the work rules and practices in effect, to see whether some supervisor has unwisely permitted an inefficient practice to continue or take root. The experience of employers is that such disclosures tie up the problem in a long series of upper echelon grievances and arbitration sessions.

Waste has never been satisfactorily eliminated by this rule. Furthermore, a steelworker official showed how dissatisfied the union was with the rule by stating "that of 186 arbitration contests in U. S. Steel which had involved (past practices) clauses, the union had lost its protest — and the employees their protection — in 145 cases, or almost 80%."[3] It shows, of course, the union's insistence on *status quo*.

Full Employment Helpful in Work-Rules Problem

There appears to be no solution to the work-rules problem, barring full employment. Full employment would be the essential guarantee desired by unions and workers in order to seek jobs elsewhere, with full mobility and without fear. Otherwise, resistance to change and the desire to maintain the *status quo* will continue. The creation of Government retraining programs in electronic methods — by Federal guarantees of training subsidies and of job vacancy and employee availability notifications — might be effective in matching openings and available jobs. Federal assistance in disposing of the house of the displaced worker who wishes to move to a new location would help facilitate mobility.

Social Change and Industrial Change

If management wants workers and unions to be more receptive to the drive to eliminate waste, the industry must be more sympathetic to the need for social change.

Recently, there was much ado in the national press about the fact that most of the new missile contracts are going to the West Coast, where skilled labor is in short supply, while contractors in the East Coast, with a labor surplus, are not getting a proper share of contracts. Secretary of Labor Goldberg immediately went into a "huddle" with the Secretary of Defense to see if this problem could be straightened out, so that national unemployment could drop. This is an example of how national planning, if received and accepted by workers and manufacturers alike, becomes a social change, mutually agreed to.

Working Rules, Displacement, and Job Protection

The number of production workers in basic steel, automobiles, longshoring, railroads, tires, shipping, sawmills, motion pictures, meat packing, and in many other industries has steadily decreased. In an effort to survive and meet the foreign competition of the fifties, firms have aimed at cost reduction and have achieved a substantial reduction as a result of automation and fuller mechanization.

Unfortunately, markets have not expanded as production facilities have been augmented by the automated equipment. This condition has led to unemployment and job displacement. It has also made the unions very unhappy and more anxious than ever to resist changes in work rules and other practices. Controversies over work rules and work practices have come to a head in the basic steel, the railroad, and the glass industries. Employers want to be flexible enough to automate and improve work practices. Unions resist these desires.

Unions Attempt to Regulate Management

Ross states:

> Working rules have an indirect effect on employment; but where displacement is serious, unions may attempt to regulate the process

directly in the name of job protection. Manning tables, restrictions on layoffs, and similar measures may be emphasized. The Supreme Court has recently held that job protection is a legitimate subject of bargaining under American labor law. . . . Two other issues have been aggravated (as employment has declined). The first is subcontracting with its overtones of union jurisdictional conflict. The second is the issue of worker assignment. Can employers redistribute duties, eliminate job titles and make assignments out of classification; or do the employees in any classification have exclusive jurisdiction to perform their customary duties?[4]

Technological displacement is creating a great deal of bitterness in labor relations and is causing much grief for arbitrators, but it has not yet become a major cause for strike. Pointed out by Ross was the fact that, of forty-nine stoppages or strikes in the years 1953 to 1959, only six centered on the issues of job displacement and technological changes. Historically, technological change and displacement have not created major bargaining issues, because the unions decided it was better to gain control of the situation rather than obstruct.

Unions have been able to control the situation satisfactorily by spacing the introduction of machinery, gaining jurisdiction over new jobs, reducing hours, providing dismissal wages, regulating entrance into the trade, and other actions. In 1950 a prominent Harvard professor, Benjamin M. Selekman, could say, "Apparently the historic resistance to the machine, and all it implied, is by this time pretty well dissipated, especially in basic industry. Majority union policy today accepts technological advance, provided there are proper protections for the interests of affected workers."

Automation and Ability to Strike

Issues of work rules and job protection grow more and more impossible of quick solution. Technological change through that highest form of mechanization, automation, will have other impacts on industrial conflict. The power to strike in certain industries has been virtually eliminated by the introduction of highly automatic production facilities. A small number of supervisors are now able to maintain operations in the face of a walkout without having to import scabs. The teamsters *could* interfere with the holdout, but unless deliveries are stopped, the employer is in a very strong position as compared with the employer in the conventional plant.

Oil refining serves as a fine example of the growing weaknesses of certain unions:

> The Oil, Chemical and Atomic Workers recently struck for 191 days against the American Oil Company's refinery at Texas City, Texas. All 1,250 employees walked out on July 1, 1959. On the same day the Company announced its intention to continue operating; and within ten months the rate of production had been raised to about 75% of normal, with 300 supervisors working 6 or 7 days a week. The same union struck for 9 months against the Standard Oil of Indiana at its Sugar Creek, Missouri, refinery in 1959 and 1960. Production was resumed after the first two days and continued at a rate of 50 to 70% until the strike collapsed. The loss of this strike badly handicapped the OCAW in attempting to organize workers represented by independent unions in the oil industry.[5]

The inability to maintain a successful strike or walkout is also illustrated by the telephone industry. Whereas in 1947 the industry took a national walkout of 350,000 workers, the dislocation was fairly serious because there were very few dial installations for long distance dialing. Today, with dial installations and associated automatic equipment, a successful national strike is almost impossible. In fact, the 1955 strike against the Southern Bell Telephone Company was unsuccessful in the ten-week walkout of 80 percent of the personnel, because of the widespread use of the dial. Even sabotage of equipment did not materially affect service or the outcome of the strike. The union (CWA) was in bad shape after the Southern Bell strike, and in worse shape after its strike against Western Electric in 1957, which was reported as follows:

> The long threatened strike of (equipment installers) in 44 states and the District of Columbia had little effect on the general public. From 85 to 90% of the nation's phones . . . . can function indefinitely without attention. There were some delays in long distance service, where much of the equipment is manned by operators. However, supervisory telephone employees moved in and operated the equipment.[6]

From the foregoing examples it would appear that employers are becoming less vulnerable to strikes as a result of technological development.

When industry after industry is finding it easier to produce goods with fewer workers, Government definitely has a responsibility for providing jobs. This sort of issue apparently cannot be settled by traditional collective bargaining techniques. In a statement about the results of the Armour automation studies, Ralph Helstein, president of the United Packinghouse Workers, made the following statement:

> I think I can say categorically, that although no final report is yet available from the Armour automation studies — one thing is clear, and that is that the problems that are being uncovered are such that no company nor no one industry is going to be able to deal with them; and that either we begin to use government as our implement and instrument or we're going to find ourselves in a great deal of difficulty . . . . by the way of our experience with the Armour Automation fund, I think there is great value from having constant meetings (between labor and management) during the time of the regular contract period. These meetings would be devoid of the pressures and the tensions which arise in the collective bargaining procedures at contract renewal time. When there is no contract renewal on hand, you can sit back and talk in much less emotional tones about many of the basic problems that you have. I think this may well lay the basis for eventual agreement when you finally get down under the gun of resolving a contract. To this extent it seems to me to make good sense to have these sessions as a continuing matter throughout the entire period of the contract.[7]

Effect of Automation on Grievances

It might be expected that automation, in its initial application, would lead to a tremendous increase in grievances. This has not been the case. Despite the fact that automation has become a major issue in collective bargaining, it has not unduly affected labor-management relations on a day-to-day basis. Naturally, frictions do develop when, as a result of changing technology, new standards and rates of pay have to be established for the new jobs. There are also problems of transfer or layoffs, but these irritants are more characteristic of the break-in period of automation and not of the period after change has occurred.

In several studies, among them Faunce's[8] of the Detroit automobile industry, it appeared that the grievance rate in the automated plants did not differ appreciably from the grievance rate in the conventional plants.

The analysts in the automobile study also checked grievance records in another plant where some departments had been automated and others had not been. It was concluded that the grievance rate during periods of normal nonautomated operation did not differ from periods of normal automated operation. It may be inferred from these findings that while automation will create grievances and friction during the introductory stage of the new equipment and techniques, it has not appreciably changed the existing patterns of employer-union relations. Unions have apparently decided to place at the bargaining table all their ammunition with respect to automation.

Automation and Seniority

The union response to the problem of spot unemployment consists of pressure for measures to minimize the costs of change borne by workers and to make changes in the work force less attractive to employers. If seniority units are broadened, workers whose jobs otherwise would fall within narrow seniority classifications and who would be unable to "bump back" shorter tenure workers outside those classifications, will be able to bid for more jobs, in the event they are affected. Extension of seniority coverage, from department-wide to plant-wide or from plant-wide to company-wide, would mean that employees could transfer more easily without loss of rights. Strengthened transfer rights and preferential hiring for displaced workers would further bolster the position of the worker who must change jobs or areas in order to remain employed.

Guaranteed wage plans are intended not only to discourage companies from laying off and rehiring workers in response to short-term economic change, but also to protect workers who lose jobs to progress or who must accept reduced or sporadic employment.[9]

Scope of Bargaining Unit

The increase in the number of nonproduction workers and the decline, both relative and absolute, of production workers, will significantly affect union membership. Will unions be able to organize white collar workers more successfully than in past years?

Some increase in labor-management conflict over the scope of the bargaining unit may be expected. For example, should a programmer who displaces a pattern maker be included or excluded from the unit? Most collective bargaining agreements are vague on such points. New kinds of jobs will probably increase jurisdictional disputes, not only between unions but between groups within unions.[10]

Procedures in Automating a Plant

Management is often confronted with the need to make a decision about staffing the newly automated plant or department. In most instances companies are bent on transferring older experienced workers from the conventional plants to the newly automated plants or departments. The usual procedure would be to poll the workers in the conventional plant to determine who wishes to transfer to the automated plant.

When a substantial majority of persons wish to transfer, it may be necessary to prepare seniority lists to determine who should be transferred. In some instances, however, discussions with the union (if one exists) should make it clear that often workers with some particular skill are necessary to set up operations in the new plant. Aside from these special situations, seniority should be adhered to.

Broadened Seniority

Nat Goldfinger, of the Research Department of the AFL-CIO, suggested that in the face of automation seniority areas should be broadened to a plant-wide or a company-wide basis. He also indicated that more thought should be given to the possibilities of "geographic area-wide preferential hiring," with all firms under contract with the union giving preference to laid-off workers in the same industry and area.[11] Reuther has made the point that "new plants should be located where displaced workers from closed plants can be absorbed and where the workers' social investment in the community is not seriously jeopardized.[12] This plan could be possible under Goldfinger's recommendations.

Problems in Seniority

In the Faunce[13] studies of automation in the automobile industry, there was no evidence that the pressure for transfers was any greater in the automated plant than in the conventional plant. Management went to great lengths to discourage transfers, because with automation lack of familiarity with machines and equipment could lead to mistakes much more costly than in the nonautomated plants.

Management was disturbed by the broad seniority units in the plant which facilitated transfers. Management believed that seniority units should be narrowed. The union, however, took the opposite position. It believed that seniority units should be broadened. Because automation does not affect all departments or plants equally, the union argued that seniority units should be broadened to protect the jobs of the high-seniority workers in the automated departments or plants.

Seniority Benefits to Management and Worker

What are the relative advantages of seniority to the manager and to the worker? It appears that "experience" is now of less value to management, since the automated operations are automatically monitored and controlled. Seniority in an automated plant has less value to management than in the conventional plant.

Seniority by job classifications or departments would work against the employee's best interest, since it would restrict transfers as jobs are eliminated by automation. Furthermore, in the automated system, there is no longer the need for the protection of the individual to the degree once necessary. Workers are no longer laid off as individuals, since the unit of labor is now one set of employees for an automated line. If the system is to run, the entire complement of workers is necessary. There is no cost gain by eliminating a fraction of the line; output would be reduced and losses would result.

Effect on Employment

What effect will automation have on employment? The chief reason for the installation of the new equipment seems to be to reduce labor costs. Savings of 75 to 95 percent on manpower are not unusual. Union leaders use the new developments as the basis for a whole army of new bargaining demands ranging from the shorter workweek to conserving natural resources.

Killingsworth describes the response of management to these new union demands:

> A great many company representatives have reacted defensively by denying that automation represents anything new or important, by being secretive about the results achieved by automation, by refusing to cooperate with academic or governmental researchers, or by emphasizing the great job-creating ability of technological change.[14]

In case studies of automation made by Bright,[15] Mann and Hoffman,[16] and special studies made by the Bureau of Labor Statistics, there is considerable agreement that in the short run the man-power requirements per unit of output have been greatly reduced. Jobs were generally found elsewhere in the plant or company for those displaced. Where a total reduction of employees was planned in the light of a forthcoming new installation, new hiring was curtailed so that attrition in a normal way facilitated the adjustment.

Management has learned that there is less resistance to automation when no one in the company loses a job because of it. Expansion in sales or the development of new markets often permits automation without a proportionate increase in the number of workers who might have to be hired on conventional jobs. This is particularly true of certain insurance companies that have expanded their businesses. What will result in the aggregate? In the past decade, while output increased annually, the number of production workers has steadily decreased. Office automation will begin to affect the possible employment of former production workers, or at least stop the employment opportunities of new entrants into the labor force.

How to Alleviate Employment Effects

A common failing is to regard technological unemployment as transitional and temporary. Mobility, which might make up the lack of jobs in an expanding market, becomes absent in a static market. Local depressions remain with us, even in times of substantial national prosperity.

In 1962 Congress passed the Manpower Development and Training Act, described in some detail in Chapter 4. Under this Act funds are provided for education and training of unemployed heads of families as well as unemployed youths, and weekly subsistence allowances up to twelve months of training are permitted. Grants are made to states for instructors' salaries, training equipment, and vocational facilities.

Without a national program aimed at this problem, unions would have to rely on time-honored measures of privately bargained insurance — severance pay, supplemental unemployment benefits, company retraining programs, and area-wide seniority.

Automation and Job Security in Automobile Industry

Faunce[17] and Mann and Hoffman[18] have reported that workers interviewed believed on the whole that automation would result in the displacement of workers. In the Faunce study of 125 workers in newly automated auto plants in Detroit, 90 percent of the sample interviewed were of the opinion that automation would result in increased unemployment.

> There was little evidence, however, that these workers felt that their jobs were less secure because of the change. It is probable that, in industries like the automobile industry where there are both automated and non-automated plants in operation, it is in the non-automated plants that workers may feel that their jobs are less secure as a result of the change.[19]

Effect of Automation on Workday and Workweek

As productivity increases, more goods and services can be produced with a given number of hours of labor. The nation has a choice of alternatives in such a situation: productivity gains can be taken wholly in the form of increased output; present productivity can be maintained, with a corresponding reduction in working hours; or part of the production gain can be applied to increasing output and part to increasing the worker's leisure time.

Since 1900 the average workweek has been shortened from about fifty-five hours to about forty or less. This means that about 33 percent of the productivity gain has gone to provide time off for workers. Unions are estimating that, with automation, a thirty-three-hour week can be expected by 1970. Some doubt has been expressed about this possibility, as the national trend since World War II seems to be in the direction of raising living standards rather than increasing leisure time. A new approach by unions appears to be in the direction of a four-day week rather than a shorter workday. This shorter workweek would permit longer weekends for workers.

Whereas the original desire of unions for shorter hours of work stemmed from the desire to improve the health of their members, this attitude changed with the advent of the Depression of the nineteen thirties. Shorter hours became the key to the sharing of work in depression times and also as a wedge against technological displacement. A principal union contention today is that the increased productivity should allow for more leisure time without reducing the standard of living or take-home pay. If labor continues to aim at shorter workweeks and workdays and longer vacations (sixty days in the maritime unions) without a corresponding increase in productivity, inflation will result and the United States will lose its competitive ability to keep up with the nations of Europe.

The traditional sphere of collective bargaining starts with wages, extends to hours, and ends with working conditions. Automation can have a favorable effect on working conditions, as newer plants of a more healthful type are developed. On the other hand, unions, by demanding restrictive work rules, can cripple the firm that lays out millions for the automated equipment and does not wind up with the expected increase in production per man-hour.

Automation and Working Hours

The number of hours and days worked per week during any period tends to be regarded as natural and immutable.[20] The five-day, forty-hour week is currently so regarded in the vast majority of firms in the United States. On the other hand, companies in the needle trades industries dealing with the International Ladies' Garment Workers Union regard the five-day, thirty-five-hour week as natural, since it has been in force since 1953. The demand made by David McDonald, in the 1962 steel negotiations for a four-day, thirty-two-hour week, sounds very extreme, but if this arrangement were in effect for about five years, no one would "bat an eyelash."

The decline in hours worked per week has averaged about three hours a decade from the beginning of this century to the present. As Seligman has noted, it is the process of reduction of working time, which appears to be "natural and immutable."[21]

In the past twenty-five years, output per man-hour has more than doubled. According to Faunce,[22] "the benefits of this increased productivity have been distributed between income and leisure on a 60–40 basis, 60 percent going into greater income and 40 percent for more leisure time." It is estimated that automation will contribute to more leisure time for workers rather than accelerate an increase in his income. Naturally, the extent to which workers share in the productivity gain from the standpoint of additional income or shorter hours will depend on how the productivity "pie" is cut, and what the pressure of labor unions is bound to be. What is the employer's preference?

> The logic of cost reduction would, in most instances, dictate a management preference for longer hours and fewer workers when the point is reached at which a decrease in hours worked no longer increases productivity.[23]

Effect of Increase in Output per Man-Hour on Short-Term Displacement

Automation has a direct influence on the possible reduction of working hours because of the productivity increases in many plants and offices where automated equipment has been installed. The resultant effect of the development of rapid-transfer machines, computer technology, and electronic inspection devices has undoubtedly influenced the increase in output per man-hour in American industry. What the increase will be in the next decade remains to be seen, but in any event this factor will be a bargaining point in union-management negotiations.

One chemical company recently opened a magnesium mill, which, under automated methods, can produce more magnesium sheet and plate than the previous total national production. A national recording company recently installed new automatic machines. Four men now turn out eight times as many records as 250 men produced previously. A specific automobile engine part, manufactured at a rate of thirty-eight an hour by two machines and five men, is now produced by one man and one machine at the rate of 750 an hour. In a newly automated automobile engine plant, twice as many engines a day are now being produced with one tenth the manpower of the conventional plant.

Pressure for Reduction of Workweek

There appears to be great pressure toward reducing the workweek for production-line workers. Barring increases in product demand, job opportunities in some industries seem to be diminishing. In the period 1947–1948 to 1953–1954, in the automobile industry production workers increased 8 percent, nonproduction workers 69 percent. Semiskilled workers today represent a smaller proportion of the total work force in that industry than a decade ago.

In Faunce's[24] study of the automated automobile industry, the workers were asked whether they would prefer a shorter workweek, increased wages, or longer vacations, if these possibilities developed through automation. About 75 percent of the respondents indicated a preference for the shorter workweek.

Faunce concludes that automation has not made the job more interesting than it was before the advent of the new technology. There are monotonous and repetitive job assignments and little requirements for increasing skill. This situation does not permit the kind of occupational involvement or identification necessary to make work a satisfying experience. When this attitude prevails, workers would like to leave the plant and enjoy more recreation as a result of their leisure-time experience.

Four-Day Week?

Seligman states:

> A majority of a sample of both union and management leadership in the automobile industry interviewed in 1957 expressed the opinion that there would be a reduction of working hours resulting from automation within five to ten years. . . . It has been estimated that if the rate of productivity continues to increase at two or three percent per year, and assuming a continuation of the 60-40 ratio of distribution of increased productivity between income and leisure, a four-day work-week may be feasible throughout the non-farm sector of our economy in twenty-five years.[25]

Evidence based upon union demands in 1962 indicates that the four-day week may come much sooner. If so, it will affect the pattern of leisure activities.

Automation and Leisure Time

Automation may affect patterns of use of leisure time, either by increasing the amount of time available for such activities or by changing the nature of the work experience. With a four-day week, the nature of leisure activities may be affected. Research indicates that the proportion of time spent in various activities increases or decreases, depending on the amount of leisure time available.[26]

> The combination of decreased physical effort required by automated jobs and decreased working hours would make possible a decrease in the proportion of time spent in recuperation from work and permit more active involvement in leisure pursuits. Since recuperative time is likely to be non-creative, there would be at least the possibility for more creative use of leisure with increased time available. Production line workers desiring creative outlets would necessarily seek such experience in leisure activities because of the essentially non-creative character of work in either automated or conventional plants.[27]

One effect of automation on some types of production-line jobs has been the social isolation of workers because of increased distance between work stations and increased attention required by the job.[28]

With this result of automation tied into a reduced workday and workweek, it appears that personnel directors may be in a position where sound planning would develop extracurricular plant social and recreational activities, of the sort to build interest in the industrial environment and the company. A worker employed only six hours a day might enjoy the use of a company gymnasium and steam room for an hour or two a day. The chances are that his income is inadequate to permit the luxury of this activity away from the plant.

Leisure Time and Acquisition of Technical Skills

In another of Faunce's studies of the automobile industry, workers in automated plants were asked about their "proposed use of leisure time." Twenty percent of the workers interviewed replied that they want to "go back to school or learn a trade."[29]

If this desire were to be effectuated by opportunity, the communities do not obviously have enough facilities to meet this need for adult education. What is required is an ambitious program of not merely the providing of technical skills through vocational training, but also the teaching and instilling of values that will have a creative effect on workers on increased leisure time.

Five-Hour Workday for Electricians

Aid and comfort to those unions fighting the effects of automation with demands for shorter workdays and workweeks were given by the New York City electricians in the construction industry, who in January 1962 gained a two-year pact with six hundred electrical contracting concerns calling for a five-hour workday.[30]

Local 3 of the International Brotherhood of Electrical Workers had been demanding a four-hour day. The union, prior to the bargaining, had called for a six-hour day and five-day week, plus one hour of mandatory daily overtime. A spokesman for the Builders Association in New York expected costs to go up to such an extent that rents might have to be raised.

Under the new pact, electricians work five hours a day at $4.96 an hour, but will get an extra hour of mandatory overtime at time and a half ($7.44 an hour). Figuring in the overtime, electricians will receive about $161 for a thirty-hour five-day week under the new contract. Should they continue to work for about seven hours a day (including overtime), as at present, their weekly pay would rise to about $198 a week.

Harry Van Arsdale, business manager of Local 3, said: "the union will do everything possible to discourage overtime. . . . the union wants shorter hours to share work and protect members against the impact of automation, not as a scheme to get more overtime."[31]

The twenty-five-hour victory (without mandatory overtime) was hailed by labor as a major break-through in a national attempt to cut unemployment and was expected to set a pattern of negotiation for other unions. This victory was attained in direct contradiction to President Kennedy's efforts against reducing the workweek because of world competition. The New York Central Labor Council was quoted as follows:

> A shorter work week is our goal in every industry — production, construction and service. We believe that this major breakthrough has opened the door to general advances in this field.[32]

It was indicated that the next big push might come in the steel industry, where a dwindling number of workers is required to operate the mills because of automation.

Four-Hour Day by 1970

Victor Reisel, a labor columnist writing in the *Philadelphia Inquirer*, stated:

> The unprecedented five hour day for New York City Electricians is a breakthrough for labor that will lead to similar hours for other workers. . . . The four hour work day . . . will become a reality within the next ten years. . . . The four hour work day will probably be attained through round-about methods: a three month sabbatical, certain days off, or other time saving methods. . . . Labor is the most powerful political group in the nation, and the man who controls it controls the destiny of millions of human beings. . . . James Hoffa wants all groups that distribute, all organizations that move, all men who make deliveries, to come together in one conference. . . . (if this were accomplished by Hoffa) then Hoffa would have the labor contracts of members of the conference expire on a common date, and be in a position to dictate his demands to industry, and to cripple the nation if his demands were not met.[33]

Forty-Hour Workweek Desired by Administration

In February 1962, President Kennedy took the lead in championing a continuation of the standard eight-hour day, forty-hour week. Automation has intensified the union desire for a shorter workweek.

The President strongly disapproved the twenty-five-hour week won by the electricians in New York City. He was concerned that the demands of the steel union during the early part of the 1962 negotiations might center on a thirty-two-hour week, thus spreading the work in the face of automation-induced production gains.

In the face of automation, job security has taken precedence over wages. Either the unions win a shorter workweek, or they want guarantees that management decisions on mergers or newly automated departments will not reduce the number presently employed.

In the latter part of 1962 most of the important national unions in the AFL-CIO, particularly those in the basic industries, came out strongly in favor of the thirty-five-hour workweek.

Management Opposition to Shorter Workweek

Management translates the shorter workweek right back into dollars. It says it seeks mechanization to cut costs and to be more competitive with foreign manufacturers. It also wants to maintain price levels. If hours are cut, management must hire more men to fill out a regular week. To the union, this action means sharing the available work; to management, it means that the cost-cutting advantages of mechanization may have been lost.

The Kennedy administration wants wages to go up if productivity goes up; thus, inflation will be negated. When mechanization means an increase in the amount of goods turned out by the same number of man-hours of labor, then this is a true rise in productivity.

President Kennedy's economic advisors believe that labor should limit its demands in the next few years to the range of productivity gains. The President implies that this rule of thumb is the same, whether the demand is for higher wages for the same amount of work or for the same pay for less work. Although most executives may agree with the President, their thinking goes even further. They desire that a substantial part of the productivity gains be translated into funds the company can use for growth.

Managers also hold that since higher productivity means larger earnings, these factors, translated into fatter dividends, also serve economic growth. Their argument is that such productivity and earnings build up capital funds to be tapped for the expansion; the Nation thus must have to provide more jobs and to compete with foreign goods.

For the individual worker, however, the problem is likely to mean security as a primary goal, either sharing the work through shorter weeks or else insuring that his own income and standard of living will not be undermined.

Problems of Maritime Industry

The maritime industry is an excellent illustration of an industry in which restrictive work practices have resulted in the building up of an American-owned foreign-flag fleet, generally registered in Panama, Liberia, and Honduras. The size of this fleet is impressive. It includes over 10,000,000 dead-weight tons and, for the most part, employs Italians, Norwegians, British, Dutch, and West German nationals. Approximately 40,000 foreign seamen are employed on these American-owned ships, and these seamen are not members of American labor unions. However, the SIU and NMU are trying to organize these seamen as a result of some favorable decisions of the National Labor Relations Board.

The reason that Americans own these foreign-flag ships is their economical performance. By avoiding the featherbedding and restrictive work practices of the American unions, the owners may operate these ships at one quarter the daily cost of an American-flag vessel.[34]

In the study of the foreign-flag fleet made by the author, the following statement appeared:

> Every effort should be made to utilize the excellent researches of the Maritime Commission Shipboard Mechanization and Manpower Study released June 20, 1961. It is obvious that the manning of a semi-automated vessel versus a non-automated vessel would save approximately 50% of the personnel required to operate a vessel and reduce the total wage cost by approximately 40%.[35]

This fact is borne out by the following data taken from operation studies of the Maritime Commission. Obviously, if automation takes place in American-flag ships, there will be less pressure to employ the foreign-flag fleet. The big question, however, is, Will American unions permit semiautomated devices to be used, in the face of a history of restrictive work practices and the large number of unemployed American seamen?

COMPARISON OF MANNING ON A MARINER-SIZE VESSEL[36]

	Nonautomated	Semiautomated
Master	1	1
Licensed Officers		
Deck	4	7
Engine	8	6
Radio	1	0
Electrical-Electronic	0	1
Unlicensed		
Deck	14	4
Engine	14	3
Steward	13	4
Total	55	26

SOURCE: Maritime Administration and SNAME Panel MO-1 Progress Report.

COMPARISON OF ANNUAL FLEET COSTS TO OPERATOR[37]

	Nonautomated ($1,000's)	Semiautomated ($1,000's)
Amortization (after construction subsidy)	$2,324	$2,368
Operating Costs (before operating subsidy)		
Wages	2,760	1,615
Other	3,655	3,535
Total Annual Costs	$8,739	$7,518
Operating Subsidy under each cost structure	$2,760	$1,885

SOURCE: Paper No. 11, SNAME ANNUAL MEETINGS, November 17 and 18, 1960, New York.

Restrictive Work Practices on Railroads

Early in 1962 an announcement that the New York Central and the Pennsylvania Rail Road might merge led to a threatened strike by Michael Quill, head of the Transport Workers Union. This threat created a great deal of bitterness, and the Pennsylvania Rail Road threatened a countersuit for several millions. Apparently Quill feared that a large railroad merger of this sort would result in heavy layoffs and in the continued and progressive use of automated equipment. The railroad problem is serving as a background for the union-

management squabbles of 1962. All these battles are related directly
or indirectly to job security. Unions see a threat to American workers
by both automation and reduced tariffs, and this fear has been
stimulated by talk of the United States joining the European Common Market. The passage in 1962 of the Trade Expansion Act appears to justify this talk.

Effect of Automation on Railroads

What can and should the railroad industry do to make the jobs
of its workers more secure? If layoffs are unavoidable, what benefits
have rail workers the right to expect? These questions have plagued
the railroads and the brotherhoods for years. In 1957 a study was
commissioned by the Brotherhood of Maintenance and Way employees, and four professors — William Haber, John J. Carroll, Mark
L. Kahn, and Merton J. Peck — were given a free hand. Out of their
investigations came a book of great value to students of automation
and technological displacement (see reference 38 at end of chapter).

The severity of the problem is evidenced by the fact that in 1957
only 44 percent as many waymen were employed as in 1921. In 1957
the railroad industry employed only 63 percent of the number of
workers employed in 1921. During this same period, rail traffic had
increased 50 percent.

The analysts found that the most important causes of job loss
were technological change and interindustry competition. Mechanization and automation were accompanied by wooing away of traffic
by trucks, buses, and airlines. It was found that thousands of waymen
were laid off at the slightest recession and that there was tremendous
seasonal unemployment during the cold months.

Haber and collaborators considered the possibility of recommending that a number of workers be retained as part of a regular work
force based on past standards, but they rejected this idea because it
would hamper technological progress and postpone innovations.
Furthermore the railroads faced interindustry competition and the
suggested plan would hamper their ability to compete still further.

The analysts likewise rejected the idea of sharing the work by
reducing the workweek below 40 hours. Such a proposal might work
in an expanding industry, but not in the railroads.

They finally came up with some positive suggestions, which will
be of interest to all industries in America facing automation:

1. *Prior Notice and Joint Consultation.* Good contract administration is essential for effective adjustment to new machines and methods. In general, the existing contracts make the rates for new positions a matter of negotiation. Effective negotiation ordinarily requires adequate notice of contemplated changes and the holding of conferences before the changes are instituted. . . . A collectively bargained national rule governing prior notice and joint consultation on changes in machines and methods might prove an effective way to raise the average practice towards the level of the best, without interfering with system-level decisions on matters of substance.

2. *Access to New Occupations.* Maintenance of way employees should have a preferential opportunity to qualify for new types of jobs in maintenance and way departments. Training for employees who can qualify in a reasonable period should be at company expense. . . . The definition of *reasonable* must evolve from negotiations or on a case by case basis. It would be affected by the qualifications of current employees in relation to new job requirements; by the amount of training outsiders would require; by the full costs of displacing regular employees; and by the costs and length of training.

3. *Job Reclassification.* Orderly wage administration requires the prompt reclassification and rerating of changed jobs or new types of jobs. Our investigations indicate that on many carriers these actions are not taking place or only after long delays. Many *laborers* appear to be operating machines.

4. *Compensation for Deterioration in Working Conditions* . . .

5. *Preferential Hiring.* Employees who must be separated from their regular maintenance of way jobs should be given preferential access, on an orderly basis, to any opening in other departments of the same carrier or in any departments of other carriers.

6. *Dismissal Compensation* (on account of technological displacement).

7. *Negotiated Retraining Provisions.*[38]

Recognition of the principle of dismissal compensation as a result of technological displacement has been added to the dicta of the Washington Agreement of 1936, which protected workers who lost jobs as a result of railroad mergers. This new principle was contained in a 1956 agreement between the Chesapeake & Ohio Railroad and the Brotherhood of Railroad Clerks dealing with the establishment of a new Univac computer center:

It is hereby agreed to adopt and apply the beneficial provisions of the so-called "Washington Agreement" of May 1936, to all employees adversely affected as a result of their work being placed in the Computer

Center from time to time; so as to provide similar treatment to those which would have been provided or accorded had the work gone into the Computer Center from two or more carriers and thus constituted a coordination as that term is used and defined in the so-called "Washington Agreement."[39]

The Washington Agreement

The Washington Agreement has been previously mentioned in an earlier chapter. It bears repetition, since unions, who point to collective bargaining as the medium by which understanding and mutual cooperation on problems of automation can be achieved, think in terms of the Washington Agreement. This agreement was negotiated in 1936 by the railroad companies and the unions. In those days, of course, the displacement problem was caused by railroad mergers. There are two schools of thought about the Washington Agreement. Railroad management believes that it added to the carrier costs and contributed to the present insolvency of many of the nation's railroads. On the other hand, the unions have been able to live under it and regard it as a kind of "bible."

The Washington Agreement included:

1. Displacement allowances based upon seniority. The displaced employee received 60 percent of average monthly pay for the previous 12 month period for as long as six months for employees with low seniority, up to five years for employees with 15 years service.

2. Job protection against downgrading of wages or working conditions for 5 years for employees retained.

3. Moving expenses for employees who keep their jobs but must move to a new location. The moving expenses, costs of the employee, and his family living expenses while relocating, and the losses from forced sale of homes, are paid.[40]

Railroad Commission Report on Featherbedding

A practical test of the power of unions to oppose technological advancement was made when a White House Commission on the Railroad Problem made its report to President Kennedy on March 1, 1962. The panel handed the President an exhaustive report recommending methods by which the railroads may eliminate many thousands of workmen it said "aren't needed to operate moving trains."

The Commission agreed in effect with the carriers that for years they have been saddled with featherbedding requirements to keep on unnecessary workers. It said that some 35,000 firemen on diesel locomotives in freight and yard service serve no useful purpose and should be gradually eliminated. The panel urged that the railroad industry be allowed to adjust to advancing technology in order to free itself of nineteenth century methods and to maintain a rightful and necessary place in the nation's transportation system.

Union Opposition to Commission Report

Only the public and management members of the panel accepted the report. The union members denounced the report as "shabby, obnoxious, a tragedy." Immediately after the release of the report, Michael J. Quill, president of the Transport Workers Union, called on the Government to seize and operate the railroads.

Said Quill, "They have decided that 35,000 yard and freight firemen are to be consigned to the slag heap of misery called structural unemployment, which grows ever larger daily."[41]

The President called on management and unions to enter into collective bargaining on the recommendation of the Commission, "being mindful that they have an overriding national responsibility." Kennedy added:

> The railroad industry is a conspicuous illustration of the problem of changing technology. While seeking ways to reap the benefits of advancing technology, it is necessary at the same time to preserve basic human interests.[42]

Principal Recommendation of the Railroad Commission

The principal proposals of the Railroad Commission follow:

1. Abolish firemen gradually, beginning July 1, 1962, from all freight and yard service locomotive crews. This alone would wipe out some 35,000 jobs within a decade — at eventual savings estimated at $250 million a year. Firemen would continue on passenger locomotives.

2. Give the railroads an unlimited right to introduce technological change, subject to the continued pay and other protections provided for employees losing their jobs.

3. Eliminate crew-change requirements at inter-divisional terminals.

4. Overhaul the complex operating employee-pay system, of "dual pay," in which workers are paid both for the time and mileage on their runs. There are widespread pay disparities and inequities which need correction.

5. Shorten work hours for many workers. Some employees work only four hours for a day's pay; others as much as 15 hours. The present 16 hour limit on a work day should be quickly reduced to 14 and eventually to 12.

6. Require more overtime pay to discourage management from working the men long hours. This would also spread jobs. Along that line, an immediate retirement for men 70 and over should be made mandatory. Over a five-year period the mandatory retirement age would be reduced to 65.

7. The net effect of the various pay proposals would raise payroll costs by 2%; three-fourths of the work group would get more pay! Pay adjustments would cost about 60 millions per year, but eliminating the firemen and having freedom to make changes would mean considerably greater economies.

8. Carriers should give considerable attention to management development and training to enable the railroads to look ahead, develop and adopt new technology as well as improve quality of service to the passenger and shipper.

9. Instead of five rail operating unions, there should only be two. One should cover engine service employees and one train service employees. The engine service union should merge the engineers and firemen, while the train service union should cover trainmen, conductors and switchmen. The mergers should not be postponed; they must be achieved if industrial relations in the railroad industry are to be improved in the best interests of the employees and the community.[43]

In November 1962 the Federal courts enjoined the railroads from effectuating any of the recommendations of the Railroad Commission, and at this writing action in this respect has been deferred.

Conclusion

The standard of living in the United States may very well be affected by a continuation of restrictive practices. Unless restrictive practices are considered and resolved by management, unions, and possibly Government, the fear of automation will tend to increase such practices.

Restrictive practices of labor and of management have no place in a competitive world, for they sabotage society. They benefit no one, and corrupt all who are subjected to them. As Goodman says:

> Born in the past [restrictive practices] are out of place in the present. Let us hope that these practices are done away with and rapidly, for they can do much to harm full employment and thus automation, by keeping down the increase in the production of wealth which is so necessary, if there is to be any considerable increase in the standard of living.[44]

References

1. N. W. Chamberlain, "Work Rules," from *Industrial Relations in the 1960's, Problems and Prospects*, George W. Taylor and Edward B. Shils, eds., University of Pennsylvania Labor Relations Council, February 15, 1961, p. 7.
2. *Ibid*, p. 9.
3. *Ibid.*, p. 10.
4. Arthur M. Ross, "Changing Role of the Strike," from *Industrial Relations in the 1960's, Problems and Prospects, op. cit.*, pp. 19–20.
5. *Ibid.*, p. 22.
6. *Journal of Commerce*, September 17, 1957.
7. Ralph Helstein, remarks made on November 18, 1960, at the University of Pennsylvania Labor Relations Conference.
8. W. A. Faunce, "The Automobile Industry; A Case Study in Automation," from *Automation and Society*, H. B. Jacobson and J. S. Roucek, eds., (New York: Philosophical Library, 1959), pp. 47–48.
9. Jack Rogers, *Automation: Technology's New Face*, Berkeley: University of California, 1958, p. 82.
10. C. W. Killingsworth, "Automation in Manufacturing," Labor and Industrial Relations Center reprint, Michigan State University, vol. 53, no. 14, May 1959, p. 13.
11. Nat Goldfinger, "Labor Views Planned Adjustment to Automation," *Advanced Management*, vol. 21, no. 5, May 1956, pp. 16–28.
12. Walter P. Reuther, "Automation," the *Detroit Free Press*, Section F (Sunday), June 3, 1956.
13. Faunce, *op. cit.*, p. 46.
14. Killingsworth, *op. cit.*, p. 6.
15. Bright, *Automation and Management*, Boston, Division of Research, Graduate School of Business Administration, Harvard University, 1958.

16. Floyd C. Mann and L. Richard Hoffman, "Individual and Organizational Correlates of Automation," *Journal of Social Issues*, vol. 12, 1956, pp. 7–17.
17. Faunce, "Automation and the Automobile Worker," *Social Problems*, vol. VI, no. 1, Summer 1958, pp. 68–78.
18. Mann and Hoffman, *op. cit.*, pp. 7–17.
19. Faunce, *op. cit.*, p. 75.
20. Faunce, "Automation and Leisure," from *Automation and Society*, H. B. Jacobson and J. S. Roucek, eds., (New York: Philosophical Library, 1959), p. 298.
21. Daniel Seligman, "The Four Day Work Week: How Soon," *Fortune*, July 1954, p. 81.
22. Faunce, *op. cit.*, p. 298.
23. *Ibid.*, p. 299.
24. *Ibid.*, p. 300.
25. Seligman, *op. cit.*, p. 114.
26. George Lundberg, et al., *Leisure* (New York: Columbia University Press, 1932), p. 123.
27. Faunce, *op. cit.*, p. 302.
28. Faunce, "Automation in the Automobile Industry: Some Consequences for In-Plant Social Structure," *American Sociological Review*, XXIII, August 1958.
29. Faunce, *op. cit.*, pp. 304–305.
30. *Wall Street Journal*, January 19, 1962, p. 11.
31. *Ibid.*
32. *Philadelphia Inquirer*, January 19, 1962, p. 1.
33. Victor Reisel, Philadelphia *Inquirer*, January 24, 1962, p. 41.
34. E. B. Shils, "The Flag of Necessity Fleet and the American Economy," *Labor Law Journal*, February 1962, p. 161.
35. *Ibid.*
36. *Increased Mechanization and Automation of Ships* (D. C. MacMillan, Chairman), Maritime Administration and SNAME Panel MO-1 Progress Report, November 4, 1960.
37. *Competitive General Cargo Ships* (D. C. MacMillan and T. B. Westfall), Paper no. 11, SNAME Annual Meetings, November 17 and 18, 1960.
38. William Haber, John J. Carroll, Mark L. Kahn, and Merton J. Peck, "Maintenance of Way Employment on U. S. Railroads — An Analysis of Sources of Instability and Remedial Measures," Detroit, Brotherhood of Maintenance of Way Employees, 1957.
39. William Haber and Mark L. Kahn, "Maintenance of Way Employment," *Monthly Labor Review*, October and November, 1957, Reprint No. 2265 (U. S. Department of Labor, Bureau of Labor Statistics), p. 6.
40. "The Impact of Automation — A Challenge to America," AFL-CIO *American Federationist*, August 1961, vol. 68, no. 8. p. 17.

41. *Philadelphia Inquirer*, March 1, 1961, p. 1.
42. *Ibid.*, p. 1 and 3.
43. *Ibid.*
44. L. Landon Goodman, *Man and Automation* (Harmondsworth, Middlesex: Penguin Books, 1957), p. 173.

▶ ▶ ▶ ▶ **14**

Influence of
Automation on Education,
Training, and Retraining
Programs

Education in general, as well as technical and vocational training, will have to be adjusted to changes resulting from automation. The progress made in education and training will determine how well society will adjust to the new technology.

Automation offers the teacher a challenge on two levels: the industrial level and the college and university level. Engineers with a variety of technical backgrounds will be needed to man automated processes. "Control" or "systems" engineers, with a wide knowledge of the technique of control, will have to be developed. Engineers versed in both electronics and mechanical engineering will be required to introduce the concept of control to traditional engineering processes. The nation will have to train and develop production engineers who understand the statistical techniques and who will obtain the best performance from complex systems of machines. There will be a new profession called "tool engineer," whose responsibility will be to find the most economic method of machining components. The college, the university, and the technical institute obviously do not have courses that successfully cut across traditional lines and meet the "integrated" approach to knowledge required under automation.

Much of the same need, evidenced at the professional level, will be manifested at the level of the junior technician and craftsman. Here, however, the urgency to train will have to be the primary responsibility of industry. Industry will have to take more direct action than it has taken to make certain that courses for technicians are available in vocational high schools and technical institutes. General training will be of value at the technician level, but many firms will want their employee courses tailored to meet their own needs.

Impact on Education Level of New Employees

A higher proportion of the new entrants into the labor force will be needing secondary school technical education and apprenticeship training up to and beyond the skilled worker level.

The changing skill requirements of industry must be reflected in the vocational training of young persons, which becomes the combined responsibility of the Government, industry, labor, and the community. The one-time emphasis on the classical trades — blacksmiths, foundrymen, plumbers, tailors and bricklayers — is running out. Training for the new skills must be developed in school at an earlier age. For example, repair and maintenance of electronic computers require new skills and knowledge, different from those needed in the classical trades.

There is current disagreement as to whether or not the training of youth should be more intensive and more technically oriented, or whether on-the-job training is the answer to acquisition of the "new" skills. Many believe that a genuine foundation in mathematics and science will enable youth to undertake many different kinds of work in a broad interindustrial field. Courses in physics, chemistry, and electricity are very important, but another school of thought still believes in systematic on-the-job training.

One well-known industrialist recently stressed the point that automation will necessitate more intensive apprenticeship training. Even those who agree with the idea of apprenticeship training believe that it will have to be changed radically to be effective. A new emphasis on group training is suggested for youth, with alternating periods of study and work. At Drexel Institute of Technology in Philadelphia, such training is termed the "cooperative" program. In the last few years in the United States, a new apprenticeship scheme has been launched for both "electronic laboratory technicians" and for "machine-tool mechanics." These programs deal primarily with machines used in automatic processes.

Since the new developing skills require more extensive basic education, the concept of vocational training will have to be changed. A broadened attitude toward the vocational aspects of education will raise the prestige of vocational education, and many a youngster preparing for the traditional four-year program because of the status factor might be interested in a two-year post high school technical institute training or in a two-year community college.

Need for Vocational Guidance

Training will be impossible without good vocational guidance. Persons who undertake training will have to be carefully selected through interviews, counseling, aptitude tests, and other means of selection. Otherwise a great deal of the firm's or the taxpayer's money may be wasted.

Vocational guidance should be attuned to job opportunities. Several years ago the Renault works in France was graduating 150 craftsmen a year at its training school. Suddenly demand changed and milling-machine operators, fitters, and turners could not be placed. In the past few years, training at Renault has been directed away from the traditional trades to machine setters for automatic lathes or transfer machines, and toolmakers for plastics. As automation moves forward, no gap must be allowed between production and training.

Vocational guidance will fail unless there are adequate community training facilities, and access to these facilities by trainees both from the standpoint of location and ability to pay.

Training and Retraining of Older Workers

Socially and psychologically, a serious impact is being felt by the adult worker. Changes in the occupational and skill structure are tending to upset the stability of the worker and his family and thus to confuse him. Industrial managers agree that retraining programs are necessary for the employed worker whose job content is changing in the automated plant. Training directors will agree that a great deal of disappointment and bitterness have resulted from attempts to retrain these persons.

Training officers and managers now agree that the older worker requires not only retraining in techniques, but also a fuller understanding of reasons for these changes. Workers tend to learn more readily when they participate and see the implications of technological development. They must not be made to feel that training is being forced on them.

Retraining cannot be a standardized and mechanized affair. A more imaginative approach is required, particularly for the older workers and especially those whose areas of skill have disappeared as a result of technological change. A retraining program for workers in the middle years, as well as of the supervisory staff, must make allowance for certain psychological and emotional problems. The retraining of skilled workers and supervisors must take into full account their instinctive desire to preserve their relative occupational and social status within the firm or organization.

Automation appears to favor for supervisory spots those men who have had more formal and technical education. In retraining programs the attempt is often made to give to the older men with seniority claims to higher jobs some of the formal education which they lack and which the younger men usually have. There appears to be some danger that the growing emphasis on education may reduce the esteem with which experience-based knowledge has been held.

Retraining is partly an industry problem and partly a community problem. In so far as a company-wide retraining program for the plant's labor force is set up to effect skill adjustments to technological advances, the responsibility lies largely with the plant, often shared by the union.

The retraining of already displaced workers is a community responsibility, shared by the Federal, state, and local governments in cooperation with employers and unions. Later in this chapter, the progress under the Area Redevelopment Act and the Manpower Development and Training Act is discussed in some detail.

Short-Term Training

Short-term training is generally carried out by supervisors in the plant or by experienced workers, or, when individual training takes considerable time, by methods, engineers, or specialized instructors.

In the Ford Company's automated engine plants, special courses, in addition to on-the-job training, were developed in cooperation with machine-tool manufacturers, to move employees from old to new operations. Training courses were arranged for maintenance personnel, including specialized training in hydraulics, lubrication, electricity, and electronics and an over-all program on automation technology.

General Mills has had an extensive program of retraining. Its experts serve as instructors in the local vocational high schools; the company provides material and specialized equipment and also works with the school in recommending and designing new courses in producing of new products or introducing and operating of new techniques.

Most other large American firms provide training to enable workers to handle new assignments. The greater part of the training is done by supervisors or through "vestibule" training schools, which run for one to two weeks in preparation for a specific kind of work.

Several highly automated enterprises, the larger corporations, employ a specialized training staff, which assists maintenance, production, and methods engineers and supervisors in preparing programs for retraining workers in case of major changeover. It is difficult for the employer to visualize how training methods and training content must change. In the past, the worker had to be shown how to run a machine or to perform a hand operation, and was given direct control over the machine or tool. With automatic equipment, the instructor's job is to teach the worker to keep his hands off the machine, leaving adjustments and repairs to the professional or technical maintenance staff.[1]

Managerial and Supervisory Staff

Training for the management of automatic processes is linked with the training of technical manpower, because these processes break down the distinction between technical and managerial skills. Managerial decisions are vitally important when they affect the maintenance and operation of the integrated plant, and they can be made only by persons who know the plant intimately as a technical system.

Control will tend to pass into the hands of technical specialists, and the institutions of higher technical education may be asked to give students more training for management. Automation will, in fact, reinforce a need that already exists, because of the growing complexity of modern factories.

Automatic production is also likely to increase the advantages of formal training in management, because each plant must operate as a unified whole, and such operation is best achieved by techniques of managerial planning and control, which have to be acquired by formal training. Industry may need to take steps to secure adequate facilities for such training, as well as technical training, and the universities and engineering colleges will be expected to contribute much more than they have contributed in the past.

Promotional Problems

Technological change may force a reappraisal of opportunities for promotion. Automation would have an adverse effect if the existing gap in skill and knowledge between operatives and supervisors becomes too great to be bridged by experience on the job. The same problem would be evident as between technicians and managers. If promotion under automation depends on higher educational qualifications on a broader scale, then the worker will find it more difficult to advance on the basis of his work experience alone. Many supervisors who have obtained long experience with the same firm are looking with distaste at the young engineers brought in by management and put over them. Will it be possible to train the young skilled worker without formal education to become a supervisor under automation? Or will he retrogress, ending up structurally unemployed because of the obsolescence of his skill? Will there be a real promotion possibility for those without too much formal education who enter automated industry as apprentices? Management can provide for this dead end only by supplying flexible and versatile training. A good foundation will be a requisite for later retraining and upgrading.

Recent technological changes are likely to emphasize the need for more adult education, not only by retraining for new types of employment of workers whose skills have become obsolete through technological advance, but in a determined way for raising the general level of knowledge and industrial skills. If adult education does not progress in this way, accelerated technological advance is likely to increase the difficulties already experienced in finding employment for middle-aged and older workers, and in impeding their promotion to more responsible jobs.

Educational advance and technological advance must go hand in hand. The education and training of adult workers is a continuing necessity for absorbing technological improvements smoothly and equitably. Retraining is not a form of skill conversion. It is a form of education.

The Automated Manager

Before the corporation executive can give anyone, human or robot, an analysis of his operations, he must think the process through for himself. He must be able to define precisely what he is doing now, and compare that to what he wants to do. Few men are prepared to undergo this rigorous discipline.

I will not be surprised if we have to wait for a new generation of managers before we put automation into full effect. I suspect it will take that long to develop the new perspective. Even then the universities will be able to complete the evolution in time only if they modernize their mathematics courses (most of which now stop three hundred years back) and add computer laboratories where physical and social sciences can be studied as the intertwined realities they are in the office-campus world.[2]

The preceding statement by John Lear, who at the time was science editor of the *Saturday Review*, explains in a nutshell what the problem will be in finding the right sort of managers for the automated plant.

While the intellectual process of preparing curriculums and training students in the new management takes place, interim automation will be processed. As competition dictates new machines with the ability to direct and inspect their own work, production will increase and breakdown costs will rise. As human operators will decline in numbers, their need for a more exact knowledge of their tools will grow. Specialized jobs will be merged into amalgams. In place of maintenance teams of narrowly skilled craftsmen will be general mechanics. Training and retraining will be of the utmost importance. Training, formerly considered a staff responsibility, will now be the most important item in the line. Supervisors will become analysts in the new system of technology and will want to know why something occurs, how to prevent it, as well as what to do about it when it does occur. In many cases supervision will be by remote control, and the psychology of leadership will change and be subjected to many strains. Foremen and workers will have to be more broadly taught both skills and the human side of production. This teaching will have to be done at the plant. The universities will not have the time to do it.[3]

Automation will give a boom to the matter of "training directors." It will often present new opportunities for the profession in training not only new workers but also old workers, many of whom will find their jobs destroyed by automation. Training and retraining should not be confined to merely showing a man how to manipulate his hands in a production operation. Today, mechanical hands are actuated by electrical nerves guided by electronic impulses; what is needed is the training of workers to understand thoroughly the new relationships between men and machines.

Training Costs

The cost of training will increase under automation. Many processes will require the retraining of those who have already passed their fortieth and fiftieth birthdays. Both the Government and the employer should be interested in retraining these workers, who are seriously affected by automation. Unions take the position that retraining should be a charge against the cost of production. Inasmuch as the employer amortizes his highly automated equipment and includes the cost in the price of the product, why should he not be required to amortize similarly the retraining costs necessary to take care of workers affected by displacement?

Training Problems Ahead

Aaron Levenstein, editor-in-chief of the Research Institute of America, has pinpointed some problems the training director will have to face as a result of the new technology of automation:

> First he will have to face the rapid obsolescence of equipment and skills. There will be a shortage in the type of personnel needed to handle the new methods and equipment. We may be facing a new kind of illiteracy in a mathematical society. A new kind of executive will have to understand what the new machines can do and how they can be put to work to solve specific business problems.[4]

Obviously executive retraining will be essential because of the entire change in the financial base for operating an automated plant. Market researchers will have to be retrained to understand the relative inflexibility of the automated plant and the need for standardizing product design to permit machined automaticity.

The nature of employee relations will change as the attitudes of workers change and as their adjustment to change in the automated plant becomes a matter of stress and strain. Training directors will have to be more skilled to accomplish what is desired by management. Workers will no longer be motivated by the end result of production, because they cannot readily see their share of the product. Automation will increase the "depersonalization" of work and make human-relations training more important.

Colleges and universities should be giving increased attention to the requirements of the new industrial technology. They should not be limiting their efforts to engineering or the training of computer specialists. They should be preparing men and women in the humanities, so that they are better able to think through industrial problems to help people use their leisure intelligently, to explore the elusive problem of obtaining job satisfaction in a depersonalized society.

Training is one of the most important responsibilities of management. Does the opening of a newly automated plant or department require special training for the upgrading of skills and abilities? Early analysis of the skill levels required in conventional plants versus those in automated plants showed rather conclusively that upgrading or extensive retraining was not always necessary in production jobs. In a number of studies, among them Faunce's work on automation in the automobile industry in Detroit, it was stated that "management in the plant did not feel that new skills were required in semiskilled classifications on automated lines and as a result training programs were not set up for machine operators."[5] There is some controversy on depth needs in training on the "new" job. At any rate, the training director is faced with a challenge: analyze each job to determine how much training, if any, is required.

Where Training Is Required

In the automobile studies, some training was given job setters and machine repairmen through special training programs in hydraulics and electrical circuits. The most important personnel problem created by automation into the new plant was the need to procure skilled salaried technicians and engineers.

With complex electrical circuits and hydraulic lines spread over a transfer machine, which may be more than one hundred yards long, it becomes very difficult to determine the causes of machine breakdown. A situation such as this requires technicians who can repair damage quickly, since expensive machinery is amortized over shorter periods than formerly, and stoppages are very costly. Engineers and technicians need to know their business, but they need also to get their hands dirty. Their jobs are not theory jobs. The Faunce study mentioned previously indicated that the automated plant required about thirty technicians who would have never been hired under the conventional system.

It has always been held true in industry that, as the worker is provided with more complex tools, he needs increased training in order to understand the operation, the adjustments, and the variety of operative tasks to which the tool or machine can be put. When power is applied to the tool, and the worker is responsible for the fine adjustments, he has to learn more and more about machinery. He therefore needs additional training to understand the principles underlying the machine's operation and adjustment.

As automaticity approaches the higher levels in the metalworking industry, operators are substituted for "machinists," because of the introduction of automatic cycling, wherein a pattern of predetermined actions can be mechanically achieved. When this stage is effected, the operator is not required to have the skill and knowledge for making fine adjustments. The control over the complex has been taken from him.

Retraining Necessary for Certain Maintenance Workers

Many maintenance men, such as carpenters and welders, do not need upgrading by additional training. Electricians, however, definitely need this training, since they are now confronted by problems of electronic circuits requiring substantial knowledge of the theory and practice of electronics. Bright reports that "one engine plant has studied this problem and concluded that almost 2,000 hours would be needed in class and shop work to provide adequate electronic training, in addition to the firm's existing journeyman electrical training program of three years."[6]

Automation also requires training of a new type of repairman, one competent in the various phases of control circuits. Considerable downtime is lost as a result of sending out individual specialists to work on the malfunctioning machine, each finding that his skill and knowledge are inadequate.

> Obtaining this kind of maintenance ability involves a training problem and a union relations problem which very few managers have tackled, and fewer still have solved.[7]

Are Competent Supervisors Available?

In newly automated plants and departments management has been complaining principally about a lack of adequately trained supervisors. The missing ingredients, management points out, are alertness, perception, and judgment with respect to equipment operation, and the implications of downtime. "The ability to see ahead — to plan, instead of to live from hour to hour — is what the old line foreman doesn't have."[8]

This unfavorable situation opens up new areas for supervisory training, and it is significant that most firms have been getting along with their old foremen, despite the many management complaints. Unless firms going into automation expect to build their own equipment, the need for a great many engineers does not appear to be present.

Training for Change

John Diebold advises managers not only to educate themselves for the fullest use of data processing, but also to fulfill educational programs for the "men and women who have completed their formal education and are now working in business and industry." He calls for "training which is more basic, broader in scope, more intensive, given in greater depth" than an understanding of only one manufacturer's computer. His strong appeal for education about data processing is phrased thus: "Of one thing I am certain: automation is going to demand better educated men, in the fullest sense of the word," and he adds: "Automation, and technological advance, demand an ability to adapt to change."[9]

Whether business management accepts this kind of advice immediately on automating or later after more experience with it, the implication to trade union people is clear. The union concern shall be that their members receive the on-the-job training they require, while they continue to receive regular remuneration and maintain their job security. The union should provide some off-the-job training as well, either by night-school or by home-study courses. The members should be encouraged to take the additional training, to benefit by higher job classification and wages and thus to realize greater personal fulfillment.

Research and Development Costs

American industry spends about ten billion dollars a year on research. Each successful piece of research is likely to make possible some new product which can be produced for the market. As time goes on, manufacturers find that new products are increasingly complex in design. Furthermore, many new products require precision in manufacture, both in the chemistry of the materials and in the exactness of fabrication, far beyond that required in anything but scientific instruments a few decades ago.

The result is that, for the successful manufacture of new products, thousands of employees with advanced skills must be found somewhere. The need for skills is increased by these circumstances at the same time that the demand for unskilled or semiskilled labor diminishes, because of new machines that perform tedious and repetitive tasks.

Industry must provide for a continuous supply of skilled manpower to replace normal turnover in the existing work force and to meet the needs of projected expansion. American mass production depends upon the abilities and skills of people — highly skilled craftsmen and machine workers as well as semiskilled employees for many vital operations. Competent persons are also required for the beginning jobs, which demand varying degrees of skills, training, and education. Before a single plane can roll off the assembly line, more than three hundred human skills have gone into its making.

Recently an automotive concern had to search the entire world for 480 tool- and diemakers it needed for an emergency retooling program. There just were not enough men around in the nation with the right kind of training and skill to handle the project.

This experience has been duplicated in many places throughout the United States. Surplus skills are available in Eastern United States but are in short supply at the West Coast Missile Centers. If there were more mobility, there might be less need for retraining to find jobs for displaced workers.

Some skills, even though developed to a high degree, gradually become obsolete as products pass out of use. The possessors of skills must therefore learn new skills if they are to keep pace with the march of progress.

Relocation is one of the prices paid for progress, but this is far outweighed by the benefits conferred upon the whole nation. Progress makes possible the gain in real wages, eliminating the drudgery and working conditions that prematurely aged previous generations. Progress provides expanding opportunities for capable men and women to escape from monotonous and unrewarding work to more challenging, more satisfying, and better compensated work.

On-the-Job Training

G. S. Brown has stated:

> Automation means employment of modern developments of a science and engineering in a mature sophisticated way, for the purpose

of increasing productivity, quality of product, and reducing the amount of muscle in industrial operations. . . . Automation will upgrade jobs and make flexibility and versatility of the workingman much more important. Management will have increased responsibility in allocation of effort to push product, to upgrade product, to keep competitive position in the market place, and to *see that people are developed and reoriented as jobs change.* . . . One way to solve problems of technical upgrading, is to make widespread use of on-the-job training especially when it is well in advance of the introduction of a new automatic process or technique.[10]

Apprentice Training

The installation of new equipment must be coordinated with retraining workers in new skills. Workers must be better trained and must possess many additional skills not required in the conventional plants. Emphasis will shift away from brawn and muscles to mental effort. I. Lubin[11] recommends the greater utilization of apprentice training, with more emphasis on a background of technical schooling. He claims this is the best method to meet the unexpected demands of industry.

However, the concept of what is an apprenticeable occupation must be enlarged, as changes in technology and industrial processes create new skill combinations that constitute new individual crafts. Lubin believes that a system of scholarships for this type of training should be set up, with the cost being shared among industry, labor, and Government.

Apprenticeship Training in Ford Motor Company The United Automobile Workers in its negotiations with the Ford Motor Company amended the traditional apprentice training program to provide an opportunity for older workers with greater seniority to obtain the retraining necessary before new job applicants could secure training. At one time, training was limited to applicants 26 years old and under. This requirement was changed so that a member with seniority, regardless of age, who could pass the mental and aptitude test could make an application for training.

Special lists were compiled of those wishing retraining, to eliminate the possibility of the young applicant outside the company being given preference in apprenticeship programs. The union also kept urging that training programs be extended to those workers already working in the highest skilled level. The UAW believes that despite the highly competent mechanics in its membership, additional training is needed to handle properly the new pneumatic, chemical, electrical, or electronic devices developed since these highly skilled mechanics first took apprenticeship training.

Proper Selection Important Prerequisite

Training will not succeed without proper selection techniques, since the key to the wider spread application is the need for greater flexibility. Ability to switch quickly from one type of assembly to another with minimum downtime on equipment is a prime requirement.[12] The search for flexibility is important, since, in the main, automation is characterized by inflexibility, its greatest weakness. This need will be especially acute in the smaller companies.

Aptitude tests will have to be devised to enable a firm to recruit the "flexible" and "integrated" personality, one "right" for the automated plant. This requirement will create some problems, for when management will want to give tests, the union will generally resist. The union will be against a unilateral approach, but may be friendly to the impartial "outsider" who is a psychological consultant. The union will fear aptitude tests because it believes they are designed to "unload" certain workers.

Training of Skilled Technician Essential

Harry Monroe, a maintenance expert, in a talk in Philadelphia before the plant engineering and maintenance show, made these remarks:

> The next essential step in the development of automated machinery is the training of skilled technicians to keep the push-button devices running. . . . The current use of industrial electricians to maintain complicated electronic equipment after a short training period — is like sending a man to medical school, and after three weeks expecting him to perform surgery.[13]

Despite the forebodings of Monroe, it was interesting to note that at the same convention A. M. Beebe, plant engineer for the Rochester, New York, division of General Motors, took the opposite position by stating that "Engineers are now working on plans to develop maintenance-free machinery — and that much of the machinery of this type developed in the last few years has cut the number of workers necessary to maintain the devices by nearly one-half.[14]

Automation and Retraining in Meat-Packing Industry

In August 1959 a two-year contract was entered into between Armour Company and the United Packinghouse, Food and Allied Workers and the Amalgamated Meat Cutters and Butchers Workmen of North America. A feature of this agreement was the provision for a tripartite committee, which has come to be known as the "Automation Committee," to be composed of four representatives of the company, two from each of the two unions, and an impartial executive director.

A fund of $500,000 was to be set up by the company to finance the Automation Committee in its work. The committee was to study the problems of automation and to report its findings in connection with new bargaining for a collective agreement in August 1961. Clark Kerr, president of the University of California, was named chairman of the committee.

In June 1961 the Automation Committee released a progress report.

Background of Automation Agreement

In the early summer of 1959 Armour and Company announced the permanent closing of six production plants. Included were two large establishments in Chicago and East St. Louis, and four smaller plants in Columbus, Fargo, Atlanta, and Tifton. More than 20 percent of the company's total plant capacity was shut down, and 5000 production employees were terminated. A year later, in July 1960, the Company closed the Oklahoma City plant, thereby adding 420 employees to the total terminated.[15]

Armour's closedowns were not unique. Each of the other three large packers has had to close down plants as a result of the increasing strength of the independents and of the additional consumption of processed meats. Shifts in population and the switch from rail to truck transportation had resulted in the opening of new plants in new areas of the nation. It was estimated that 30,000 workers had been affected as a result of the various closings of the "big four."

Studies Made for Armour Automation Committee

A three-city study was completed under the direction of Professors Richard C. Wilcox and Walter H. Franke, of the Institute of

Labor and Industrial Relations at the University of Illinois. The three cities involved were Columbus, Fargo, and East St. Louis, and the data pertained to more than 80 percent of the former employees. The composition of this group by age, sex, race, and other factors, was as follows:

53.1 percent of all former employees in the three cities were over 45 years old and had a record of long service with Armour and Company; 18.8 percent were women. 57.6 percent of the former employees in East St. Louis and 8.6 percent of the former employees in Columbus were Negroes; there were none in Fargo. A high proportion of the former employees had relatively little skill, and most of these skills were largely nontransferable.[16]

General Findings of Armour Analysts

1. The analysts found that plant closings created severe hardships on the displaced workers, particularly when there was possible discrimination on the basis of age, sex, and race.

2. The unemployment experience of the former Armour workers was much worse than the average for the communities in which they worked. In East St. Louis, a year after the shutdown, 56 percent of the employees were still out of work compared to a rate of unemployment for that city of between 4 and 7 percent. In Fargo, one year after shutdown, the unemployment rate for the meat packers was still about 30 percent.

3. In the year following the layoff, those under age 45 had an easier time getting work than those over 45. One year after layoff, the unemployment rate for the younger group was only 33 percent; that for the "over 45" group was 47 percent.

4. Women found it more difficult to get jobs. The unemployment rate for the female group was 52 percent one year after layoff; that for the males only 39 percent.

5. When unemployment is generally critical, Negroes find it more difficult to get jobs than whites. In East St. Louis, one year after layoff, 61 percent of the Negroes were still out of work, but only 36 percent of the whites.

6. The greatest unemployment rate, one year after layoff, was found among those with the least education and also with the lowest level of skills.

7. Little mobility was revealed among the unemployed. Although 50 to 65 percent of the displaced workers indicated at the time of separation that they would be willing to move to another job in the Armour plant, only 4 percent voluntarily moved more than 100 miles from their original communities.

8. The state employment services were of little help in finding jobs for the displaced employees, partly because of the high earnings at Armour, which averaged $2.20 an hour. Those former employees who got work after separation averaged only $1.86 an hour.

9. Fifty percent of those separated in the three cities under study indicated that they would use severance pay to pay old debts, so that they would not have this money as a means of support during the time they were job hunting.

Oklahoma City Experience With Retraining

Although the three-city study involved plants closed in 1959, the Oklahoma City shutdown came in July 1960, after the committee was already in existence. The committee retained Professor Edwin Young of the University of Wisconsin to help the unemployed get new jobs. Lists of the former Armour employees were carefully prepared, with details of their experience and their qualifications. The press, TV, and radio were used to help procure job placements. Every area was studied for employment, but little was accomplished.

In addition to efforts made at seeking positions for the displaced, training was attempted. The State Employment Service tested the unemployed for aptitudes. Counseling was made available. Of 431 production workers invited to take retraining, only 143 men and 27 women completed both the tests and the interviews. In other words, only 41 percent of the men and 35 percent of the women were interested and motivated.

It was ascertained that, of the former production workers at Armour, 59 percent who were still unemployed participated; only 20 percent of those employed in other jobs were interested in retraining. Furthermore, most of the former workers who got jobs were younger persons, so that the bulk of those accepting the idea of retraining were in the advanced age group.

Of the 170 tested, only 60 showed promise for retraining. The remainder of 110 were told that the "best chance for employment would be in casual manual labor."[17]

Training in Oklahoma City Experiment

In the Oklahoma City experiment, training was given in typing, office methods, blueprint reading, upholstery, welding, basic electronics, beauty parlor techniques, real estate business methods, air conditioning, and auto mechanics.[18] The committee paid the first $60 toward the tuition, plus 50 percent of the balance, so long as the total did not exceed $150.

The greater part of the cost of the courses was paid by the committee, thus helping the morale of the small group who took training. Unfortunately, however, job opportunities in Oklahoma City decreased further, owing to a general wave of unemployment, which increased the city rate from 3 percent to 7 percent.

Conclusions on Oklahoma City Endeavors

Careful advance planning and close cooperation with the State Employment Service will be of greater benefit to the displaced workers than attempts at a "crash" program. No matter how great the promotion, there will not be a significant number of job opportunities while total unemployment is rising. Regardless of its cooperation, the public employment office can be helpful only in a minor way. Since most of the employees desiring retraining are middle-aged, the chances are small that these persons have satisfactory formal education to begin with.

It appeared that a carefully thought-out program of retraining, *while a person is still employed*, might create the skills needed to procure a job in time of crisis.

Experimental Transfer Plan

The committee retained the University of Chicago to investigate eight situations of labor-management relations, where programs for interplant transfers had been worked out. The study was directed by Professor Arnold Weber of the Graduate School of Business at the University of Chicago. Surveyed were Lever Brothers and the International Chemical Workers; International-Harvester and the UAW; Libby-Owens-Ford and the United Glass and Ceramic Workers; Continental Can and the Steelworkers; Ford, Chrysler, General Motors and the UAW and various railroads represented by the Brotherhood of Railway Clerks.

As a result of this study, the Automation Committee determined to begin an experimental transfer plan between Oklahoma City and Kansas City. Letters went out to 304 employees working for Armour at the time the plant closed in Oklahoma City in July 1960. The employees were promised the same wages and working conditions in Kansas City, but were told that for purposes of severance pay, pension rights, and departmental seniority, they would be treated as new employees in Kansas City but would be permitted the regular vacations, sick leave, and other benefits.

The plan required that job offers would have to be accepted within a short period and Armour would pay the moving bill to Kansas City up to $325. Workers would receive $5 a day in Kansas City until joined by their families. If layoff occurred in Kansas City within the first year, actual moving expenses up to $325 would be made available back to Oklahoma City, less any per diem allowance previously received by the worker.

Approximately 50 percent of those queried said they would like to transfer. Unfortunately the employment situation in Kansas City deteriorated before the plan could be made effective. The basis, however, could be used for future planning.

The Armour situation serves as an instructional basis for proceeding with company-union retraining programs and illustrates that planning for placement must come early. The best retraining is that which takes place while workers are still employed. Despite the serious attention paid by national groups to developments in training at Armour, results have been negligible.

Oilworkers Union Attitude Toward Retraining

The oil union looks with distain on worker retraining as the answer to layoffs. Says O. W. Knight, union president:

> Retraining is unworkable, a few people can be trained to run automated equipment, but the general retraining idea seems to be to take an oilworker and make him a steel worker or a butcher. But the new steelworker and butcher will find these industries are laying off too! Besides the retrained man wouldn't have any seniority in his new job, and without that he doesn't have a chance.[19]

The attitude of this labor leader indicates the difficulty of launching successful retraining programs without the full cooperation of labor, management, and Government. Too many persons involved in this problem stand "pat" and say "show me."

School Dropouts

Arthur Goldberg, as Secretary of Labor, agreed with James B. Conant that the mounting social and economic problems raised by large numbers of youths who end their education without finishing high school is "the most dangerous social situation in America . . . social dynamite . . . and a terrible waste of our youth."[20]

The U. S. Office of Eduaction recently made clear the magnitude of the problem. Some 2.5 million of the 10.8 million students now enrolled in grades 9 through 12 in the nation's public and private schools will drop out before graduation. Secretary Ribicoff stated: "The percentage of youth who enroll in school but do not graduate ranges from 17 percent to 42 percent in 50 states."[21] In most states youngsters are free to leave school when they reach the age of 16.

The advent of these youngsters into the labor market at ages 16 and 17 presents a serious unemployment problem, with the current emphasis on advanced technology. The unemployment rate for those without a high school education is about 6.5 percent, just about double the rate of those with a high school diploma.

An unskilled job, such as that of elevator operator, used to be available for young boys; now elevators are automatic. A young boy with a ninth grade education certainly cannot be employed in the maintenance or the manufacture of elevators.

Not being able to get jobs, hundreds of thousands of young people will be added to the relief rolls, and great numbers may become juvenile delinquents and criminals.

Vocational Schools and Technical Institutes

Because many dropouts leave school after having failed one or more courses, counseling services should be improved. These young persons need to be encouraged and their potentialities identified through testing. For those not destined for college, greater emphasis should be given to vocational training; for those who do not have funds or the ability normally required in the traditional four-year college, a two-year post high school education should be provided at the technical institute level.

The National Committee for Children and Youth estimates, however, that 20 to 25 percent of the dropouts have superior intelligence, but have either economic or cultural problems.[22] Many of these superior children come from slum homes, where the parents are separated, and such handicaps are too great for them in the face of their school responsibilities.

Vanishing Opportunities

In former days, other jobs were available for youngsters besides running of an elevator. Many stronger ones took unskilled jobs with the railroads. The Atlantic Coast Line Railroad, with headquarters in Jacksonville, Florida, reports that it has only 2750 jobs for unskilled workers, whereas ten years ago it had 5300. The reduction in the number of laborers required to maintain the roadbeds, for example, has been due to the installation of machinery. Today, three or four men lay crossties and rails, as compared to the 100 men formerly needed for the same job.

The semiconductor division of Sylvania Electric Products, Inc., cut the number of unskilled workers on a transistor testing line from 102 to six when it installed new testing equipment a year ago.

The Kendall Company, which employs 5400 hourly workers in textile and cotton mills in New England and the South, discourages applications from nonhigh school graduates. "For one of our employees to advance beyond a shipping or packing clerk, it is necessary that he have a high school diploma,"[23] stated L. E. Schildein, Kendall's personnel director.

Federal Works Program Advocated

James B. Conant, former president of Harvard, has suggested that a Federal public works program might be necessary to alleviate the problem of unemployment in the age groups 16–21 in large cities. It is necessary to get these youngsters off the streets and into useful pursuits. Such an experiment was successfully attempted by the Government in the late nineteen thirties with the Civilian Conservation Corps.

Technical Institutes and Community Colleges

If greater opportunities could be provided for high school graduates to take technical training and general education for at least two years after graduation, the nation would accomplish three important results:

1. The current rate of additions to the labor force would be slowed down for at least a few years.

2. The nation would be providing the technical skills necessary for a fuller mechanized or automated economy. It is clear that the unskilled soon will provide the greater part of the unemployed.

3. By providing for two years of general education in addition to technical training, the nation would be strengthened with better citizens in the sense of political and social awareness. This type of combined training is possible in the better technical institutes and community colleges. Of the thirty California community colleges awarding associates degrees or certificates, seventeen are technical schools offering abundant opportunities for modern employment openings.

For those who are able to learn the new skills desired by the changing American technology, facilities should be available in secondary schools and in post high school institutions. Although the secondary schools can be of much help, the burden will fall on the post high school institution. More community colleges and technical institutes, both public and private, should be planned in coming years.

Higher educational institutions should help in every possible way to see that programs are made available to students. Proprietory and trade schools can also do much to fill the vacuum of facilities, which will become more obvious in the next decade. Tuition in all these planned institutions should be nominal, as many students who will attend will not be well off economically. The development of needed skills should add to the nation's resources. The investment will pay off in more creative citizens and in less unemployment in coming decades.

The problem of numbers is not gross calculation. The holding power of the schools is on the increase. In 1940, 15 percent of the college-age group was in colleges; by 1955 this figure had risen to 30 percent. By 1975 it will be something like 50 percent throughout the nation. All these high school graduates will want something different. There will be millions who will want a combination of technical and general education of less than four years. The labor market will demand this additional training and study. Automation requires technicians who will have a preparation quite different from the skilled trades of yesterday.

Job Retraining Under 1961 Area Redevelopment Act

Under the 1961 Area Redevelopment Act, the Government offers aid to areas of high unemployment so that qualified jobless persons can learn new and needed skills. Shortly after the Act was passed, the program had already enrolled 4400 jobless persons. Federal officials expect the figure to have reached 18,000 by early 1963.

No one claims that job retraining will wipe out unemployment, but it may be a means of attacking long-time unemployment in areas where industry has emigrated and the population refuses to move. Huntington, West Virginia, is such an area in which the ARA program is being tried out. This community was formerly a coal-mining center. Since 1955, work in the mines has dwindled and twenty-eight industrial plants have moved from the area, leaving 4000 displaced workers in the community. The unemployment rate in Huntington was 8.7 percent of the labor force, as compared to a national average of less than 6 percent.

Among the difficulties encountered in beginning this retraining program was a reluctance by the unemployed to train for new skills, an inability to retrain many of the persons who need jobs first, and a real problem in finding jobs for those who have been retrained.

By the end of 1961, the ARA program had been approved for thirty-five communities in fourteen states. Early in 1962 applications were received from the Government from an additional one hundred communities. The success of the ARA plan influenced the passage of the Clark-Holland proposals for retraining programs in major metropolitan areas where automation and technological change have resulted in a high rate of unemployment, but where the city cannot qualify for ARA funds.

The first three areas to set up ARA programs — Huntington, West Virginia; Ansonia, Connecticut; Providence and Pawtucket, Rhode Island — enrolled over seven hundred persons for retraining during the first six months of 1962.

Weekly Allotments to Trainees Under ARA

Currently, qualified applicants are trained from two to sixteen weeks in one of thirty skills, ranging from waitress to machinist. Some four million dollars has been appropriated by the Federal Government to pay for training and another ten million is available for weekly allotments equal to the average weekly unemployment compensation for the state in which the trainee resides. A trainee has the option of receiving these benefits or unemployment compensation, if he is still eligible.

Aptitude Testing

Civic leaders in Huntington, West Virginia, set up, and won state approval for, an economic development plan as required by Federal law. Included in the application was a list of skills needed for the region, after a survey of local businesses was made. State and local officials then went to work with ARA officials and set up a training program in Huntington East High Trade School and two local hospitals.

Postcards were sent to over one thousand long-time unemployed. Only 640 appeared for the aptitude tests, and of these only 240 qualified for retraining. Some officials believe that the response was poor because the postcards were sent out shortly before Christmas, and that a good number of the unemployed had temporary jobs at the time.

One major problem, according to retraining supervisors, is that poor education renders many of the unemployed unsuitable for retraining. The aptitude test frustrates many of them. One manager in Ansonia, Connecticut, said that of eighty-three candidates who took a test for basic machine shop aptitude, only twenty-five passed. The test requires two years of high school and some understanding of algebra.

To meet a demand for nurses' aides in Huntington, a program was set up. By the time the trainees finished the four-week course, untrained persons had snapped up most of the jobs. Only ten graduates have been placed so far.

Some instructors believed that a four-week course was inadequate to prepare anyone for a skill. There have, however, been some good results with the courses.

After taking a machinery course provided in Ansonia, Connecticut, seventeen graduates were placed with five major employers, and the firms requested an additional twenty-seven students, who were halfway through a second course. In Providence, a local bank offered to supply calculating machines for a retraining course in bookkeeping and to hire all the graduates. Recently West Virginia officials were able to lure Lockheed Aircraft Corporation to Clarksburg because of a state-sponsored course for aicraft riveters. Twenty-one graduates were placed with Lockheed and the company requested an additional seventy-five. Federal concern with retraining will certainly help focus interest in existing state and local programs, which until recently had not been properly promoted.

Manpower Development and Training Act

The Clark-Holland proposals previously referred to in this book were passed by Congress in 1962 as the Manpower Development and Training Act. The Act will provide $435,000,000 to train and retrain approximately one million persons from 1963 through 1965 who have been displaced in their jobs by automation, foreign competition, industrial relocation, and similar causes.

The Government will foot 100 percent of the cost of the training program during the first two years the Act is in operation. In the third year, the Government will pay only 50 percent of the cost.

Secretary of Labor Arthur J. Goldberg termed the program "an essential step necessary for our country to maintain economic growth, while at the same time assuring that workers shall benefit, not suffer, from rapid technological change."[24]

The initial impact of the program will employ a combination of state and local school district planning. Later, it is intended that the Government will assume the full cost of on-the-job training courses. The OJT program will be deferred until the vocational school programs get under way.

The training courses are not permitted to exceed fifty-two weeks, and during that period trainees are eligible to receive approximately $35 a week if they happen to be heads of families and households. The Act is expressly designed to favor retraining of heads of families who have had not less than three years' experience in gainful employment. The new law, however, does provide for youth within the specified age bracket of 19 through 21 years. These young people may receive $20 a week subsistence. If heads of families are still eligible for unemployment compensation, they may receive such benefits until they are exhausted, provided the unemployment payments are greater than the $35 subsistence, but in no event can a trainee receive both payments simultaneously.

As a result of a special study made in September 1962, New Jersey was ready to retrain 1370 workers idled by automation. The state's share of the total three-year appropriation will be $15,600,000, or 3.6 percent of the national total.

Approved training courses in New Jersey were as follows:

Camden: auto-body repairmen; Hackensack: combination welders; Middlesex County: engine lathe operators; Newark: junior draftsmen (tracers), general machine operators; Salem: automotive mechanics.

Other proposed projects in the state would call for the training of sheet metal workers, lathe operators, spray painters, chemists' assistants, storm window assemblers, nurses' aides, nuclear pipe fitters (for work on nuclear ships), salesmen, secretaries, and fork-lift operators.

Conclusion

The old-fashioned notion that education is completed at a certain point must be dropped. Skills and knowledge possessed at the age of 22 cannot be assumed to remain unaffected for an entire working lifetime. The rate of obsolescence of skill and knowledge is rapid in this changing economy. Experts believe that it will speed up, rather than slow down. Changes in skill and skill requirements will apply to a wider range of tasks and to a growing segment of the labor force, both in the office and the plant.

Training and retraining appear to be massive problems, which will grow in size and complexity, rather than diminish. The general problem will also affect what fundamentals curriculums, for example, mathematics and science, should be taught in the elementary and secondary grades. Also introduced will be programs of education designed for technicians at the technical institute and community college levels. The better prepared for change the new entrant into the labor force is, the greater the ease with which he can switch jobs in the new technology. The major problem will be with senior workers who do not have the basic formal education to be flexible. In earlier times, when most workers were semiskilled at best, such workers could transfer from declining to expanding trades and industries with relative ease and little loss of skill or earning power. This possibility has almost disappeared.

In the next decade, at least most new work skills will be acquired on the job, not in the school. Dissemination of new knowledge and skill would come at a snail's pace if the new entrants into the labor force were alone to be depended on. The greater part of the supplies of new skills is the product of self-education, of work experience, of training programs (conducted by forums, unions, and Government), and *not* the formal school system.

The main problem will not be the resources for retraining and replacing of obsolete skills, but the knowledge of how to use these training sources to the best advantage. When a business firm sets up a training program to provide skills not available on the labor market, or to retain displaced workers for available openings, it knows what skills it needs, and approximately how many workers it should train for them.

However, when the Government undertakes training and retraining programs, as it is now doing under the Area Development Program and as it will soon do under the newly enacted Manpower Development and Training Act of 1962, it is looking at the requirements in a large perspective and actually lacks complete knowledge of the prospective demands for skills. This lack of information must be remedied, else public retraining programs will fail.

Vocational schools may train excessive numbers of students in carpentry or tinsmithing, but few, if any, in the expanding skill requirements of medical technicians or of the electronic or nuclear age. Part of this problem lies with the teachers, whose skills are obsolete. In effect, this condition is due to a cultural lag.

In summary, the nation lacks a detailed knowledge of present and prospective market demand for specific skills, as well as comprehensive guidance programs for both teen-agers and adults. The nation has data on the number of persons without jobs, their geographical locations, their occupations, and their industry. What is required is job data, with greater detail on available job openings by occupational classification and location. This information would improve guidance and training. It would not solve all problems, because job opportunities would have to be reconciled with educational freedom and occupational choice.

Who is responsible for retraining displaced workers and for providing some income maintenance? The employer, whose innovation has displaced them? The workers themselves, whose labor is no longer in demand? Is it society at large? From an ethical point of view, all share responsibility. Employers should provide for retraining where it involves employment in their own firms. Consideration should be given to these displaced workers; else their fellow workers, also fearing displacement, will join forces to block progress through collective bargaining or collective action. The residual burden for retraining must be borne by the state, local, and Federal governments. Employers can help a great deal by advance notice, by retraining for possible transfers in the plants, and by helping the displaced workers find work elsewhere, or by directing them to appropriate counseling or Government agencies for assistance.

References

1. "Your Place in the Changing Scene," memo of Research Institute of America, New York, 1956.
2. D. H. Fryer, M. H. Feinberg and S. S. Zalkind, *Developing People in Industry* (New York: Harper & Row, 1956), p. 10.
3. *Ibid.*, p. 10.
4. *Ibid.*, p. 18.
5. Willaim A. Faunce, "The Automobile Industry; A Case Study in Automation," from *Automation and Society*, H. B. Jacobson and J. S. Roucek, eds. (New York: Philosophical Library, 1959), pp. 45–46.
6. James R. Bright, "Skill Requirements and Wage Aspects of Automation," presented at the University of Pennsylvania Labor Relations Conference, from *Industrial Relations in the 1960's Problems and Prospects*, George W. Taylor and Edward B. Shils, eds., p. 21.
7. *Ibid.*, p. 22.
8. *Ibid.*, pp. 24–25.
9. John Diebold, "Applied Automation: A Practical Approach." *Keeping Pace With Automation, Practical Guides For the Company Executive*, special report, no. 7, New York American Management Association, 1955.
10. From an address delivered in Atlantic City in 1954 at the Seventh International Convention of United Steelworkers of America.
11. I. Lubin, "We must Increase Our Investment in Skilled Manpower," address before the Eleventh Annual Seaboard Apprenticeship Conference, Monticello, New York, June 1, 1955.
12. W. R. G. Baker, "Automation As the Engineer Sees It," Automation-Engineering for Tomorrow, Michigan State University, East Lansing, Michigan, May 13, 1955.
13. *Philadelphia Inquirer*, January 23, 1961, p. 7.
14. *Ibid.*
15. Bureau of National Affairs, no. 419, June 23, 1961, 16:621, "Automation: Report of the Armour Committee," p. c-2.

16. *Ibid.*, p. c-3.
17. *Ibid.*, p. c-5.
18. *Ibid.*
19. *Wall Street Journal*, January 19, 1962, p. 19.
20. *Ibid.*, November 14, 1961, p. 1.
21. *Ibid.*
22. *Ibid.*, p. 14.
23. *Ibid.*
24. *Philadelphia Inquirer*, March 1, 1962, p. 3.

Clerical Automation
and White-Collar
Organizing Drives

The advent of automation, with assistance from the computer, is having as sharp an impact in the office as in the factory. In fact, the time-honored distinctions between the blue-collar environment and the white-collar environment are fast disappearing. It is growing more difficult to determine readily where the information part of the plant ends and the manufacturing operations begin. The former mass-production atmosphere is on its way out. The numbers of direct production workers have decreased, and relative increases in the service areas of the plant are noticeable. Technicians, engineers, statistical-control, personnel, and maintenance experts are beginning to replace the worker with the greasy overalls. In fact, it is difficult to distinguish the worker from the supervisor. Both are checking dials, gauges, and pressures; both are fairly well dressed — in grease-free clothing.

At first, it appeared that the production workers had most to fear from the new technology, in terms of job displacement. Now the experts tell us that the white-collar workers are to be exposed to a type of automation which will outpace that experienced by factory workers. Thus the clerical worker, the technical, and the professional are susceptible to the overtures of union organizers.

Influence of Automation on Formation of
White-Collar and Professional Unions

Union Reasons for Attempts to Organize "White-Collarites"
Unions are trying their best to organize the white-collar workers now that they see this group gradually making inroads, through automation, into industries formerly served by the production worker.

The unions are hiring a new type of organizer, the man with a college degree who can appeal to the office and professional workers. Unions are looking at the statistics. Beginning in 1956 the Bureau of the Census announced that a turning point had come in the history of the United States. They said that for the first time the number of white-collar workers exceeded the number of blue-collar workers. Since that time the trend has become more pronounced.

In January 1962 there were 28,000,000 white-collar workers versus 24,000,000 blue-collar workers. The Bureau of Labor Statistics expects that by 1965 there will be 31,300,000 white-collar workers versus 28,000,000 blue-collar workers.[1] This situation will be quite a change from 1950, when blue-collar workers outnumbered the white-collar group by more than 2,000,000.

Organization Problems

If the economy expands to the degree predicted by the Labor Department, production unions may look forward to some slight increase in membership. The gain, in the number of white-collar workers, however, will be sharply accelerated during this period. Many unions are pessimistic that blue-collar jobs will not expand further, and they see an attrition in union membership during the next decade. This possibility has caused them to extend their jurisdiction to the white-collar, professional, and semiprofessional workers and technicians.

Of the 28,000,000 white-collar workers in 1962, only about 10 percent, or 2,500,000,[2] were organized; of the 24,000,000 blue-collar workers, about two thirds, or 15,000,000, were organized.

If union leaders could organize the unorganized 90 percent of the white-collar workers, things would be wonderful in the union movement. Not only are unions losing membership in relation to the entire population, but they are losing out in absolute numbers. The Labor Department analysis of 1959 showed that in 1956 unions in the United States had 18,500,000 members, whereas in 1958 they only had 18,100,000 members. Thus, while population was increasing, union membership declined by a net of 400,000 members. Among the major gross declines during the two-year period was a reduction of 293,000 members in the United Automobile Workers and of 290,000 members in the United Steelworkers.

Reasons for Desire of White-Collar Workers to Organize Despite the opportunity of ultimately moving into management, many office workers have been discontented with their hourly earnings and fringe benefits compared to those of production workers. This was not always so. At one time the white-collar worker had a sense of security, he was closer to his boss when businesses were smaller, and from 1890 to 1920 he enjoyed a differential in earnings from 50 percent to 100 percent greater.[3]

In other words, until 1920 he was much better off than the blue-collar worker. By 1954 the white-collar worker's comparative earnings were 2 percent less than the production worker's. This situation has continued to change, so that the organized blue-collar worker is much better off than either the organized or the unorganized white-collar worker.

Before World War II the white-collar worker had a two-week vacation and paid holidays. The blue-collar workers had little in the way of fringe benefits until the wage freeze of World War II. After the war blue-collar workers not only received vacations and paid holidays, but were also granted insurance, hospitalization, pensions, and many other benefits. Not only has the blue-collar worker caught up on fringes, but is now running much ahead. The white-collar worker has been losing out by remaining unorganized. Their employers have not volunteered increases and fringe benefits equal to those enjoyed by the blue-collar worker; the only way that the white-collar workers were able to catch up in part was through tandem increases. Generally, these increases followed the blue-collar workers' raises, by months or years, and only after much discontent and bitterness.

Automation and Absence of Security in the Office   Automation in the office is another factor contributing to the feeling of insecurity in the office worker. In many organizations the clerical worker had a feeling closely akin to that of civil service worker — that the job was for life. James J. Bambrick states the problem in this way:

> . . . office workers see the work they used to do being taken over by machines, and their placid assurance is gone. In one such organization a supervisor said: "I used to feel secure, now I no longer feel secure. . . ."

Planning for automation is not merely planning for machines, it is planning for human beings. Long ago the Bell Telephone Companies decided to go in for automatic equipment throughout the nation. They also made the fundamental decision to gear the introduction of automation with their normal rate of attrition. Through this human relations planning, "Ma Bell" has achieved a high rate of automation. She has thousands fewer employees, and she has no lay-offs. "Ma Bell" has thus maintained her enviable record of taking care of her own — and she has done it along with installing one of the most widespread systems of white-collar automation this country has ever seen.[4]

Desire for Systematic Grievance Procedures   Most unorganized white-collar workers long for a well-worked-out grievance procedure, which they believe the unions can provide. They will turn to unionism for this reason — and more and more their desire to organize will be related to grievances arising from office automation. White-collar workers wish recognition, as do all workers. The absence of recognition has led to bitterness and a desire for union affiliation.

Difficulty in Organizing the White-Collar Worker   The traditional unions have not been successful in organizing white-collar workers because they used the wrong approach. They had inept organizers — blue-collar organizers instead of white-collar organizers. In the Wall Street strike, they used the Seafarers International Union to man the picket line. Rough language and the jostling of girls caused a negative feeling toward unionism in the Wall Street area. Instead of planning sound methods, unions battled about who should grab whom — and their organizing efforts have been so amateurish that there have been more decertifications of white-collar groups from the traditionally blue-collar unions than new certifications.

Inaccessibility Eliminated   For years organizers wandered around the home offices of large corporations and were told to "get off the premises." There was little cultural rapport between organizers and workers; they did not move in the same social circle.

Today, with automation sweeping the nation, more and more jobs in the plant might be classified as white-collar work. The computer and programming have come to the automated work place; and it should be easier to organize the workers.

Similarity Between Professional Unions and Other Unions?   Professional unions perform the elementary functions of unions in the American setting. The high earnings of the union members among pilots, actors, engineers, and scientists have not prevented them from bargaining with management over wages, hours, and working conditions in great detail; nor have these unions been spared the traditional contests for office; nor have hotly contested jurisdictional disputes been prevented; to mention one instance, the air line pilots with the flight engineers. High earnings have not prevented professionals from engaging in costly, wholesale, and long-lived strikes over what they consider vital issues.

Where are these professionals to be found? Many of them are in public institutional locals, such as the American Federation of State, County and Municipal Employees. Although some professionals constitute separate locals, they are part of such industrial unions as UAW, IUE, Steelworkers, and IBEW, all affiliated with AFL-CIO, of course.

Other professional national unions affiliated with AFL-CIO are limited to professional members only, such as the Hollywood talent guilds, the Federation of Technical Engineers, and the Teachers Union. Professionals may also be found in unaffiliated groups, national in scope, such as the Engineers and Scientists of America. Still other professionals are members of a local or company-wide council — as, for example, the RCA engineers or the Council of Western Electric Engineers. Then there are the professional associations with articulated bargaining interests, as, for example, the nurses. Finally, there are professional associations that may be very hostile to union-oriented collective bargaining, such as the National Educational Association.[5]

Management Sensitive to White-Collar and Professional Unionization Management is concerned lest, with automation, unions will invade the white-collar and professional fields. Observe, for example, the main headings of a series of suggestions recently made by the National Association of Manufacturers for dealing with the professional employee:

> (1) Realize that the professional employee wants to be recognized as a member of a profession. (2) Insure credit and recognition from top management for outstanding work and unusual accomplishments. (3) Give proper dignity to the title of each position held by a professional employee. (4) Provide work that will challenge the professional employee's technical competence. (5) Afford professional specialists opportunity for promotion and salary progression equivalent to that of members of management. (6) Accept the professional employee as a member of the management team. (7) Adopt liberal policies with respect to time off for personal reasons. (8) Provide physical facilities and equipment which meet the standards expected by professional employees. (9) Assist the recent professional graduate to identify himself with his specialty early in his training period. (10) Encourage professional employees to take part in the activities of their engineering or technical

societies. (11) Provide opportunities for research and development personnel to pursue independent interests, if practicable, with due recognition for achievements.[6]

Management is fully aware of its experience with the blue-collar workers, for whom the unions provided what management did not provide. The NAM states further:

> The salaried employee today is being wooed by both unions and management. The contest for his support will be won by the one which recognizes the real needs and desires of the salaried group and provides the answers which will bring satisfactions. The outcome of this contest may very well rest on management's action at this critical juncture.[7]

Socialization of the Work Situation The largest factor working in favor of unionization is what might be called "the socialization of the work situation." This is described by Jack Barbash as follows:

> The individualistic bent which constitutes the hard core of the professional's values is having to give way to the realities of the industrial discipline. The realities are first the technological requirement of concentration of numbers in one place. Automation has underscored and accentuated this socializing tendency by requiring the concentrated presence of professionals at the worksite, (At the same time, incidentally, that it seems to be having the opposite effect on industrial workers).[8]

The growing technology in the plant requires that scientists, engineers, technicians, maintenance personnel, and operators work closely together. This situation brings up another reality that may drive the engineers and scientists into automation — the need for more rules, regulations, and procedures.

A recent study of industrialization has aptly stressed this need:

> The inevitable structuring of the managers and the managed in the course of industrialization [has resulted in the developing of] a complex web of rules binding the worker into the industrial process, to his job, to his community, to patterns of behavior.[9]

Will this factor lead the minority, who are the elite among the employees, into unionism?

Automation and Management Standardization People working together in one place require management standardization. Regardless of the level of skill or professional ability, employees like to organize both formally and informally. This tendency to organize and to standardize is the stuff out of which unions are made. The fabric is present in the new technology. The automated plant brings together to the production work place not alone production workers but white-collar convertees as well.

The ultimate in industrial discipline, as it is known, is well described by the International Labor Organization:

> [an office-work environment] characterized by rationalization and integration of work processes in one continuous workflow, the operations to be performed to the maximum degree by mechanical means with a minimum of operator intervention.[10]

The unions are impressed by "socialization and hyper-organization"[11] of the professional work situation, and, noting the implications of automation and data processing, are attempting to appeal for the protection of the "individuality" of the clerical or professional worker. They base this appeal by making statements such as the following, which can shock anyone — even a professional employee, who usually has substantial education and intelligence:

> Much of what we call decision-making is nothing more than action based upon the perception of data in terms of a given system of rules or instructions. Every computer has a logical component which can operate to perform this function, and to the extent that we define a set of coherent, internally consistent rules, this component can make an almost endless variety of decisions.

> We need to know a great deal more about the nature of decision-making and administrative processes in general before such programming can become effective. At the present time organizations are structured in such a way that major units, such as departments or divisions, are defined in terms of the data or information over which they have cognizance.

> Each department has right to, or interests in, certain classes of information. If we view the organization as a vast system of information of many types flowing in and out of departments pigeonholed (in such a way as to provide a means for sorting of data). But as data-processing applications of computers advance in scope and efficiency, this vast system of information will tend to become integrated under a single unit of information specialists. When this happens, departmental lines will begin to dissolve and structural changes in the organization will be inevitable.[12]

Such warnings of what automation will do to the individual are "scare" statements helping the cause of unionism. The following statement also tends to give one the "jitters":

Information technology is going to do to thousands of middle managers what *scientific management* did to the workers; break their jobs down into routine, repetitive activities demanding little imagination and involving no important decisions. The change is based on new equipment, and new ideas for processing information.[13]

Emerging Philosophy of Union Professionalism The emerging philosophy of union professionalism is being matched by reorientation of professional union structure, functioning, and operating concepts. The structural keynote is to keep the "professional" identification. This is evidenced in collective bargaining by emphasis on merit-rating, special layoff, and recall-rating systems, which include both education and merit and almost completely de-emphasize seniority.

Employee Reaction to Clerical and Office Automation

Clerical Automation Overtaking Factory Automation At one time it appeared that the displaced blue-collar workers who could be retrained might find jobs in the offices, since production workers were less needed in the automated factory and there would be a much greater need for information. This need has been realized, but with the realization has come automation in the office — a situation resulting from the development of new machines capable of producing information better and faster than the clerks could produce — but not safeguarding the jobs of the present conventional office employees.

Some companies have been overbuying this new equipment. W. H. Johnson[14] reported that about ninety clerks must be replaced to pay for one advanced machine. Such an experience is expensive for any company to undergo. Yet experts are saying that the small firm can automate the office. Johnson pointed out that one benefit of automation is that the routine work of the conventional clerk is disappearing and that the work is becoming more complex and more interesting. The implication is that more professional training is required to do the "new" job in the office. It is questionable whether former production workers or conventional clerks have the ability to take this training and to be upgraded.

Labor Turnover Helpful When Automating The Bureau of Labor Statistics[15] reports the success of a large insurance company with the installation of an electronic computer. The company prepared the employers of their plan in advance. The factors contributing to the success of the new installation were the company's growth to meet a greater volume of business; a shortage in, and a relatively high turnover of, clerks; and the basic similarity of job requirements among many of the company's divisions, which permitted easy transferability.

Resultant Employment and Human Relations Problems   Ida R. Hoos,[16] writing in the *Harvard Business Review* in 1960, presented an informative picture of what occurs when the computer takes over the office.

This account covered a two-year study of nineteen business concerns and Government agencies introducing data processing techniques and equipment and showed that the results of automation in the office are somewhat similar to those in the plant.

As to displacement, the author found that for every five positions eliminated, only one new position was created. As to upgrading and review of job skills, these too were reminiscent of the experience in the plant. For example, while a new class of programmers and analysts was developed (like the maintenance jobs in the plant), the remaining jobs showed little upgrading in skills. They also became duller and more machine regulated than ever before.

Centralization of record-keeping and accounting functions was effected in these companies and agencies studied, which seriously upset the job opportunities of personnel in the regions or branches. Instead of job opportunities being opened up with the advent of automation, the reverse was true. The electronic data processing executives appeared to be empire builders. Expansion did not take place in jobs in other clerical departments. Opportunities for middle management positions, outside of the data processing group, became fewer, and substantial bitterness between the data processing personnel and the ordinary operating personnel developed. Apparently the data processing personnel were in a strategic position in terms of adjustment to change, while failure of communications and a lack of the best human-relations techniques contributed to the sensitivity and lack of good morale of the regular supervisory staff.

Similar findings to those in the Hoos study were reported by C. E. Weber[17] in 1959. Weber tested the hypothesis that electronic data processing requires a higher type of clerical skill or ability. The author tried out this hypothesis in two manufacturing companies and learned that although some highly skilled jobs are set up, by and large the advent of the computer tends to downgrade most of the clerical force. He also found that in manufacturing firms clerical workers generally have more latitude for judgments and decision-making than do the ordinary clerical workers in insurance companies, banks, and Government offices. It followed, therefore, that there was more room to downgrade jobs in the manufacturing firms than in banks and insurance companies.

Employee Reaction in Medium-Sized Insurance Company In 1960 Einar Hardin, of Michigan State University, reported on a comprehensive study he had made in a Midwestern insurance company. He was interested in the characteristics of changes made in the work environment by the installation of an IBM 650 electronic data processing machine. Hardin was interested in both the affected and the unaffected departments in terms of their attitudes both before and after the installation of the computer. His conclusions were as follows:

> 1. The installation of the computer did affect the work environment of a number of the employees. By and large the results were thought to be desirable by the affected employees.
>
> 2. Employees in the computer area (which gained work tasks) and employees in unaffected departments liked the idea of the computer better than employees in other affected departments (who lost work tasks because of the computer and who in some part had to adjust to new methods and procedures).
>
> 3. Employees in the affected areas other than the computer area showed less gains in job satisfaction than did the unaffected employees or the computer area employees.
>
> 4. Computer area personnel were less satisfied with job tenure, pay, relations with supervisors, etc. than were employees in other departments. They thought of themselves as indispensable and believed themselves to be a "new elite."
>
> 5. The author also concluded that in the main there was little reaction to the installation of an IBM 650 computer. Perhaps, it was not concluded to be a radical enough automation innovation.[18]

Findings similar to these were concluded by a research group in still another insurance company study.[19]

Acceptance of Office Automation Important In 1960 B. Miller[20] prepared for the American Management Association an excellent research report on how management has to go about gaining the acceptance of supervisors, methods analysts, workers, and others concerned with the possible effect of office automation.

Miller's study involved six companies. He concluded that the chief sources of conflict during the process of automating the departments were the inept methods analysts, who had many problems in dealing with other employees. These companies also had trouble with the outside consultants on whom they became overdependent.

Instead of being able to plan well and think clearly, pressure was obviously brought on management to get the job of automation over with quickly. This situation created tensions and mistakes in judgment. Most of the firms were hit by manpower shortages during the switchover period, when it became necessary to operate two systems simultaneously, the old and the new.

A lack of participation among front-line supervisors also stemmed from the inability of management to secure such participation, a condition that led to confusion and lack of information about results. Furthermore, the situation was aggravated by poor planning and management was incompetent in handling transfers and reclassifications.

The greatest proponents of automation were the methods analysts. The least positive group was the first-line supervisors and the ordinary employees. Once the changes were established, the early critics reacted more favorably to automation. Age of the employees did not seem to be a factor in the response to the problem.

The problems encountered by Miller may be further clarified by the study by M. Stewart[21] on work resistance to technological change. Stewart presents two interesting theories: (1) Resistance is not to change itself, but to the way it is introduced. He definitely recommends the active solicitation and participation of employees. (2) Worry about job security, psychological status, compensation, and job rating affect reaction to change. Stewart concludes that, whereas both theories may be partially true, understanding of response to change in a specific set of circumstances requires a comprehensive study of the employee's attitude derived from his record with the firm up to that point.

Effect of Automation on Clerical Employees   Jack Stieber,[22] of Michigan State University, offers some interesting conclusions on how office automation will affect the eight and one half million employees engaged in clerical work.

He has found that, generally, management is using normal attrition to take care of displacement. This procedure appears to raise fewer problems than are encountered in industrial situations. Many of the office workers are not unionized, hence management has much more flexibility in these instances. In the long run, it appears that automation may displace office workers relatively more rapidly than it does plant workers. Certainly, office jobs will not continue to provide for an increasing percentage of the labor force.

Stieber believes reports on the influence of office automation on upgrading of workers and on raising of skills have been exaggerated. The level of work seems to be about what it was before, except that machines are now used.

Most job opportunities provided by the office computer are being filled from within, after some retraining. It does not follow, however, that all employees whose jobs are abolished will qualify for programming the computer. Still, they appear to have a better chance than the outsider for consideration. Most management people would rather utilize experienced employees with no computer experience than outsiders with computer experience but with no company experience in operations.

So long as there are no sharp layoffs in those firms that install computers, employee attitudes will not be unfavorable. When businesses stop expanding, then such reaction may be expected. The one easement is the continued higher rate of normal turnover in office situations than in plant situations, a condition due partly to the employment of women, who marry, have children, or resign for other reasons. This fact helps cushion the blow of office automation.

Data Processing An electronic data processing system is a management tool which, in a predetermined manner, stores, handles, and manipulates vast quantities of data, carrying out any necessary calculations. The selected results are presented in a printed, typed for coded form.[23] For the most part electronic data processing is used in the office, but has important uses in manufacturing as well.

Insurance companies, banks, Government departments, mail order houses, airlines, and factories are some of the places where electronic data processing is at work. Many types of clerical work are handled, including general and payroll accounting, inventory control, airline seat reservations, and market research. In factories, computers can deal with production, purchase orders, work scheduling, machine and process loading, and order issuing.

These systems cannot think; they can do only what they are ordered to do. The machine will never fully replace the human being.

Computers can also operate in the field of management: they can aid in decision making when given the necessary information.

Savings Made Possible Through Data Processing The application of electronics offers many advantages in suitable cases in office work. Clerical costs are reduced because of the smaller staff required, or increased output is made possible with the existing staff. Savings do not usually reach the estimated figure, however, because of an increased load on the business owing to business growth, as well as more extensive use of the computer by management as soon as it becomes completely familiar with the system. The flow of information is speeded up, so that action can be taken more quickly as trends are noted. The new methods permit storage of a vast amount of information in a very limited space; thus, there is considerable savings in floor space.

Some of the complex decisions to be made by management today require relatively advanced mathematical theory. Examples are queuing theory, input-output economic analysis, and linear programming.[24] These techniques are powerful tools in ascertaining optimum objectives and programs.

The growth of an organization often leads to a subdivision of work, groups of employees doing what was once a consolidated task. In larger insurance companies, each department usually has its own files, rather than one central file. One insurance policy might need ten sets of card files. Under the conventional system, in some insurance companies the payment of a death claim required a trip first to a filing division to obtain the original application for insurance, then to another file to determine how premiums were paid, then to another file to determine whether there had been a loan against the policy, and perhaps to other files before the final payment was completed.

With electronic data processing, the computer can perform all that needs to be done. The computer can pay the death claim, with all details handled in one place at one time. Thus, central operations are substituted for the former departmental decentralization.

Trend Toward Management Decentralization Reversed The introduction of computers may reverse the trend toward management decentralization, for the system is as applicable to several factories or offices as to one. Centralization is practical and desirable. Management decisions can be concentrated at one point. With a computer installation, a study of the whole company is vital and necessary, for the use of data processing will cut across existing departmental boundaries. After a study has been made of paper work for the whole company, methods and procedures can perhaps be corrected and improved to eliminate the need for the computer.

The computer is only a tool; management must prepare facts in a logical manner for presentation to the computer. The right information must be available, for the wrong information, when fed into the computer, will only give the wrong answers — faster! The reasons for computer installation in the office must be sound, for it will cost as much to learn how to use the computer as it will to buy one. Quite often the justification for a computer is based upon savings in clerical help, but management also plans to use it for managerial planning and decision making. There is often a conflict between these two objectives. Clerical operations must be performed continuously and require only the simplest of arithmetical computations. Equipment for this type of work is simple and not too costly. On the other hand the necessary mathematical and statistical calculations required in managerial decisions are as complex and difficult as those associated with science and engineering.

Electronic data processing requires a new type of management education. For persons involved in this new activity, not only is management ability required, but also conceptual and analytic abilities. It is necessary to gain the good will of the employees affected by the computer as well as those in related activities.

Purchasing and Other Business Functions of the Computer The computer can determine the economic quantity for an order. It can carry out shop scheduling; that is, determining when the various production orders will be worked on machine tools and other production facilities. In large plants particularly, with the aid of the computer, machine shops can be efficiently changed over from making one type of product to another type, when the demand for the second increases.

Market research is aided by the computer. Goodman tells a story of the use of linear programming in distribution work. One product of a large company in England, with eight factories, was sold in bulk in fifty-six depots. The product in question was made in each factory. The cost and output of each factory was known, as was the cost of shipping from each factory to each depot. The problem was to ascertain which factory should serve which depot, in order to reduce the cost of transportation. The problem was solved by a systematic series of trials. Since it would have taken months to do this by human calculations, the problem was presented to the Ferranti computer at Manchester University in the form of 64 equations with 448 variables. In one-half hour the machine had provided a reasonable answer. It brought down the transportation costs from 1,000,000 pounds sterling a year to 640,000 pounds sterling a year.[25]

Payroll Accounting Many companies have had beneficial experience in using computers for payroll work. One in particular uses its computer to handle the payroll for ten thousand employees, and this task is completed in four hours. Previously thirty-seven full-time clerks were engaged in this task. The same computer is borrowed part time to handle the payroll for another large firm. In addition, it performs many other assignments for the company owning it.

Banking A new machine, introduced by the Bank of America in San Jose, California, and called ERMA (meaning "electronic recording machine accounting"), can handle the books for fifty thousand commercial accounts, and will look after the work of four branch banks. The machine is able to sort checks by reading the magnetized numbers printed on them; it handles deposits and withdrawals of individual accounts and presents the latest balance. It reports when accounts are overdrawn and accepts stop-payment orders. Information is stored on a magnetic drum, which revolves constantly. It is capable of storing three hundred thousand individual account numbers. Although the use of ERMA effected a substantial reduction in personnel, since only nine operators are required to operate it, there was no displacement; the released employees were assigned to other duties to improve general banking services.

Air Traffic Computers are being used in Indianapolis and other terminals for air traffic control. The human operator is relieved of the clerical detail involved in separating traffic in the air. Information on all air routes is stored and can be brought up instantly on demand. The controller types out the flight plan on punch cards fed into the computer, which searches a storage drum and prints a series of strips giving the controller a continuous program for the proposed flight.

Pan American found that its present accounting system had become saturated. Now, a computer is able to do in fifteen hours accounting that previously required 750 hours. The computer also provides sales information, solves new scheduling problems, speeds up billing, and provides for a more precise control of inventory.

Computers are in use at LaGuardia Airport. At American Airlines the city offices contact the central computer to find out which flights still have seats. Annually the computer handles about ten million transactions and has effected savings of 10 percent of its cost in the first year of operation, while at the same time improving the service.

Advantages of Computer Over Present Clerical Systems   The computer can do work (suited to its talents) faster and more economically than any other method. The computer is more accurate than people or earlier machines. The computer can effectively expand the scope of mechanized systems by absorbing the quasi-analytical functions of clerical work.

The computer can easily perform operations previously considered economically impractical if not impossible in analysis and research. Through the program of instructions prepared by systems personnel, the computer applies the best technical knowledge to the processing of the simplest clerical functions.

Types of Applications   Three distinct types of problems are suitable to computer applications:

1. Engineering and scientific problems
2. Business analysis problems
3. Business clerical problems

The ability to solve complex engineering and scientific problems on the computer will assist in taking the guesswork out of product development and will accelerate technological progress.

The ability to analyze business problems on the computer will materially assist management in making better business decisions.

The ability to process clerical work on the computer will reduce overhead costs and improve reporting methods. Business applications must be of sufficient volume to justify the high cost of program development. If large-volume single functions are not available, justification can be found in the following approaches:

1. Integrated function application
2. Consolidated function application

The integrated function application involves grouping a number of related functions dependent upon one another for input or output. They may be processed economically only if processed together; when the output of the first job becomes the input for the second, there is the opportunity of developing an economic package. An example of integrated processing is the package of unit inventory control, billing, cost of sales, sales analysis.

In this case a single program can be developed to maintain the unit inventory quantities on a master record and at the same time draw off the usage to prepare a tape for billing purposes; another tape to record the data required for cost purposes; still another tape to summarize the sales by classification from the billing data.

The consolidated function approach involves centralizing a single function from a number of locations to provide sufficient volume to warrant economic computer processing. Centralized payroll activity is an example of a consolidated function. Consolidated functions can in turn be integrated for further efficiency.

Program Development A program for computer processing is usually developed jointly between the operational department and the computer activity. The operating department's intimate knowledge of the current methods and objectives of the job, combined with the computer technician's knowledge of programming for automation, insures the most successful application.

Operating departments can, however, develop programs on their own initiative. In either case the personnel assigned to the task of programming must take a four-week formal course in programming techniques. This course is necessary not only in view of the complexity of programming but also to prepare the programmer to exploit the computer's abilities to the fullest extent.

Program development is a detailed, laborious, and time-consuming job. Applications can take from several months to several years to develop and use from two to twenty employees in the process. Only highly qualified systems personnel and experienced punch-card machine personnel should be utilized in programming.

The steps in developing the program are as follows:

1. Train operating department personnel in the techniques of the computer.

2. Thoroughly document every step in the current system from source records to end product.

3. Restate objectives of the activity in terms of management requirements.

4. Chart the approach to the job for computer processing.

5. Develop layout of master records as they will appear on punch cards and tape; prepare block diagram showing flow of processing; and prepare coded machine instructions.

6. Develop detailed instruction manuals for console operator, for nonmachine personnel, and for converting present records to the new system.

Increasing emphasis is being placed upon reducing the cost of clerical functions and providing more complete management data on a timely basis. The successful application of computer techniques to the payroll function is a good example of the improvements that can be accomplished through office automation.

Office Automation in Federal Government Because the Government has a large volume of routine record keeping, Federal administrators and technicians have been greatly interested in the economy of personnel, time, and money made possible with electronic data processing. In an article prepared by Richard W. Riche and William E. Alli, of the Division of Productivity and Technological Developments, U. S. Department of Labor, an interesting summary of developments in the Federal Government are made available to the student of automation.[26]

The Bureau first introduced a large-scale electronic computer in 1951; in 1959 414 computers were located in Government agencies.

Treasury Department and Related Agencies Two business applications in the Treasury Department involve hundreds of millions of transactions annually: the payment and reconciliation of Treasury checks and the auditing and accounting of United States Savings Bonds.

The Treasury Department adopted a policy of informing employees of changes well in advance, in some cases nearly a year before work was to be scheduled to the computer.

Employees involved in the Treasury Department conversion, as well as those in the General Accounting Office, also confronted with the computer problem, were invited to take aptitude tests. Of 470 persons tested, seventy-seven were selected for training and twenty-three were assigned to electronic positions. Final selection of the twenty-three employees, who were to become regular programmers or operators, was made on the additional basis of marks achieved in programming school. Most of the training in electronic data processing was carried on by the computer manufacturers. The Government paid salaries, tuition, and transportation cost of trainees.

Computer application was utilized simultaneously in the Treasury Department, the General Accounting Office, and the Federal Reserve System. The electronic system went into operation in June

1957 after seventeen months of phased conversion from a mechanical system. Seven hundred and fifty-five persons were affected and only 174, or 23 percent, were retained in the same unit for continuing operations. Over one half were transferred, most going into other activities within their organization; only thirty-one employees, 4 percent of the total, went into the new computer unit. Through special placement effort, 11 percent went to other agencies. Nearly 14 percent resigned or retired, and only 2 percent were laid off.

In the Bureau of Public Debt of the Treasury Department 889 persons were affected. The auditing branches in Chicago and New York were closed. Electronic data processing of punch-card savings bonds was started at a new office in Parkersburg, West Virginia, at that time a labor-surplus area. Of the 889 employees in the Bureau of Public Debt, over one third, mainly in the lower clerical group, were laid off. Sixteen percent resigned, giving such reasons as ill health, home responsibilities, and a desire for further education. Three percent were transferred to other Public Debt offices; 35 percent went to other Government agencies; 9 percent obtained jobs with private industry. Few of the employees desired to move to Parkersburg when offered jobs there. The 458 employees required in the Parkersburg installation were recruited locally.

Veterans Administration In the Veterans Administration a large-scale electronic processing system was to be used to establish and maintain insurance records for over six million policyholders. This was to be "the most extensive computer application undertaken by any major life insurance operation."[27] The program was eventually to draw the premium loan dividend and building records into one major file. The system was to be used to perform high-speed posting, billing, and accounting operations, and to store a complete up-to-date record on magnetic tape, which was to constitute a master record file.

The Veterans Administration has a policy of informing employees in advance of technical change. A constant stream of bulletins and newsletters informed the employees about the imminent installation of computers. Employees were given reassurance that the agency would do everything possible to minimize displacement.

A basic orientation course on electronic data processing lasting from three to forty hours was given to 17,500 employees.

The VA estimated that automation would create 1259 surplus jobs in its offices throughout the country during fiscal years 1960 to 1962. A spokesman for the VA stated: "The need for reassignment actions will be anticipated in sufficient time to take full advantage for outplacement of employees."[28]

Employees in the Department of Insurance of the Veterans Administration in Philadelphia had an opportunity for extensive training. Representatives of computer manufacturers gave on-the-site courses to employees directly involved with computer operations. Twenty persons were each given 150 hours of programming; five employees, twenty-four hours of peripheral equipment operation; and five persons, twelve hours of digital computer console operations.

In preparation for other clerical jobs for this data processing installation, several hundred employees and administrators were given classroom training dealing with the use of records and documents involved in programming. In addition, all 2700 employees received orientation courses lasting one and one-half hours.

In tests given to trainees in order to weed out unsuitable candidates, periodic review of material covered was required, with the result that in certain training groups 25 to 30 percent of the trainees were dropped.

Attitude of Government Employee Organizations   Officials of Government employees' unions stated that they did not oppose automation, but wanted specific efforts made to avoid hardships arising from data processing installations. Some approved the advance preparations made by the VA and felt that similar efforts should be made prior to future technological changes. They suggested a number of specific protective measures.

Vaux Owen, president of the National Federation of Federal Employees, recommended a five-point program:

1. Thorough and definite planning ahead . . . of all departments and agencies prior to adoption of automated procedures.
2. Retraining programs . . . for all employees before they are displaced by automation so that (they) may be qualified for reassignment to other positions.
3. Positive reassignment procedures . . . so that employees can feel some assurance they will get reassignments in their own or another Federal agency. . . .
4. Definite placement programs . . . to place in suitable jobs in private industry those who cannot be reassigned in the Federal service.
5. Advance information . . . about plans for installing automated procedures, and just which categories of employees, and how many, will likely be affected, and when.[29]

Owen also proposed "an inventory of the skills of the people in the different agencies" as well as an inventory "of those who want to develop new skills."

Justice Department Use of Electronic Devices for Price-Rigging Investigations The Department of Justice is throwing electronic detectives into their war on price rigging. Giant computers are being turned loose to scrutinize thousands of sealed bids, which, on being opened by the Federal, state, and local governments, turn out to be identical with those of competitors. The computers will be able to detect patterns not apparent to human beings. It would take hundreds and possibly thousands of persons to do this work and the collection of data would become almost unmanageable.

Informal Retrieval A new system, called "IR" or "information retrieval," has been developed by the use of computers. IBM estimates that Government, business, and university groups are already spending some twenty millions a year for information retrieval, and this figure will mushroom. The saving to industry and Government from speedier access to information is tremendous. The solutions to many research problems lie buried somewhere in more than 200,000 journals, books, and reports prepared by the world's scientists and published each year. To break this bottleneck the first step is to have a computer index the contents of a library, usually by feeding it with titles and then having it pick out the key words under which to list them.

The Central Intelligence Agency (CIA) is having its 99,000,000 reports microfilmed and then filed into one hundred wash-tub-sized cabinets. Each specific microfilm can be removed from the cabinet in less than one minute. Each microfilmed document will again be microfilmed to turn out a stamp-sized copy. This copy will then be mounted on a filmstrip with ninety-eight other similar images, and a control card will be punched out to note its location.

Fifty filmstrips are inserted into each of two hundred narrow holders, each holder fitting into a slot in a storage bin. While this is going on, a computer indexes all the material by key words. When a request is made for information, a librarian will edit the request into key words and feed the words into the computer. The machine will match these key words against the key words it has indexed and report which documents are indexed under these words, which cabinets they are in, and on what control cards they are listed. Control cards for the desired documents will then be fed into a retrieval mechanism on the storage bin. The mechanism signals a mechanical arm to dip into the storage bin and pull out the requested filmstrip. A camera then blows up the filmstrip to standard microfilm size, and the microfilm is projected on a viewer so that the agent can read the type.

Hospitals and Automation The nation's hospitals more than any other institution have been hit hard by rising labor costs during the past decade. For this reason the new group of trained hospital administrators seeks solutions through improved efficiency and automation. Under pressure of rising expenses and demands for improved service, hospitals are experimenting with a host of new devices and procedures. Some of these aids are successful; others are complete failures. Also adding impetus to the automation push is the increasing nursing shortage. In 1962 it was estimated that hospitals had a shortage of 23,000 professional nurses.

In 1960, the Roosevelt Hospital in New York City installed a $16,000 experimental electronic system to check the pulse rate, heart performance, and other critical functions of seriously ill patients. The machine was built to the hospital's specifications by Epsco, Inc., of Cambridge Massachusetts; "the monitoring system was publicized as a device to cut costly nursing surveillance."[30]

The system's centralized panel showing conditions of several patients was designed to be located in the hallway, thus reducing the need for time-consuming room-by-room checks. Because some difficulty has been encountered with the unit, it had to be rebuilt. Hospital officials at Roosevelt had originally hoped that the unit would enable them to drop one nurse on each of three shifts, thus effecting savings of up to $15,000 a year.

Another monitoring system was built by Gulton Industries, Inc., of Metuchen, New Jersey, for the purpose of improving patient care by freeing nurses from purely mechanical procedures, such as taking blood pressure. The Minneapolis-Honeywell Regulator Company is also introducing a patient-monitoring system. All developments need further study based upon advance reports.

Automation and the Bible James B. Carey, president of the International Union of Electrical, Radio and Machine Workers pointed out two recent illustrations of automation and the Bible.[31]

Some 311 manuscripts from the third to the sixteenth centuries were programmed for the computer; four chapters from St. Luke were used. Since all these, and the rest of 4600 extant ancient Bible manuscripts, are copies of copies, exegesis through the search for text variations was an apparently unending job.

The Harvard University Computation Laboratory put a computer on this job, thus undertaking the huge and complicated task of determining which manuscripts were copies from the same copies of the original text. Scheduled for completion within one year, this enormous task, without electronic assistance, would otherwise have consumed many thousands of years of work by individual scholars.

The second illustration is the new Bible Concordance, a commercial publication. It reached the market after less than two years' work. The digital computer made it possible to list and identify 310,000 entries from the Revised Standard Version. The earlier, similar project with the King James Version of the Bible was the fruit of thirty years of toil by the Reverend James Strong.

Automation in Communications   Joseph A. Beirne,[32] president of the Communications Workers of America, believes that the communications industry is witnessing a good deal of upgrading as a result of automation. He points out that the number of the higher paying positions has increased. Beirne found no ground for fear that automation would result in vast layoffs.

Nevertheless, there is still dissatisfaction among telephone workers because transfer to automated methods and the resulting personnel problems have not been adequately handled. According to Beirne, help should be given in clarifying what automation means to a worker. He claims that this is a joint responsibility of Government, business, and labor in planning technological change.

Railroad Industry   Automation is making advances in the railroad industry. Automatic signals were formerly accepted with the pride of progress. Now, however, freight cars are being sorted and assigned with computer control. A new installation costing $36,000,000 was built near Pittsburgh and consists of two yards, each of which handles 4500 cars a day. Cars are taken to the top of a hump and then permitted to run downhill by gravity alone into one of a number of tracks. In this way trains can be broken down and sorted and new trains made up. The wagons are automatically switched to the right track in accordance with information as to classification, which is fed into the control system from a teleprinter tape, previously made out from a switching list for an entire train.

There are three control systems. The first is a weight-control classifier. The cars are automatically weighed and classified as light, medium, or heavy for automatic operation of the primary and secondary retarders on the downgrade. A second control is a kind of measuring equipment, which automatically determines the rolling resistance of each freight car or groups of cars, in order to predict the speed and distance the cars will travel after leaving the retarder section. The third control automatically records the number of cars on each classification of track and transmits into a computer information about the distance each car must roll. This process affects the speed of each car as it leaves the group retarder.

Lastly there is the electronic computer itself, which correlates the information from the three systems described above. It then dictates the distance each new car should roll along a given area of track. This system permits tremendous savings in crews. An entire train can now be classified without the requirement of operators or crewmen pushing buttons or doing other work at the actual point of operations.

Building Industry   Cleveland is the location of an automatic plant producing mixed and ready-to-use concrete. There is no labor used anywhere in the process; the entire operation is controlled from one central panel. A teleprinter tells the controller what particular mix is to be delivered. The controller selects a punched card for the mix and puts it into the card reader, then automatic controls take over. Correct quantities of the required materials are delivered by conveyors to the mixing bins, where they are automatically mixed and delivered to cars. All water quantities are automatically determined. In fact, concrete of possibly 1500 different formulas can be delivered. The plant has a capacity of 200 cubic yards of concrete an hour.

Work formerly done by per diem employees on the outside has now been turned over to the computer and the office and administrative staff.

Conclusion

By virtue of the computer, planning and control, formerly done in the plant, is being switched to the white-collar worker. As a result of automating the manufacturing processes, firms have found themselves top-heavy on office and administration levels. The move to automate the office has shown an acceleration in the degree of automation as compared to the factory. Unless markets expand for a firm or the nation, the time may come when the total proportion of the labor force involved in office work may begin to level out and perhaps decrease.

The white-collar worker, the technician, and the professional worker is being made the subject of intense organization drives by traditional unions. So far, they have not been too successful, since their techniques have been clumsy and they have not been employing the white-collar organizer.

Sooner or later, there may arise a group of powerful white-collar and professional unions, which will not be part of traditional industrial unionism. When this occurs, many a current national labor leader will begin to lose influence.

If further unionization of white-collar workers comes, one most likely place will be in the office contiguous to the already unionized plant. Unionism can be extended without the necessity of setting up a new organizing base. Also, the blue-collar union has access to the white-collar worker. Day-to-day associations always direct themselves to problems of status, wages, and security. In these situations, white-collar workers are in a good position to observe if their employers have a double standard as between union and nonunion workers.

White-collar unionization is apparently not inevitable. Unions result when management is deficient. Employers should examine their personnel policies with respect to white-collar workers.

Employers should follow several procedures in order to forestall union organization among white-collar workers. First, the firm should have a written personnel policy, which should be adhered to at all levels. This policy would be an acceptable substitute for the blue-collar contracts, about which white-collar workers know a great deal, and would provide something of the same kind of assurance and certainty inherent in labor contracts. Policies of this sort would go far beyond the normal contract in terms of constructive results.

A second item of importance would be to install a systematic wage program, based upon the equitable principles of job evaluation and wage administration. The white-collar worker wants fairness in wages and fringe benefits within his own group, as well as in relation to the production workers.

Third, the white-collar worker would be interested in a written statement of seniority, so that layoffs, either because of automation or for other reasons, would take place "by the numbers," and not arbitrarily or capriciously.

Fourth, the white-collar worker would like written into the personnel policy procedures for presentation of grievances. He wants to know who is responsible for handling grievances and the channels for handling the dispute from bottom to top.

Fifth, if management were to assure a good two-way system of open communications, so that white-collar workers would know what was going on in the company, the chances of union organization would be reduced. These procedures should permit communications to go up the line from the worker and should provide the opportunity for information to go down the line from management. Included would be discussion groups, suggestion systems, training courses, bulletin boards, attitude surveys, and other sounding-board organizations.[33]

Last, personnel techniques would be improved by a personnel department headed by a director who had the support of top management and the boss. These procedures, if applied, would help reduce the chances for unionism among white-collar workers.

References

1. "Manpower, Challenge of the 1960's," *U. S. Department of Labor*, p. 10.
2. "Directory of National and International Unions in the United States," *U. S. Department of Labor*, BLS Bulletin no. 1267, 1959.
3. Robert K. Burns, "The Comparative Economic Position of Manual and White-Collar Employees," *The Journal of Business*, October 1954, p. 257.
4. "White-Collar Unionization," James J. Bambrick in *Industrial Relations in the 1960's: Problems and Prospects*, George W. Taylor and Edward B. Shils, eds. University of Pennsylvania, February 15, 1961, vol. 11, p. 14.
5. *Ibid.*, p. 3.
6. *Satisfying the Salaried Employee*, National Association of Manufacturers, 1957, pp. 14–16.
7. *Ibid.*, p. 6.
8. Jack Barbash, "Unionizing the Professional Worker." Speech at University of Pennsylvania Labor Relations Council, Philadelphia, November 18, 1960 (mimeo.), p. 12.
9. Clark Kerr, John T. Dunlop, Frederick Harbison, and Charles A. Myers, *Industrialism and Industrial Man*, (Cambridge, Mass.: Harvard University Press, 1960), pp. 7–8.
10. International Labor Organization Report III, Advisory Committee on Salaried Employees and Professional Workers, *Effects of Mechanization and Automation in Offices*, 1959, p. 13.

11. Barbash, *op. cit.*, p. 16.
12. Carl H. Rush, Jr., *Implications of Electronic Data Processing for Industrial Relations Research* (Paper) 1957, Industrial Relations Research Association (mimeo) pp. 8–9.
13. *Esquire*, April 1960, p. 109.
14. W. H. Johnson, "Installation of Automatic Office Equipment and the Manufacturer." *Man and Automation:* New Haven, Conn., The Technology Project, Yale University, 1956, pp. 17–22.
15. "The Introduction of an Electronic Computer in a Large Insurance Company," *Studies of Automatic Technology*, no. 2, Washington, D. C., U. S. Dept. of Labor, Bureau of Labor Statistics, October 1955, p. 16.
16. Ida R. Hoos, "When the Computer Takes Over the Office," *Harvard Business Review*, 38 (4), 1960, pp. 102-112.
17. C. E. Weber, "The Impact of Electronic Data Processing on Clerical Skills," *Personnel Administration*, 22 (1), 1959, pp. 20–27.
18. Einar Hardin, "The Reactions of Office Employees to Office Automation," *Monthly Labor Review*, September 1960, pp. 925–932.
19. E. H. Jacobson, D. A. Trumbo, Gloria Cheeck, and J. Nangle, "Employee Attitudes Toward Technological Change in a Medium-Size Insurance Company," *Journal of Applied Psychology*, 43, December 1959, pp. 349–354.
20. B. Miller, "Gaining Acceptance for Major Methods Changes," Research Study 44, New York: American Management Association, 1960.
21. M. Stewart, "Resistance to Technological Change in Industry," *Human Organization*, 16 (3), 1957, pp. 36–39.
22. Jack Stieber, "Automation and the White-Collar Worker," Reprint Series of the Labor and Industrial Relations Center of Michigan State University, 1957–1958, p. 11.
23. L. Landon Goodman, Man and Automation (Harmondsworth, Middlesex: Penguin Books, Ltd., 1957), p. 55.
24. *Ibid.*, p. 56.
25. *Ibid.*, p. 76.
26. *Monthly Labor Review*, Washington, D. C., U. S. Department of Labor, Bureau of Labor Statistics, September 1960, p. 109.
27. *Ibid.*, p. 110.
28. *Ibid.*
29. *Ibid.*, p. 114.
30. *Wall Street Journal*, December 19, 1961, p. 1.
31. James B. Carey, "The Impact of Automation on Production and Employment," *The Religion and Labor Foundation*, Columbus, Ohio, 1957, pp. 3–4.
32. Joseph A. Beirne, "Automation and the Communications Industry," *Daily Labor Report*, December 1, 1960, F-1–3.
33. "Engineer Union Fights For Life," *Fortune*, May 1960, pp. 246–51.

▶▶▶▶ 16

Workers' Health
and Safety in
Automation Era

Automation does more than develop new techniques in the
plant or the office; it actually influences a new way of life involving
biological and social values, as well as technological ones.

Importance of Industrial Health

Generally speaking, the health of an employee is influenced by
his environment. When a change in the industrial environment
becomes apparent, it creates anxiety. In anticipation of automation,
employees display a great deal of anxiety, which affects their health
and well-being.

A company's employees are valuable assets, and it is important
to anticipate the health problem. In fact, employees become even
more valuable under automation, since the capital investment per
worker becomes twice as much as in the conventional establishment.
As jobs grow more technical, since they involve maintenance and
repair of complex machinery and monitoring of automatic equipment,
greater skills and education will be required. Mistakes in decision
making will be costly. Thus, automation may create in the employee
a feeling of tension, which may undermine his health. Absence due
to health in an automated industry will not only disrupt production,
but will also result in possible errors in the operation of the equipment;
and such errors will be more disastrous than is absence from work
under conventional operations.

The investment in the electric power generation industry, which
is almost completely automated, amounts to approximately $106,000
for each employee.[1]

Preventive Medicine

Just as managers believe in preventive maintenance, so must they believe in preventive medicine. "Preventive medicine is concerned with the total physical and mental well-being of the workers both on the job and at home," stated Dr. C. Richard Walmer, managing director of the Industrial Hygiene Foundation, at an Industrial Relations Conference on "the impact of automation," in Philadelphia, Pennsylvania, on April 4, 1956.

Dr. Walmer also reported that one of the members of the Industrial Hygiene Foundation reported a reduction of 63 percent in absenteeism due to illness in the past five years because of concern with preventive medicine and environmental control.

Even the most comprehensive medical program will be less costly than worker absenteeism. Health counseling and education will enable the worker to learn how to take better care of his health and to avoid injury. The source of most accidents at the machine are to be found in man's constitution and behavior when confronted by a machine.

Implications of Automation for Health Programs

In the ideal plant, atmospheric contaminants are well controlled. Automation will provide the solution to many environmental health problems. Contaminants will mostly be eliminated, because manufacturing operations will be enclosed. In many cases workers stationed at the control panels will be isolated from actual processing areas. Such factors as ventilation, temperature, humidity, and noise will no longer affect performance. Automation eliminates much of the actual handling of materials by the workers, and thus makes possible the use of ingredients formerly too toxic to be handled safely.

In a conventional plant manufacturing large metal containers, manual soldering of side and end seams was required, a process necessitating dangerous exposure to lead and solvents. Later, the plant installed automatic equipment, which permitted better ventilation and completely eliminated exposure to toxic materials. However, workers could still be exposed to toxic materials if there is a rupture in the line when maintenance work is in process.

Accident Prevention

Automation will lessen the safety department's task with respect to prevention of physical injury and will eventually eliminate most traumatic injuries. With complete automation, workers will hardly ever come in contact with machinery. Manual handling of heavy stock and loading and unloading of machines are often eliminated, so that there is less danger of physical strain or injury, such as crushed feet. At the Ford Motor Company, where automatic equipment has been installed, an 85 percent reduction in the number of hernia cases was reported.

Automation, while it does not eliminate the need for decisions by human beings, replaces some of man's sensory apparatus with regard to the operating functions of the machine, and thus relieves the chance of error in human perception, which is too often affected by such factors as mental stress and physical fatigue. Man no longer needs to strain himself or pace himself to the rhythm of the machine. Thus, tension and possible accidents are virtually eliminated.

Effect on Medical Department

In view of the reduction of safety hazards, certainly less staff time will be used for treatment of injuries, but the medical department will have more responsibility than ever in carrying out the modern concept of industrial health — prevention rather than cure. Industrial psychiatry, health counseling, selective placement through evaluation of the applicant's physical and mental condition, will all become more important responsibilities.

The preplacement physical examination will be more important than ever. This examination will uncover physical defects, which can often be corrected if caught in time. Employee and job should be matched, so that work will be a source of satisfaction rather than a source of dissatisfaction, tension, and stress.

Anatomical or physiological requirements for work in automated industries will have to be reviewed. Physical strength will be less of a factor, and many handicapped workers can be employed. The use of periodical examinations will be important in the automated plant. Such examinations will enable the physician to detect a change in the physical condition of the worker since the preemployment physical examination. It will be important to check for strain.

"Human engineering" will also become imperative. Automation will require that all physicians, both in industry and in private practice, know much more of the tolerance of the human organism to the occupation stresses. The design of instrument panels and control panels for the employee in automated industry must be developed with his physiological capacities in mind.

Safety of Workers Enhanced by Automation

J. B. Stirling reports that the elimination of much heavy handling of production materials in the factory, as a result of automation, should considerably reduce foot, back, and internal injuries. Stirling also found that on jobs particularly susceptible to herniation of workers, there was an 85.5 percent reduction on comparable automated jobs.

Automation eliminates the need for repetitive exposure to the point of operation. While this will cut down the chance of accident for the production worker, there is a greater chance, however, that the maintenance worker, involved on repairs during an emergency breakdown, may be exposing himself to working parts of equipment. Stirling concluded that a definite trend toward longer accident-free periods is possible through automation.[3]

Even when production workers are assigned to new duties away from the machines, the chances are that management will be more interested in the welfare of the worker than ever before. Most automated plants are already beginning to think in terms of the preventive approach in industrial medicine.

General Health Problems

One school of thought believes that automation provides other benefits besides the reduction of accidents. Walmer claims that environmental health problems are reduced, that fatigue is lowered, and that there is less mental stress on decision making.[4] He also points out that it is unnecessary to continue the pacing of work and body functions to the unnatural rhythm of machinery. Furthermore, Walmer says, older workers may be retained for a longer period.

Improving Safety Record

There is growing evidence that safer and healthier working conditions can result from increasing automatic production, because the machine will be more remote from its human supervisor. In a study carried on in France of the accident record in metal, chemical, and cotton textile industries in Normandy, within a given seven-year period, when there was a marked trend toward automation in the factories concerned, the frequency rates of accidents due to handling machinery and chemical substances fell in those industries by 42 and 54 percent.[5] In the French Renault factory, automation reduced materials handling, and in many operations accidents were reduced 90 percent.

A low injury rate in highly automatic plants is considered by many observers to be the natural consequence of attention to design, which is necessary to sustain mass production by modern methods. Many new chemical plants are being built to the highest standards of health and safety, resulting not only in a low accident rate, but also in the reduction of the incidence of injuries due to other causes. This type of plant attempts to assure that remedial action will be taken in the case of a failure, which in an explosives plant would normally be disastrous.

Accident Increase Possible During Installation Period

Experience has shown that during the installation period of the automated machinery the accident rate may increase during the transition period.

Maintenance work on the equipment also involves new hazards. The large size and the complexity of the equipment makes some maintenance work dangerous, particularly when such work is done while the machinery is in motion. Electrical hazards, as well as falls from greater heights, are a greater possibility than with the conventional systems.

Physical Fatigue Versus Mental Fatigue

The emphasis on improved human engineering — that is, relating engineering design to man's physiological and psychological capacities — should reduce mental fatigue, which is the worrisome phase of automation, just as physical fatigue is the weak point in the conventional system.

Designers, machine manufacturers, research workers, safety engineers, and industrial physicians must cooperate to see that the individual produces with a minimum of fatigue.

Because of mental fatigue, machinery must be guarded properly. Legislaiton might be required in this area. The finest technique in

lection and the best type of training are necessary in the
d plant to assure safety of workers, where the risks are

Conclusion

Automation will bring unquestionable advantages in the field of
safety and health in industry. The environment will improve and the
place of work will be more attractive to workers. Mental fatigue,
however, will replace physical fatigue, and workers must be properly
assigned, trained, and supervised to prevent accidents and illness.
Some aspects of the automated machinery present an increase in
hazards to those who are ignorant or badly trained. Human engineering will have to be applied to get the best results from the equipment
with a minimum of employee dissatisfaction and accidents. If everything works out well with the present automated plants, industry
can gear itself for the plants of tomorrow, which doubtless will provide
for the generation of atomic power as part of the manufacturing
processes.

References

1. Clyde Williams, "Trends in Industrial Research," *Battelle Technological
   Review*, September 1955, p. 17.
2. John B. Stirling, "Automation, Safety's New Ally," *National Safety
   News*, February 1955, pp. 22–23.
3. *Ibid.*, vol. 71, no. 2, February 1955, pp. 22–23.
4. C. R. Walmer, "Workers Welfare in the Era of Automation," *Keeping
   Pace With Automation Practical Guides for the Company Executive*,
   Special Report no. 7 New York, American Management Association.
5. "Automation," International Labor Conference, 40th Session, Geneva,
   part I, 1957, p. 78.

▶ ▶ ▶ ▶ # 17

Several Case
Studies of Automatic
Technology

In the previous chapters a functional approach has been taken to the problems of automation. This chapter presents four cases in which automation was first contemplated, then applied. Described are the problems of advance planning, the impact of displacement fears, and the atmosphere and environment in which transition and conversion from a conventional to an automated system become possible. The first three cases involve materials prepared by the Bureau of Labor Statistics; the last case is taken from the studies of Floyd C. Mann and L. Richard Hoffman.

Case 1   A Manufacturer of Radio and Television Sets

The Y Company is a large manufacturer of radio, TV, and phonograph sets.[1] The manufacturing process had previously consisted of purchasing standard components and installing them in company-made cabinets. In addition, a great deal of hand-wiring and -soldering work was done on the assembly line.

Several years prior to automation, the Y Company substituted printed circuits for hand-wiring operations, which later developed into the use of photo-etched circuit boards. Mechanisms were developed to attach components automatically. Printed circuits were also used in testing.

The new technology created some new machine-tending jobs for which only two weeks of training were necessary. Certain new machine operations utilizing higher paid labor were created. These operations include the use of skilled maintenance men; at the same time, the ratio of engineers to production workers has increased. Some unskilled job opportunities were eliminated, but, according to the company officials, no worker was laid off as a result of the changes. Because of increased responsibility in the new jobs, the pay for the automated job was generally set at 5 to 15 percent above the straight-time rates for workmen at conventional plants. Group incentives were also established.

Advance Planning Two weeks before the new methods were applied, the vice-president in charge of production informed the production foreman of the changes. The union officials were also told in advance that the company was trying to improve production procedures. The conversion was successful largely because the new techniques were produced at a time of model change-over and employment expansion.

Case 2   The ABC Life Insurance Company

The ABC Life Insurance Company[2] is a large company selling diversified forms of insurance. It had been constantly plagued by increasing paper work and labor shortage. In early 1954 the company installed a large electronic computer. One hundred ninety-eight employees were in the classification section of Division X. It was expected that, as a result of the new machine, a number of these employees would be available for reassignment. Installation of the computer resulted in an estimated 50 percent net reduction in the budget for the classification section. The change-over freed 15,000 square feet of space.

Advance Planning The company planned most carefully both the personnel adjustments and the mechanical aspects of the change-over.

The affected employees were advised in advance of the impending installation, and no attempt was made to gloss over the implications for employment in the classification sections. Individual employees were interviewed with meticulous concern for job preference in the operations of the company. Except for normal turnover, the employees were successfully placed in other company jobs.

Top management met regularly to discuss the personnel problems and to provide a nucleus of computer operators. One to six months' training was provided by the computer manufacturer. Every effort was made to use persons already in the classification section. As a result of this successful start, most of the company's clerical operations in other sections and departments went on a more mechanical basis of operations with little impediment.

The factors that contributed materially to the success and easy adjustment to change-over related, however, to an expanded volume of business, a relatively high labor turnover with an accompanying shortage of women clerks, and the basic similarity of jobs among many of the company's divisions, permitting easy transference of employees.

Case 3 Large Bakery

The Z Bakery[3] employed 575 workers in the conventional system of processing. After two years of study, management decided to relocate the company's several facilities into a single modernized unit. The major effort was directed toward a great degree of mechanization in material-handling practices.

The bread-making process has been integrated mechanically in the new bakery so that, with the exception of one stage in bread mixing, there is no manual handling of the product from the receipt of the dried bulk ingredients to the delivery of the finished loaf of bread. A pneumatic conveyor system was especially designed for the bakery, and the plant is located near a railroad siding. Flour and sugar, which formerly came in bags, is now delivered in bulk by special railroad cars and trucks. The cars are unloaded through tubes and hoses by a worker operating from his position at the control panel. Flour moves from railway cars into bins at the rate of 20 tons an hour, with one man operating the system. Previously it took twenty-four men six hours to move 50 tons into the plant. Output per hour is forty times greater than before the change. The entire material handling department formerly had twenty-four workers. After automation it was reduced to seven. New mechanical methods have been adopted for handling oils and liquids in bulk. These are now pumped into the plant through steam-heated pipelines, which hold the liquid until they are stored into special tanks and metered directly into the mixing machines.

In the bread department, semiautomatic bread-making lines have been replaced by automatic lines. Ingredients were formerly weighed by hand and loaded and unloaded manually. Now they are automatically weighed by scales and automatically fed into mixing machines.

Advance Planning By advanced planning, management and union officials resolved the problems of displacement, downgrading, and changes in skill levels and earnings. Full information was exchanged at every step of the way, and suggestions were offered by the union for cushioning the impact of the changes on the workers. Few workers were displaced because the firm went on a shift basis, which required extra workers; workers who were reassigned to less skilled duties were guaranteed their former earnings until labor turnover would occur. In the early years of automation, employment of production workers fell 8 percent as production expanded; however, employment ultimately increased so that several years later there were more employees in the firm than had existed before automation.

New Job Classifications   A new job classification of "material-handling equipment man" was established in connection with the operation of the pneumatic material-handling system. At first, an engineer had been appointed to handle this system because it was thought that no one at the plant could operate it. When some dissatisfaction with the engineer's performance occurred, a worker in the maintenance department was given several weeks of on-the-job training at the control board, after which he proved quite capable. This procedure was then followed with respect to many of the new jobs.

Conclusions on Bakery Automation   Of the twenty nonworking foremen employed before the change, ten were successfully retrained on the job to meet the requirements of the new plant. The remaining ten were replaced by men especially trained as foremen, some of which were promoted from the ranks and some hired from the outside. From the standpoint of the company the effort to modernize has been successful. Capacity has been enlarged; unit labor costs reduced, despite the fact that wages have risen steadily. Losses due to waste and spoilage have been reduced. Faster materials handling has made it possible to deliver fresher products to the consumer. The workers appear to be satisfied, and both the union and the company take pride in the orderly transition made possible by well-established collective bargaining. The change in work schedules, which minimized displacement, and the decision to maintain wage rates of downgraded employees are particularly satisfactory aspects of the change. The local union believes that workers share in the greater productivity through wage increases and fringe benefits newly obtained.

Case 4   Automation in Power Plants

An interesting study made by Mann and Hoffman[4] concerns reductions of the work force as a result of automating power plant operations. In fact, personnel requirements of the new plant are less than one half of what they were in older plants. This reduction in personnel has occurred primarily in operating groups. Whereas in the conventional plant, forty-two operators, six foremen, and one operating engineer were required on each shift, in the automated plant only fourteen operators and one foreman are required. The development has produced insecurity and anxiety among older workers. In the conventional plant, they saw fewer operating jobs; in the new plant, they are aware of the growing obsolescence of their present skills.

The Mann and Hoffman study also shows a change in the organizational structure in the automated plant. By eliminating such classifications as "boiler," "turbine," and "electrical," the company has been able to eliminate one level of supervision from the new plant. In the older plant, there was a foreman for each production function — boiler, turbine and electrical — as well as an operating engineer to coordinate the activities of the three groups. In the new plant, a single shift foreman is responsible for the entire operating force. He reports directly to the plant-operations engineer.

An interesting result of the reduction in supervision has been the increased influence of the foremen in the automated plant. The foremen in the new plant have proportionately greater responsibility for the activities of subordinates than did the foremen in the conventional plant. Naturally there are fewer foremen.

Centralization of Equipment Controls The placement on a single floor of the new plant of the major control boards for the operating units has had an important effect on the attitude of the men in operations. Centralization has eliminated many of the isolated jobs that existed in conventional plants. Centralization of the control functions has forced considerable contact among operators in the new plant. The enforced contact in turn has created a high degree of psychological identification with the group and with the common objectives of its members. Despite the substantially shorter time that the operators in the new plant have worked together, their feelings of group attraction are greater than in the conventional plant.

Effect Upon Job Structure in the Power Plant In the conventional plant, there were three major operating groups: boiler, turbine, and electrical operations. Electrical switchboard operator's pay was much higher than that of operators in either the boiler or the turbine groups. The top-grade wage rate for the boiler and the turbine groups was three grades less, or 25 cents an hour, than the counterpart in the electrical group. This distinction in pay was criticized by men in the conventional plants.

In the newly automated plants, boiler and turbine functions were integrated and a new job title "power plant operator" was set up. It was decided that there should be further job enlargements, and that electrical functions could possibly be performed under the same operator. The job enlargement would have eliminated all distinctions in pay. A greater feeling of interdependence and a greater group coordination was evidenced among men in the automated plant than in the nonautomated plant.

Training for the New Job in the Power Plant Operators in the new plant were given training programs, which added to their job satisfaction. The training efforts were concentrated in two programs: (1) a series of classes on technical aspects of a power plant; (2) "cross-the-wall" training of men in the conventional plants.

When a man was selected for transfer from a conventional plant to a new plant, he was immediately relieved of his specific job responsibilities. He remained in the older plant, however, for "cross training" — training in parts of the power plant operations other than his own speciality.

> The fireman would then be assigned by the foreman to the electrical switchboard to learn what he could about distributing the electric power produced by the plant. One of the major complaints the men registered about this phase of the training program was that the operators who were doing the jobs generally refused to let the transferees try to do the job themselves. "Watch, but don't touch," they were told. The incumbent operators appeared to resent the assumption that these men could learn in a few weeks what it had taken them years to become skilled at. They were jealous of their equipment and did not want these "outsiders" tampering with it. Observation was fine; actual operating was not.[5]

The instructors showed a great deal of resistance to this program, because they felt that cross training offered a threat to the established pattern of promotion and the prevailing status system. It had been traditional that operators be promoted within their own group — for example, from electrical helpers to switchboard operator second class. The idea of a man who had been in boiler work trying electrical operation with only short training was resented by men who had gone through normal progression over a period.

Classes in the Power Plant Classes were held for the new operators, in which sets of notes containing technical information were distributed. In the older plant, a two-hour class was conducted every other week for the purpose of transferring men on each unit in the manual. Technical engineers and manufacturer representatives taught these courses. In addition, the transferred men were instructed to qualify for licenses required by the company for men working with boilers and turbines. There was also some training by use of the on-the-job method.

Continuous Operation and Shift Problems Workers in the automated plant reported that they adjusted to shift changes more rapidly than they did as workers in the conventional plant. On shifts, workers seemed to find it easier to get together with their friends and family than they could in the conventional plant. This may have been the result of easing of the physical efforts as compared to shift work in a conventional plant.

The new era of automation will increase the percent of the total workers assigned to shifts. Management, social scientists, and biological scientists will have to join forces in the search for a new solution to problems of continuous operations. Many shift workers in the automated plant were concerned that they could not utilize the fringe benefits available to day workers; gymnasium, library, bowling alley, boat club, and other facilities.

Supervisory Training Required in the Automated Plant It is a mistake to believe that with the reduced number of employees and a much heavier capital investment in machinery, the foreman should be concerned only with the technical aspects of his job. If anything, the human-relations side becomes more important.

One school of thought believes that the supervisor should be concerned more than formerly with the administrative and interpersonal aspects of his job. Many workers will be expert technicians; they will, therefore, require greater attention as individuals from the supervisor, and the job of coordinating their efforts will be even more crucial.

This study revealed that workers in the automated plant seem to be more impressed with a supervisor's competence in human relations than they were in the conventional plant. In both the automated plants and the conventional plants, this aspect of the foreman was found to be more highly correlated with employee satisfaction than with his technical or administrative competence.

There seems to be little difference between technical supervisory requirements in the automated and the nonautomated plants.

In the automated plant, where decision making on immediate problems of the men was delegated to the foreman by the plant superintendent, the atmosphere was conducive to the practice of certain good human relations behavior. An analysis of the effects of management identification and power emphasized the importance of the foreman's awareness of his dual responsibility — to the company and to the men. The more effective the foreman was in meeting both responsibilities, the more satisfied his men were with him.

Organization Readiness for Change

The impact which a major technological innovation will have on an organization cannot be isolated from the history of employee relations with the company. A supportive atmosphere, in which the workers feel that management has previously considered their needs in any situation, provides more receptive ground for such change than one in which management is seen as being insensitive or hostile to the workers' needs.[6]

The readiness of an organization for change, the state of management relations, the level of employee satisfaction with the company, and trust and good will are all important factors in the acceptance of innovation. Management must try to sense whether the company is ready for the disruption involved in the introduction of entirely new productive methods. In those cases where management has neglected human relations functions and where good will is lacking, there will be a difficult period of transition. It might be cheaper in the long run to have better human relations of employees in the conventional systems of manufacture rather than convert to automation in an unfavorable climate.

Where human relations are poor, the introduction of new processes is seen by workers as a threat to their stability and security. The elimination of the old skills and the need to adjust to a new work group will create considerable resistance to change. Those companies with a history of stability in employee relations have the best chances for a successful conversion to automation.

Working Environment in the Automated Power Plant   The Mann

and Hoffman study brought forth some interesting ideas on the influence of the working environment on the employees. A greater number of large pieces of equipment creates a complex environment of machines. In the automated department, the number of men is sharply reduced and the ratio of capital per worker is considerably higher. In the automated power plant, the control consoles were immaculately clean, well-lighted, air-conditioned rooms, located several floors and several hundred feet away from the actual production processes. This arrangment provided a pleasant working environment for the men.

The newness of the automated plant had negative aspects. The complex equipment brought new tasks to be performed and new procedures in skills to learn. There is a fear of the unknown — that something might go wrong with the system — an uncertainty about what to do if something does go wrong.

An additional negative factor was the pressure by management to expect full production in the shortest possible time. Attempting to operate at full capacity with inexperienced personnel created apprehension and anxiety.

Training Responsibility The principal inadequacies of the training program in the power plant studies revealed a failure by management to recognize that different methods were needed for acquisition of intellectual as opposed to motor skills. The jobs continued to enlarge, and this broadening required a better understanding of the entire production system. The operators received a great deal of training on new equipment in the preparation stage, but did not have any real operational practice to try out the new equipment. These men reported to the analyst that they learned more about the jobs when they were assigned to work at the equipment than through classroom briefings. Mann and Hoffman recommended that, in order to have a successful program, trainees ought to be given the opportunity to try their hand at the new procedures. Despite the economic pressure to get the new units in line as soon as possible, this objective should be tempered with the warning that the operation of new machinery by inexperienced personnel may result in losses that would outweigh any initial advantage.

It is also important to pace training in the speed of transition from one job to another, as such pacing may determine a man's future in his work. Tension rises with rapid transition. There is a natural way of learning. Often the number of ideas to be incorporated and the number of skills to be learned at any one time are wasted by the capacities of the workers involved.

Evaluating Effectiveness of Workers The Mann and Hoffman studies showed that traditional systems for measuring the work of the individual based on his productivity are inapplicable in automated systems, since the worker no longer controls production. Self-regulation mechanisms control the operation of the machine complex by maintaining the rate by which manufacturing proceeds. Sometimes the operator has nothing to do except to hold himself available for machine breakdown. The ability of the operator to limit the effect of breakdown or to reduce downtime is a measure of his effectiveness as an operator. Studies in the automated power plant indicated the possibility that downtime may provide a measure of organizational effectiveness as an operator.

References

1. *Monthly Labor Review*, U. S. Department of Labor, Bureau of Labor Statistics, January 1956, p. 79.
2. *Ibid.*
3. *Ibid.*, p. 84.
4. Floyd C. Mann and L. Richard Hoffman, *Automation and the Worker*. New York: Holt, Rinehart and Winston, 1960, pp. 193–207.
5. *Ibid.*, pp. 94–95.
6. *Ibid.*, p. 199.

Conclusions
and
Recommendations

In the long run, automation should make for more interesting employment and a higher standard of living. The United States must be as efficient as possible to compete with the other nations of the world. Extreme efficiency is most important in view of this country's desire to join the European Common Market. If we achieve greater productivity and a reduced unit cost of product, our citizens will have an improved living standard.

Meanwhile, there are dire prophecies from certain quarters. Labor leaders and certain key figures in Government look grimly at the progress of automation and predict mass unemployment and mass displacement. On the basis of available information and statistics on the subject, it is impossible to determine whether there is cause for serious alarm. Careless talk, however, can result in cumulative gloom and the development of attitudes on the part of workers and unions that will obstruct advances in technology.

The responsibility for seeing that displacement is not the harsh, cold measure it is made out to be should be shared by employers, labor unions, and Government. Previous chapters have pointed out the wisdom of advance consultations with workers and labor unions. Retraining should be made available for workers to transfer to other departments and to other positions in the same concern where possible. If displacement is necessary, then improved public employment placement techniques and opportunities for retraining at Government expense should be made available.

For the success of such a program, job counselors must know where and in what quantities job opportunities are available, and retraining must be adapted to such needs.

Unions are generally taking the position that in phase with expanding markets, automation is a good thing. On the other hand, they are generally obstructive to automation unless they are satisfied that certain security provided through collective agreements will alleviate the impacts of technological change. A logical procedure for the employer is to work closely with the union in advance of automating, but employers should not surrender their managerial prerogatives to unions. The accomplishments of this nation have resulted from progress, and it has the highest employment rate in its history.

With increased productivity comes the opportunity for additional leisure. Unions are pressing for a shorter workday and a shorter workweek. If these are possible without sacrifice of an industry's competitive position, consideration should be given to the suggestions, of course.

Automation raises many problems of employee classification and pay. These matters will have to be carefully worked with the unions. Where job content changes, the change must be so recognized. Like all automation-related problems, action must not be taken too swiftly, else every firm will have a wage program "out of kilter." Conventional departments will have one pay and classification system whereas automated departments will have another.

The challenge in the field of education and training is immense. Managers and labor leaders should get together and review the traditional apprentice training programs of the skilled trades. These classifications are rapidly being superseded by the need for technicians and engineers. Much can be done with proper on-the-job training.

The most important brake on progress will certainly be the existing and prospective shortage of technicians and managers. Automation increases both the need for them and the requirements of qualifications and skills. It implies an expansion of training facilities within the educational system and a reassessment of the needs they serve, for so far as technology is concerned, the needs cut across the existing boundaries of professional training. Automation implies also that firms should seek to train and promote the potential managers and technicians of all grades who are still in ranks. Finally, it emphasizes the importance of cooperation among technical specialists, and between them and the managers on one hand and maintenance craftsmen and operatives on the other. Qualities such as versatility, adaptability, and capacity for understanding other viewpoints will be increasingly valued in managers and professional staff.

At the same time, automation is likely to create serious problems, most of them common to all forms of technical advance, and industry must solve these problems if automatic processes are to spread widely without the social and economic dislocation marring the early history of the Industrial Revolution. Like all innovations, it entails risks, and at each stage of development, a sufficient number of firms must have the resolution and the imagination to take chances and act on informed guesses, where necessary.

Report of President's Advisory Committee

Possibly, a combination of energetic private and public action will permit the advancement of automation and technological change without the sacrifice of human values. The entire problem was reviewed in depth by the President's Advisory Committee on Labor-Management Policy, in its report of January 11, 1962. Recommendations of this outstanding group of labor, management, and public leaders follow:

We recommend that serious consideration be given the following measures:

1. Adoption by the government and others of policies which will promote a high rate of economic growth and fuller utilization of resources. A much higher rate of growth is essential and is the best device for reducing unemployment to tolerable levels. We will include in our forthcoming report on economic growth, suggestions in this area.

2. Acceptance by government agencies of the responsibility for collecting, collating, and disseminating information with respect to present and future job opportunities and requirements in a rapidly changing society.

3. Cooperation between government and private organizations in the field of education in improving and supporting educational facilities to the end that:

    a. New entrants to the labor force will be better qualified to meet the occupational demands of the future.

    b. The dropout rate at grade and high school levels will be reduced.

    c. Better vocational, technical, and guidance programs will be available.

    d. Rural and depressed areas, where surplus workers reside, will be better served.

e. Financial support will be available for deserving and needy students.

f. There will be a general upgrading in the quality of our education.

4. Acceptance by management of responsibility for taking measures, to the maximum extent practicable, for lessening the impact of technological change, including:

a. Adequate lead time.

b. Open reporting to the employees involved.

c. Cooperation with representatives of the employees to meet the problems involved.

d. Cooperation with public employment services.

e. The timing of changes, to the extent possible, so that potential unemployment will be cushioned by expected expansion of operations and normal attrition in the work force (through separations resulting from retirement, quits, and so forth).

5. Support from both public and private organizations for retraining of workers who have been and will be displaced.

a. Private employers and unions faced with automation or technological changes should make every reasonable effort to enable workers who are being displaced, and who need to be retrained, to qualify for new jobs available with the same employer, and to enjoy a means of support while so engaged.

b. Where it is not possible for the employer to reabsorb displaced workers, appropriately safeguarded public support in the form of subsistence payments should be available to industrial and agricultural workers who qualify for and engage in retraining.

c. Unemployment compensation laws should be liberalized to permit and to encourage retraining.

6. Support from both public and private sources, with due consideration to the circumstances of the enterprise involved, for the displaced worker who is seeking new employment.

a. The duration, coverage, and amount of unemployment compensation, where inadequate, should be increased and made subject to realistic uniform minimum requirements under the Federal-State system.

b. Employer supplementation of public unemployment compensation should be accomplished through severance pay, supplemental unemployment benefits, and similar measures.

c. Attention should be given to provision for the special case of the worker who is displaced during the period when he is approaching retirement. This may appropriately include consideration of provision for early retirement, through private arrangements or social security measures; but alternative possibilities of more constructive temporary uses of such services warrant exploration.

7. Support from both private and public sources to the end that a worker's job equities and security may be protected without impairment of his mobility. This will warrant consideration, taking into account relevant cost factors, of such measures as:

   a. Financial aid in the transfer of employees to other plants in a multiplant system, and protection of existing rights for individuals so transferred.
   b. The use of public funds in order to give financial aid in the transfer of unemployed workers from one area to another where the result will be to provide continuing employment.
   c. The improvement of public and private protection of pension rights.
   d. The recognition by unions, individual employees, and employers of the necessity of adapting seniority and other rules in order to facilitate mobility of workers, while providing protection for the equities of employees.

The Committee notes particularly the need for further study and exploration of this vital area.

8. Vast additional improvement of the public employment service so that it can effectively place, counsel, and relocate workers both locally and across State lines. We note with approval the start which has been made in this direction.

9. Vigorous and unremitting efforts by all segments of the population — including government, employers, unions, and employees — to eliminate discrimination in employment because of race, creed, age, or sex.

10. There are pressing national needs to be met, and an abundance of manpower available to meet these needs. This matching of manpower and national needs, which is part of the vital context of the automation and technological advance problem, will obviously be affected by various broader governmental policies. Reserving fuller consideration of this area for our economic growth report, we nevertheless note here that:

   a. When technological changes or other factors develop particular pockets of unemployment, this becomes an additional reason for the undertaking, particularly at the State and local levels but with Federal assistance where this is necessary, of public development projects for which there is need independent of the employment need itself.

b. Every effort should be made to maintain on an up-to-date and ready-to-go basis a schedule of needed public development projects, particularly those which could be started most quickly and which would be of short or controllable duration, so that the initiation of such projects can in the future be advanced, and the flow of projects already under way can be speeded up, if the manpower situation warrants this.

c. If the operation of the economy, including the effect of automation and technological change, creates or leaves an intolerable manpower surplus, consideration should be given to monetary and fiscal measures, including the possibility of appropriate tax reductions — which would give promise of helping alleviate this situation.

d. Governmental action along the lines suggested here, stimulated in part by the need to meet unemployment situations, would obviously have to take into account other considerations, including particularly the maintenance of national economic stability and security. We simply assert, however, the coordinate importance of stability and growth.

11. The need for goods and service must not be left unfilled, particularly in a time of international crisis. At the same time, high unemployment is intolerable. In the light of our current responsibilities to meet world conditions and in view of our unmet needs (we do not favor) a general reduction in the hours of work. A reduction in the basic work period has, however, historically been one means of sharing the fruits of technological progress, and there may well develop in the future the necessity and desirability of shortening the work period, either through collective bargaining or by law or by both methods. In connection with such a development, consideration would necessarily be given to the extent to which purchasing power could be maintained along with a reduced work period.[1]

Reaction to Committee Report

The nation's reaction to this comprehensive group of recommendations was encouraging, on the whole. They relate directly to the problems of automation as set forth in this book. They have been more expressly pinpointed to our national dilemma than anything so far brought to the author's attention.

What are the weaknesses of this report, if any? Arthur Burns, a member of the Committee, believed that too much emphasis was placed on automation as the cause of present unemployment, although there is some truth to this contention. The uninformed citizen is prone to blame all unemployment on automation. However, the quantitive importance of the different causes of unemployment need to be assessed. Much unemployment in this nation is caused by loopholes in the law. There is partial unemployment, cyclical unemployment, and "structural unemployment;" there are also "unemployables." Many so-called "unemployed" are "secondary" wage earners, women who are unemployed in the off-seasons, as in the garment industry.

Some fear too much Government action as a result of these recommendations, which would affect both the employer in costs of production and the size of Government outlays. How would further liberalization of the unemployment insurance laws affect the volume of unemployment itself? Is the report overpessimistic?

Henry Ford, also a member of the Committee, in a minority report took the position that when an economy is prosperous, displaced workers quickly find new employment. Ford believed that the Committee was more concerned with the "secondary" matters of training and mobility than with the primary matter of creating new jobs. He stated:

> When wages rise faster than productivity in the economy, costs will rise and then either prices will go up or profits will come down — or both will happen. If profits come down, then incentive to save or invest savings in new job creating plants, enterprises and industries must suffer.[2]

Ford thought that the most important step the Committee could have taken was to find ways, consistent with a free economy, to keep wages and other costs from causing either unemployment or inflation.

Other reactions to the Committee report centered on the fact that no one knows what may be the probable consequences of the massive program recommended for both public and private action. Fears have been expressed that a greatly expanded Federal assistance program could destroy the incentives that stimulate private economic activity and generate individual initiative.

The Committee's recommendations for improving the school systems received a very fine response. The millions of new entrants into the labor force in the coming years require a basic educational preparation that will prepare them for the changes in the industrial scene under automation.

An attempt has been made in this book to recognize the nature of the problem generated by automation. Such an attempt is impossible without a whole set of "control" statistics to isolate that portion of the present unemployment problem which results from automation. The new technology may be a blessing indeed, without which America might lose its industrial leadership in a changing world.

Technology is a material force, whose use and benefits must be dictated by the social objectives and decisions of the entire community. The social controls developed to assure that automation is used in the service of mankind will determine in part the ability of this nation to dominate and control the mighty technological forces that have been unleashed.

Labor-management cooperation can be achieved by some simple principles of cooperation, which are somewhat familiar, nevertheless sound:

1. Deal with all in good faith.
2. Consult together at all stages.
3. Agree on changes that promote the welfare of the community, the employees, and the firm.
4. Divide as fairly as possible the benefits of automation among workers, employers, and consumers.
5. Seek justice in distributing the burden of change.
6. Remove special hardships wherever possible, and deal generously with special cases that may arise.
7. Work together to see that Government will spread a cover of social protection to care for those injured by change.

The above principles can be translated into rules of practical conduct for each undertaking. The detailed applications will strengthen the structure, and widen the area, of labor-management cooperation, and foster the spirit of enterprise and growth essential to progress.

References

1. "The Benefits and Problems Incident to Automation and Other Technological Advances," Report of the President's Advisory Committee on Labor-Management Policy, January 11, 1962. Release of the U. S. Department of Commerce, pp. 3–5.
2. *Ibid.*, p. 9.

► ► ► ►

Index